SLIMMING MAGAZINE of the YEAR 2017

January 2018

Less CAKE More EXERCISE magazine

incorporating
It's Not Fucking Rocket Science Monthly

> **I lost 4 stone by eating less cake and doing more exercise**

Read one woman's inspirational story inside!

● **Drop a dress size in TWO WEEKS** with our fantastic **Less Cake, More Exercise** plan

Forget The Atkins, The Cambridge and The Macrobiotic... The **L.C.M.E.** is the only diet you'll need!

> **What I DID & DIDN'T do!**

Less Cake More Exercise **Slimmer of the Year 2015** Ada Trimble reveals her **Two Golden Rules**

Get into last year's jeans with our terrific TWO-STEP programme

Cake!
New scientific study shows too much leads to BIGGER BUMS!

Exercise:

"**I gained 20lbs by not getting enough**"

Read one man's shocking cautionary tale inside!

PLUS... One Month's **FREE MEMBERSHIP** to your local Less Cake More Exercise club for every read...

ON SALE NOW!

Look out, here it comes...

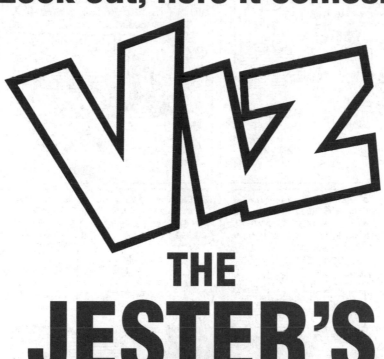

Viz

THE JESTER'S SHOES

The Eagerly Anticipated Cream of Issues 242~251

Turkish Slippers
Graham Dury and Simon Thorp

Elvis's Legs
Mark Bates, Peter Brooker, Alex Collier, Terry Corrigan, Simon Ecob, Tom Ellen, Chad Elliott, Matt Hindle, Hunt Emerson, Barney Farmer, Lee Healey, Davey Jones, Marc Jones, Shaun Madrid, Alex Matthews, Alex Morris, Paul Palmer, Tom Paterson, Joe Shooman, Terry Stickney, Cat Sullivan, Kent Tayler, Keir Thomas, Neil Tollfree and Nick Tolson.

Up and over like a pan of milk
Kerin O'Connor, Dharmesh Mistry and Stephen Catherall

Published by Dennis Publishing Ltd
31-32 Alfred Place, London WC1E 7DP

ISBN 9 781781 065792
First Printing Autumn 2017

Subscribe online at www.viz.co.uk
Find us at facebook.com/vizcomic and twitter.com/vizcomic

7

LETTERBOCKS

Viz Comic, P.O. Box 841, Whitley Bay, NE26 9EQ
letters@viz.co.uk

ABOUT two years ago I sent you a letter saying my beloved mother-in-law closely resembled the late North Korean dictator Kim Jong-il. I feel ashamed about this, because after my new eye test she actually looks a lot more like a cross between Sir Alex Ferguson and Gollum from *Lord Of The Rings*. But with a bigger chin.

Dr Richard Evans, Colwyn Bay

AFTER my wife trotted out the old cliché that men can't multitask, I quickly retorted that it wasn't true, because the last time we had sex I was imagining that she was someone else at the same time. Sometimes it's better to lose an argument than be right.

Mike Tatham, St Andrews

WHEREVER you look these days you see rust; rusty cars, rusty bikes, you name it. Yet I've had several frying pans in my life and none of them has ever shown signs of rust. It doesn't take a genius to conclude that we should build everything out of frying pan metal.

Danny Lewis, Southampton

THEY said on the news that the police were going to try to recreate a murder so they could see exactly how it all happened. But I don't know why some other poor sod has to die. I think this makes the cops no better than the thugs they're trying to catch. No wonder they have such a bad reputation.

Ben Nicol, Mernda

THEY say *"if you want something done right, you have to do it yourself."* But I beg to differ. I recently had a very successful triple heart by-pass and no way would I have managed the operation myself.

Frampton Ballspond, Luton

DON'T believe those types of bleach that claim they "Kill All Germs And Viruses". When I had flu, I drank almost three pints of the stuff and if anything, it made me feel worse.

Boris Scumramp, e-mail

WHEN a fire alarm goes off late at night in a hotel, the fire brigade are okay with people milling about outside in their underwear. Yet when a burglar alarm goes off at a young woman's house the police make a right song and dance about me being in her back garden wearing only my underpants. Yet again it's one rule for hotel guests and another for keen ornithologists.

James Brown, Edinburgh

WHY can't those street artists who draw stuff with chalk on pavements just get a proper job? I can't think of anything off hand, but what about becoming one of those coppers that draw lines around dead bodies when they've been found?

Hamilton Jackdaw, Rhyll

APPARENTLY writer Ian Fleming named his 007 story villains such as Hugo Drax, Ernst Blofeld and Francisco Scaramanga after fellow pupils he was at Eton with. It's a good job he didn't go to my school, or Bond's adversaries would have been called Mark Todd, Chris Scoltock and Barry Duckworth.

Andy Brown, Wakefield

IF anyone was wondering, my favourite National Lottery draw machine is Guinevere, and my favourite set of balls is number 6.

Timetus Buktu, Reighton

IF I had a time machine I'd go back to Hitler's time and I'd buy up the all the cheap land adjacent to his underground bunker. Then, when all the others arrived in their time machines I'd charge them a massive fee to park there while they tried to kill him. Then I'd come back to the future with all the profits and go on a massive weekend bender in Sunderland town centre.

D Mixture, East Clintwood

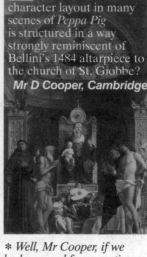

HAS anyone else noticed that the character layout in many scenes of *Peppa Pig* is structured in a way strongly reminiscent of Bellini's 1484 altarpiece to the church of St. Giobbe?

Mr D Cooper, Cambridge

∗ *Well, Mr Cooper, if we had a pound for every time a reader has written in to point that out, or indeed to suggest a Top Tip whereby you save money on personalised number plates by changing your name by deed poll to your existing number plate, we'd have a bankful of cash.*

CAN any of your readers tell me if the superstition that says it's bad luck to pass someone on the stairs applies to stairs outside the home? I only ask because I've been here on the concourse at Crewe station for 4 hours, I've missed my train and I really need a shit.

Scotty, Crewe

THEY say beggars can't be choosers, but I was stood behind one in our local corner shop the other night, and he took ages to decide on what brand of cider he wanted. In the end he went for the cheapest.

Hector Moleskin, Leeds

IT'S recently been brought to my attention that when the band Chumbawamba get knocked down, they get back up again. What a shining example to set in this day and age. Well done to them.

R Swierc, Burnley

THEY say you can't teach an old dog new tricks. Well, the bloke next door has just taught his twelve-year-old springer spaniel to lick Nutella off his dick.

Dave Edwards, Bridport

WHAT'S all this I hear about motorists being given points when they are caught speeding? If anything, surely we should be punishing them.

Marjorie Dribble, Goblin Combe

WHILST staying at a hotel recently I noticed a sign saying 'In the event of fire do not use the lift.' However, I can't ever remember seeing a fire in a lift Surely they are the safest place to be in the event of fire. Once again an example of health & safety gone mad if you ask me.

Fluff Freeman, Halebarns

WHY on earth was Adam tempted by an apple in the garden of Eden when he had a naked woman with him? Maybe he should have tried his luck with her first.

Ross Kennett, e-mail

ALL that David Attenborough does is go on about is bloody animals all the time. Doesn't he have any other interests? Home baking or playing the drums or something? The man is obsessed.

Hucky, Corfu upon Strawberry

ONE of my balls looks like a chicken nugget. Do anyone else's genitals look like anything off the McDonald's menu?

Alan, Windsor

∗ *Well, readers, do YOUR genitals look like anything off the McDonald's menu? Perhaps your foreskin looks like the lettuce off a Big Mac, or maybe your glans looks like a quarter pounder with cheese. Take a photo of it and send it to Embarrassing Bodies at Channel 4, your local GP's surgery or anybody else except us.*

I NOTICE that in his advert, Mo Farah is shown eating some Quorn mince then running along a road to prove how well it works. However, when Pele did his advert for erectile dysfunction counselling, at no point did he whip his cock out to prove that that had worked.

Garry Clarke, e-mail

IF New York is supposedly the city that never sleeps, then why are there numerous shops there selling both beds and bedding? I'm no expert, but something doesn't add up and I'm not prepared to just "forgedda bowdit".

Jamie Cuffe, Isle of Man

I CALLED my area manager a cunt during a recent investigation and she replied by telling me not to call her a cunt. However it was too late, as I had already called her a cunt just moments before.

T Hollingdrake, Lancs

RECENTLY in Lincoln Square in Manchester, I noticed a statue of Abraham Lincoln. Have any other readers come across similar incredible coincidences?

Matthew Vash, Marvelment

DESCRIBING someone as being one in a million means there are another 64 like them in the UK alone. Hardly a compliment, I feel.

Grogg Wallash, Liverpool

DO any of your readers' wives have such a venomous opinion of a kids' TV favourite as my missus, who has just told me that she thinks Paddington Bear is "a complete fucking knob"?

Stu Perry, e-mail

I'VE always wondered why washing machines have windows but tumble driers don't. After I'm finished with the enthralling viewing on offer from my washing machine, I'm left provided with absolutely no entertainment from my drier.

Richard D Tergent, Kettering

MY boss told me to kiss her arse when I asked for a pay rise, but when I did she sacked me.

Russ Poore, Littlehampton

DID you ever discover who that bloke was in that picture of that bloke kissing that bird's arse? It would be interesting to know if he's still having his photograph taken kissing birds' arses today, or if he has a son or lesbian daughter who has carried

on the tradition. When I say interesting, I meant for some of your readers. Personally I couldn't give a fuck what he's doing these days.

Lee Helium, Dartford

IF any readers are considering trimming the pubic hair on their scrotums with hairdressing scissors, be careful. Be very, very careful.

C McSpleen, East Sheen

THE fashion for shaving pubic hair has left the pubic louse on the verge of extinction, yet the

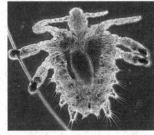

so-called environmentalists have remained silent. If it's not cute and furry these hypocrites just aren't interested.

James Brown, Edinburgh

I'VE just seen in the TV listings that *Hitler's Hidden Drug Habit* is on Channel 4 at 8pm. Now I don't know about you, but I've already made my mind up about him and, no shocking revelations about him are going to change it.

Charlie Ryan, North Shields

I DON'T know why everyone raves about Michael Palin travelling all over the world. I bet if the BBC refused to pay his travelling expenses, like my boss did to me, he wouldn't move out of his fucking living room.

Terry Waterfall, Croydon

Matthew Kelly's
TAR'S IN THEIR EYES

TONIGHT, Matthew, these celebs will be receiving urgent treatment at the nearest eye hospital! That's because they've had industrial coal tar flung in their faces to disguise their identities. But can YOU still recognise them under a thick coating of free carbon resin? Send your answers in to *Tar's In Their Eyes, Viz Comic, PO Box 841, Whitley Bay, NE26 9EQ*, and you could win a year's supply of coal, pine or petroleum tar for you and three friends!

OH-OH! Looks like there's been a massive "wiki-leak" of hot tar into this vaguely creepy, fugitive whistleblower's eyes. Let's hope they keep a stock of white spirit and swarfega at the Ecuadorian Embassy!

TAR DATE 21.50.33, and this space captain's five-year mission to to explore strange new worlds, to seek out new life and new civilisations has hit a snag. He won't be boldly going anywhere with all that tar in his eyes.

OH MOTHER! This saintly Albanian Bible-thumper's been slumming it in Calcutta and got a faceful of hot bitumen for her troubles. Time to get to work scrubbing it off with a wire brush until there's "nun" left!

TAR MAC! This observational comedian constantly takes the "Mickey" out of everything from white dogshit to wire coathangers. But funnily, he didn't observe an assailant approaching him with a bucket of hot tar.

Mrs BRADY OLD LADY

TSK. THAT MINNIE FEATHERSTONE AT NUMBER 243'S GOT A **MAN** ROUND, DOLLY.

A MAN? EEH.

HOW BRAZEN CAN YOU GET?

AND HER STANLEY NOT YET DEAD THIS FIFTEEN YEAR GONE.

OH HE WAS A LOVELY MAN, HER STANLEY, DOLLY.

HE WAS, ADA. A LOVELY MAN. I ALWAYS SAID WHAT A LOVELY MAN HE WAS, WAS HER STANLEY.

HE SUCCUMBED TO A COLO-RECTAL HIATUS WHILE OUT WALKING THE DOG.

EEH. STILL, IT WERE THE WAY HE WOULD'VE WANTED TO GO, I SUPPOSE... A BIG PROLAPSE.

MIND, I'M GLAD HE DIDN'T LIVE TO SEE THE WAY HIS WIDOW WAS CARRYING ON.

YES ADA. A MAN ROUND BOLD AS BRASS IN BROAD DAYLIGHT.

THE SHAME OF IT..!

HE'D BE TURNING IN HIS GRAVE TO SEE IT, DOLLY, IF HE WAS ALIVE.

YOU'RE NOT WRONG, ADA. IT'S DIS-**GUSTING**.

SHE'S A **HOO-ER**, DOLLY, IS THAT MINNIE FEATHERSTONE... A COMMON FILTHY DIRTY **HOOER**!

YOU'RE RIGHT. SHE'S NO BETTER THAN A COMMON **TROLLOP**..! A **SLUT**, SHE IS. A **SLUT**!

IT DUN'T BEAR THINKING ABOUT, WHAT HER AND THAT MAN ARE GETTING UP TO IN THAT HOUSE.

AYE.

RELATIONS, DOLLY, I SHOULDN'T WONDER... AND THE REST...

THE REST?

YOU KNOW, DOLLY... WATERSPORTS... TEA-BAGGING... SNOW-DROPPING...

NO!

OH YES!...BOSTON PANCAKES...CREAM PIES...PEGGING... YOU COULDN'T MAKE IT UP, LOVE.

EEH! I COULD VOMIT!

WELL I'M NOT GOING TO SIT HERE AND LET A RUDDY SEX ORGY TAKE PLACE ON ME OWN STREET, DOLLY.

ARE YOU NOT, ADA..?

I'M NOT.

HELLO...POLICE..?

=SLOOP!=

JUST A ROUTINE CALL, MRS FEATHERSTONE... DO YOU MIND IF I COME IN..?

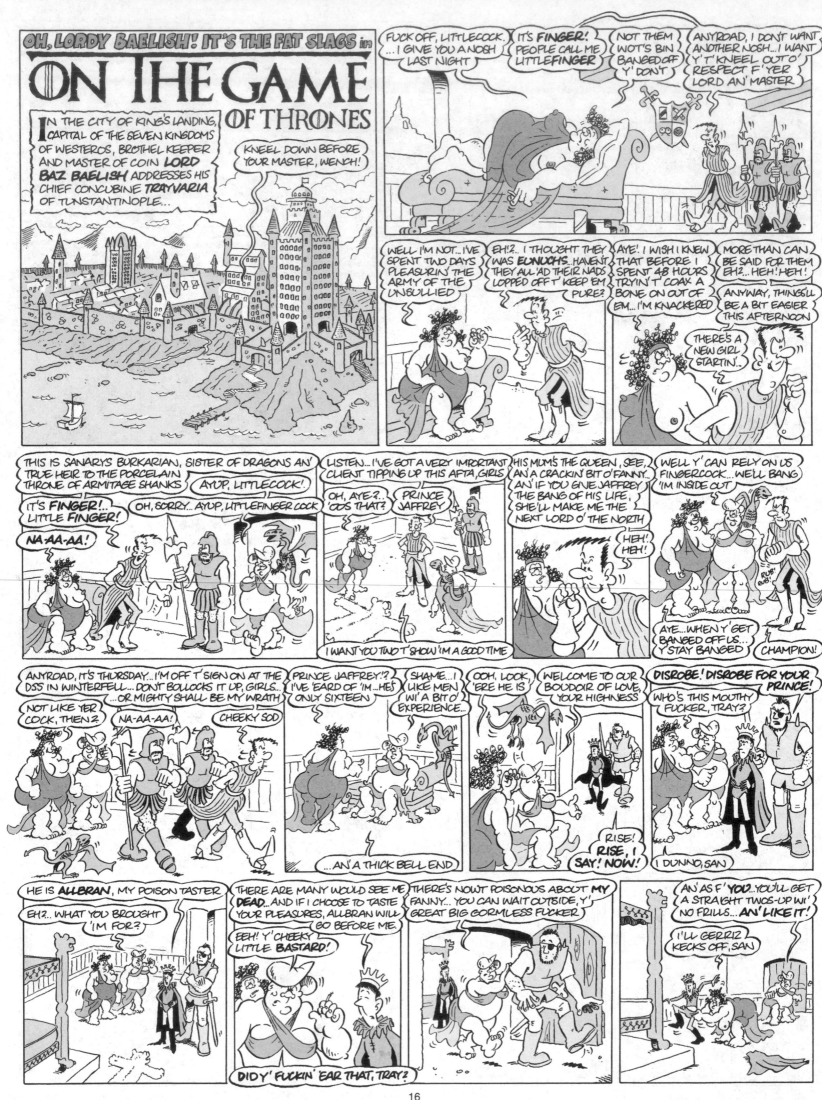

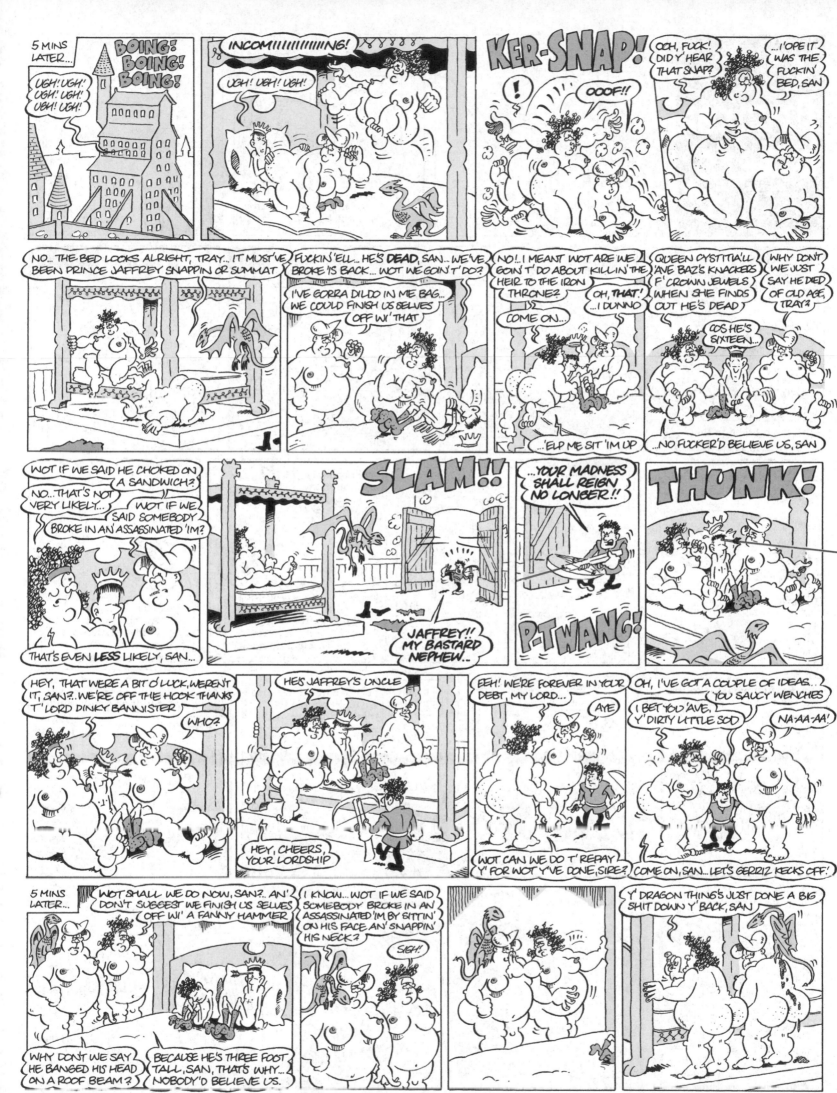

17

WOULD YOU ADAM 'n' EVE IT!?

with **Charlie ADAM** and **Trevor EVE**

Each week, the Stoke City midfielder and Shoe-string actor present the craziest and most belief-beggaring stories from around the globe

BOGOTA, Colombia

They say lightning never strikes twice - but no one told Bogota district postman **GUILLERMO JEGGINGS**. For the 38-year-old father of two has been struck by lightning **TWICE A DAY** for the past **SIXTEEN YEARS!** Luckless Guillermo has found himself on the receiving end of nearly 12,000 cloud-to-ground electrostatic discharges, each one a staggering 2 million volts. But plucky Jeggings refuses to let it get him down. "I'm about used to it by now," he told the *Bogota Herald* from his bed in the city's Severe Burns Unit. "And there's plenty of people out there have it much harder than I do."

Would You ADAM 'N' EVE It?!

SHEFFIELD, UK

Professional snooker player **DENNIS TAYLOR** has been admitted to a private hospital in Cheshire to undergo an extremely unusual operation. For the 66-year-old former world champion is going to have his eyes removed and put back in **UPSIDE DOWN!** For the last 25 years, the cheeky Irishman has worn his glasses the wrong way round, and the resulting inverted vision has caused him to have more than a few accidents. "I've had enough of tripping over pavements because they're at the top of my field of vision," he told the *Sheffield Probe and Enquirer*; "Once this op is done, I'll be able to wear my specs the wrong way round in complete safety."

Would You ADAM 'N' EVE It?!

OHIO, USA

You often hear old folks complaining that policemen are getting younger. Well, in the case of one US copper, it's true! Detective Inspector **HANK OYSTERBERG** of the Ohio state police department has shed a whopping **49 YEARS** in the space of 6 months, leaving the former 56-year-old at the sprightly age of 7. Despite his Benjamin Button-esque antics, the newly Infantile Oysterberg continues to oversee high-profile criminal cases, as his superiors can find no grounds on which to dismiss him. "There's nothing in the handbook that says you can fire an officer just because he's started ageing in reverse," said Ohio state commissioner Newt Snapple. "So, we've just got to wait this thing out till Hank hits the 'terrible twos', and then we'll stick his ass in daycare."

Would You ADAM 'N' EVE It?!

AUCKLAND, New Zealand

When 45-year-old **ANDY NIMROD** dumped his elderly mother in a Berkshire nursing home and relocated to New Zealand, he thought he'd seen the last of her. But heroic Mrs Nimrod wasn't giving up that easy. The loyal grandmother of three swam an incredible 26,000 miles across the perilous Atlantic and Indian oceans to be reunited with her beloved son. An overjoyed Mr Nimrod told the *Auckland Informer*; "After such a display of loyalty, we couldn't take her back there. We're going to keep her this time."

Would You ADAM 'N' EVE It?!

CARLISLE, UK

A Tarraby bachelor has managed to sleep with **ALL FIVE** Kardashian sisters - despite never having met them! Unemployed **TERRY ARSECHAT** wears a state-issued ankle bracelet that proves he hasn't been more than 2 miles from his flat in 25 years. However, the 46-year-old is adamant that this has not stopped him having full sex with every one of the curvy reality TV siblings. "I've shagged the lot of them", Arsechat told the *Brunstock Chronicle*. "Kim first, then Khloe, then Kourtney and Kendal at the same time, and then that Kylie just the other week. Believe me or don't, I couldn't give a fuck either way, because it's true."

Would You ADAM 'N' EVE It?!

More crazy-but-true stories next time, folks!
Charlie 'n' Trev

THE BACONS

JOHNNY FARTPANTS

QUACK!

THERE'S ALWAYS A COMMOTION GOING ON IN HIS TROUSERS

AND YOU JOIN US HERE AT THE CRUCIBLE THEATRE FOR THE FINAL FRAME OF THE 2015 WORLD SNOOKER CHAMPIONSHIPS, WHICH SEES JOHNNY 'THE HURRICANE ARSE' FARTPANTS TAKE ON JUDD 'HAIR PRODUCT' TRUMP.

AND THE BIG NEWS IS THAT YOUNG JOHNNY HAS LEFT HIS CUE ON THE BUS, JOHN.

YES, HE'S GOT A MOUNTAIN TO CLIMB IF HE'S GOING TO WIN THIS FRAME WITHOUT A CUE, DENNIS.

AND IT'S FARTPANTS TO BREAK ... WIND.

BRAAAP! KER KLACK! KER-KLACK!

OH, WHAT A WONDERFUL BREAK, DENNIS.

HE FARTED SO MUCH TOPSPIN ON THAT CUE BALL HE'S POTTED ALL THE REDS.

HE'S ONTO THE COLOURS. IT LOOKS A FAIRLY SIMPLE YELLOW.

CHALKING HIS NIPSY THERE, JOHN.

SQUEAK! SQUEAK!

THAT'S RIGHT, DENNIS, A BREAD AND BUTTER SHOT. BUT HE'S TAKING NO CHANCES.

HONK! KER-KLACK!

WHAT A SHAME FOR THE LAD. HE'S OVER-FARTED THAT ONE A LITTLE, DENNIS.

YES, HE'S LEFT HIMSELF A LITTLE SNOOKERED THERE, JOHN. HE'LL HAVE TO PUT A BIT OF SIDE ON HIS NEXT SHOT. AND THAT'S A TALL ORDER IF YOU'RE USING BUM GAS RATHER THAN A CUE.

BRAAAP!

VREEEE!

OH, A BEAUTIFUL SHOT.

JOHNNY JUST ASKING THE REFEREE TO CLEAN A BIT OF ARSE CRESS OFF THE CUE BALL THERE.

HE'S LEFT HIMSELF A TRICKY BROWN. IT'S GOING TO NEED THE LIGHTEST OF SILENT BUT DEADLIES TO KISS THAT ONE IN.

FLOOOF! CLICK!

OH, MARVELLOUS. THE LIGHTEST OF ZEPHYRS.

YES, A REAL WHODUNNIT, AND IT'S LEFT HIM PERFECT ON THE BLUE.

COUGH! COUGH!

A FEW MEMBERS OF THE AUDIENCE SUCCUMBING TO THE HOY OFF THAT ONE HERE AT THE CRUCIBLE.

YES. IT'S LIKE SOMEBODY HAS OPENED A TIN OF BUTCHERS TRIPE MIX. JOHNNY TAKING HIS TIME, HAVING A SIP OF CABBAGE WATER WHILST HE WAITS FOR THE CROWD TO SETTLE DOWN.

A LITTLE BIT AWKWARD, THIS ONE, DENNIS.

YES, HE'S HAD TO GET HIS LEG UP ON THE TABLE TO GET THE ANGLE ON HIS RING.

BROMP! KER-KLACK!

A LOVELY SHOT. JUST THE PINK AND BLACK TO GO NOW.

JOHNNY LINES IT UP. HE'S ASKING THE REFEREE TO PULL HIS FINGER.

TUG! SQUONK!

OH, DEAR, HE'S MIS-BREWED IT.

YES, HE GOT A BIT OF AN EGGY KICK ON THAT ONE, JOHN. THE REFEREE MIGHT HAVE TO LIGHT A MATCH.

AND IT'S LEFT HIM WITH AN EXTREMELY LONG BLACK TO CLEAR THE TABLE.

YES. HE'S ALREADY CLEARED THE FIRST THREE ROWS.

HE'S TAKING A LONG TIME TO BREW THIS ONE UP, JOHN.

I DON'T BLAME HIM, DENNIS, IT'S GOING TO TAKE A PILE-DRIVER TO SINK THIS BLACK.

HNNNNG! BLATCH!

OH, NO! IT'S A FOUL SHOT!

PANDEMONIUM HERE AT THE CRUCIBLE.

NOOOOO!

OH! PHEW! I MUST HAVE FALLEN ASLEEP WHILST WATCHING THE SNOOKER ON THE TELLY...

...IT WAS ALL A DREAM.

YES, JOHNNY. EXCEPT FOR THE BIT ABOUT YOU FOLLOWING THROUGH ON THE BLACK.

OOOPS!

Meteor Shower Set to Let Down Public Again

Annual non-event leaves stargazers closed-mouthed!

THE annual *Disappointids* meteor shower, billed by space buffs as *"nature's most lacklustre firework display"*, is set to thoroughly underwhelm skywatchers once again tonight.

As the earth passes through the debris field from Comet Knott-Visibull, which didn't streak spectacularly across the heavens in 1998 when it passed within 12 billion miles of the earth's orbit, astronomers expect an insipid trickle of shooting stars to fail to light up the night sky in an awe-extinguishing display of celestial mediocrity.

shit

"Quite frankly, I wouldn't even bother going out in the garden to look for it," Astronomer Royal Sir Martin Rees told *The Sky at Night*'s Maggie Aderin-Pocock. "We'll be watching it through a great big fuck off telescope at Greenwich Observatory and it'll still be shit. It always is."

A Disappointid. Or perhaps a plane going over. (Picture © NASA)

How to get the best out of tonight's meteor shower...

23.14:00 The bombardment will reach its dreary crescendo when, assuming it's not cloudy, which it will be, up to six streaks of light per hour will not be discernible.

23.15:00 Go out into the garden and stand on the wet lawn in your slippers for about thirty seconds until your neck starts to hurt.

23:15:30 Rub the back of your neck and then look in a different part of the sky where nothing is happening either.

23:15:45 Go back inside and watch the second half of *Police Interceptors*.

FATHER SEXMAS!

THE EROTIC confessions of a discount shop Santa Claus have set tongues wagging in the quiet town of Clipstone, North Notts. For local Father Christmas *Trevor Gumrot*, 67, claims that over the festive period he has bedded over 500 "yummy mummies" who have brought their children to see him in his grotto at the *Justakwid* store in the Byron Shopping Centre.

"The worst excesses of Sodom and Gomorrah are as nothing compared to what goes off in my grotto," says poundshop Santa

Milf marketing board: The pound shop in Clipstone, Notts, where Santa Claus Trevor Gumrot had full sex with more than 500 yummy mummies over the festive season.

"I don't know whether it's the white beard, the ruddy cheeks or the uniform that gets them going, but these milfs just can't keep their hands off me," he told us. "They say that Santa only comes once a year, but let me tell you, it's tons more than that."

However, Gumrot is at pains to make one thing abundantly clear. *"None of the little kiddies were present when these things went off,"* he told us. "It all happened after hours or round the back of the chair where they couldn't see anything. I don't want people getting the wrong idea and putting my windows in again."

sleepy

Now Trevor has written a steamy memoir about his grotto-based adventures. *Fifty Shades of Red and White* is an explicit, no ho-ho-holes barred account of his XXXmas sexploits, and it's already got the residents of the previously sleepy market town gossiping furiously. "The Clipstone rumour mill has gone into overdrive since my book came out," he told us. "But let me reassure the local lovelies that their sexy secrets are safe with Santa."

WARNING - The following extracts from Trevor Gumrot's book are of an extremely explicit nature, and contain detailed accounts of actual sexual activity that really happened. Any readers who are easily offended are advised to read no further.

"Christmas seems to start earlier each year, and that's certainly the case in a pound shop; I opened for business on November 1st, the day after they cleared all the Halloween stuff away. Situated in a quiet corner at the back of the store between the dog shit bags and the biscuits with Arabic writing on, my festive grotto was the unlikeliest love-palace you could imagine. A 2-metre square pop-up garden gazebo with some tinsel over the front flaps, some cardboard icicles, polystyrene packing chips "snow" on the floor and a sign reading 'Santa's Grotto - North Pole.'

sneezy

As I settled down in my fairy light-bedecked chair for my first shift, I was prepared for a quiet start to the festive season. How wrong I was. As soon as the shop opened, customers were queuing all the way back as far as the useless Chinese batteries, with mums desperate to get their kiddies in to meet Father Christmas and pick a present from one of his crepe paper-covered dustbins.

The very first customer through the grotto door showed me the shape of things to come. She was a gorgeous blonde in her early thirties with a three-year-old boy in a pushchair. As she lifted the toddler onto my knee I couldn't help noticing her sexy, voluptuous figure, like one of those bored housewives you get in sex videos. She looked like the kind of woman who would go out without any knickers on, those ones who let you do the lot.

dopey

Whilst I was talking to her son, I made a few mildly flirtatious remarks about "stuffing a bird at Christmas" and asking him whether his mum was a "naughty girl" and so on. Before long there was a definite sexual chemistry between her and me, let me tell you, although needless to say it all went over the little kiddie's head.

Once he got off my knee I told him to dip into the blue boys' bran tub and take a gift, but he wasn't listening and instead took one out of the pink bin.

The little brat was devastated when he unwrapped his parcel to reveal a knock-off *Little Mermaid* purse, and threw a tantrum. His mum asked me if he could change it for a boy's present,

> *Eventually, after I had given my yummy mummy a series of multiple organisms, I couldn't contain myself any longer and the inevitable happened...*

but I told her that it's strictly one dip in the tub per customer. That's when the atmosphere went from charged to fully electric; suddenly ten thousand volts of sexual tension crackled through the air in that grotto, lighting it up like a Christmas tree.

grumpy

"Well Santa, I'd be very grateful," she told me whilst fluttering her eyelashes, licking her lips seductively and toying with the buttons on her blouse. "I'd make it worth your while."

Well my blood's as red as Rudolf's nose, and there was no doubt in my mind what was on offer. I quickly strapped the kid back in his buggy and pushed him out of the grotto. "This visit to Santa is for grown-ups only," I chuckled as I wheeled him into the stockroom. I parked him up safely behind the forklift and kicked his pushchair brake on.

When I got back in the grotto, his mum was waiting for me. She had stripped down to her sexy underwear, which was exactly like some I had seen in a video on my computer the night before.

I quickly lowered my Santa trousers and we got down to business there and then. There was no time for foreplay. This was just down and dirty sex amongst the polystyrene snow. The idea that there were customers just

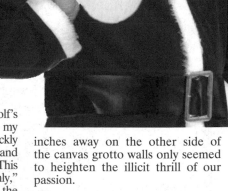

inches away on the other side of the canvas grotto walls only seemed to heighten the illicit thrill of our passion.

I tried to keep my moans of ecstasy down to a minimum, as I didn't want the store manager to guess what was going on. Eventually, after I had given my yummy mummy a series of multiple organisms, I couldn't contain myself any longer and the inevitable happened. It was a shattering climax that left me gasping for breath through my nylon beard.

happy

As soon as we'd finished, I pulled up my Santa trousers and went to fetch the toddler. He was a bit upset after being left on his own in the warehouse, but none the worse for his ordeal. I kept my half of the bargain and let him have a dip in the boys' bran tub. He pulled out a knock-off *Pirates of the Caribbean* set, comprising of an eyepatch, a moustache and cardboard Jolly Roger hat. As he left the grotto he had a big smile on his little face, but not half as big as the one on his mum's face... or mine.

But if Trevor thought that his saucy tryst with his first customer was a one-off, he had another think coming. For the very next mum through the grotto door, who had brought her two daughters to see Santa, also gave him the come-on.

This bird looked like the sort of viewer's wife who'd take a video of herself and send it in to *Television X*. She was a thirty-something brunette in a short skirt, just how I like them, and she looked like she could go a bit.

Anyway, her little girls were telling me all about what they wanted for Christmas; dolls, colouring books, that sort of shit, and I made a little joke about whether their mum would like Santa to come down the chimney and stick something in her stockings. Of course, it went right over the kiddies' heads, bless them, but mum knew what I was talking about alright, and gave a dirty laugh.

bashful

Our eyes met, and you could cut the sexual tension with a knife. "Come on girls, time to go home," she said, gathering up her daughters and swiftly ushering them out of the grotto. My heart sank; I thought I must have gone too far and scared her off with my fruity banter.

doc

So I was a little surprised when, two minutes later, my brunette milf returned on her own. "I've given the girls their bus fare and sent them off home," she announced. "Now it's time to ask Santa what *he* wants for Christmas."

From the sizeable bulge in the front of my red felt trousers, I think it was already obvious what I wanted. But I explained anyway, and let me tell you

I got it, right there in the grotto. It was a mind-blowing sex session. We did it all over the place; in my chair, up against the present bins and then behind my chair. We literally re-wrote the Kama Sutra in that grotto. We did it in every position you could imagine... *and a few you probably couldn't.*

billie

We must have been making quite a din, because we attracted the attention of the store detective - a stern, middle-aged woman with her hair up in a bun and horn-rimmed glasses. She poked her head through the grotto flaps and caught me *in flagrante delicto*, mid-thrust up the brunette. I froze in horror when I saw her, assuming I would be instantly dismissed for inappropriate behaviour on Justakwid premises. But nothing could have prepared me for what actually happened.

The store detective quietly informed me that it was forbidden to have it off with the lady customers... *unless she could join in!* And with that, she took off her glasses and shook her hair down. I was amazed to see that, underneath her ice maiden exterior, she was extremely sexy, a bit like that dark-haired piece who keeps you on the phone forever on Babestation. Then she took off her trousers and Doc Marten boots to reveal she was wearing stockings, suspenders and high-heeled shoes beneath.

Me and my yummy mummy had re-written the Kama Sutra just moments earlier. Now the three of us ripped it up and set about re-writing it all over again. It was like all my best sexual fantasies come to life, and it wasn't long before the inevitable happened. Then,

The store detective informed me that it was forbidden to have it off with the lady customers... unless she could join in!

when I was lying spent and exhausted in the afterglow of my passion, the two birds put on a lesbian show to finish themselves off. I would have thought I was imagining things if it hadn't really happened, which it definitely did.

By the time my sexy lovers had dressed and left the grotto, the queue of impatient kiddies and sexy mums was stretching all the way round the corner into the next aisle as far as firelighters. This was going to be a long, hard day.

Word soon got round the town that the Father Christmas at Justakwid was not only giving presents to children, he was sorting their mums out as well. Indeed, it wasn't long before the sex-hungry housewives of Clipstone started turning up at the grotto on their own.

It was usually pretty quiet in the middle of the day, so I took the opportunity to hang my 'Gone to Feed the Reindeer' sign outside and have a swift lunchtime can before the afternoon rush.

I'd just finished it and was having a handful of Tic-Tacs to keep the fumes at bay when a sexy redhead came into the grotto. I asked her where her kids were and she explained she had left them at home watching Jeremy Kyle. Then she came over and sat on my knee, just like the woman did in a film I'd seen with Ron Jeremy where he was a boss and she was his secretary.

She started toying with my false beard, teasing the elastic and letting it slap back sharply against my ears. To say the atmosphere was erotically charged would be no exaggeration, because it was. 'I like your white beard, Santa,' she whispered, and I could feel her hot breath on my ear. 'I was just wondering whether the collar matches the cuffs, because mine does.'

summer

With that she stood up and let her coat slip to the floor. She was completely naked underneath, except for black stockings and suspenders, coincidentally just like in the Ron Jeremy film I mentioned earlier.

And she hadn't lied. There was definitely 'fire down below', and I immediately set about fanning the flames. I started to undress but she told me to keep my costume on. She clearly had a thing about men in uniform, and my red suit, black wellingtons, plastic belt and Santa hat turned her on like nothing else.

twist

Never mind feeding the reindeer, I was soon feeding the pony and it had an insatiable appetite for oats, I can tell you. I'd pulled a Christmas cracker this time, and I don't mean the sort that goes bang. Although this one did. Like a shit-house door in a gale.

Modesty forbids me from going into too much detail about what we did over the following two hours, suffice to say that red-headed minx gave me a "Christmas box" I'll always remember. Her ginger fanny.

The job in the pound shop was turning out to be much more fun than Trevor had ever imagined. However, after just three days playing jolly Saint Nick, he was called in to see the manager.

"Apparently there had been some complaints from customers about so-called 'inappropriate behaviour'. A few dozen mums, probably feminists or lesbians, had accused me of ogling them and making indecent comments in front of their kiddies.

What's more, my boss said he'd been doing some digging around and discovered I'd filled in false details on my CRB check form. He said he'd found out that I was actually on the sex offenders register. Which is not true, because I'm pretty sure I'm not.

I explained that it must be somebody else with the same name as me, and who lived at the same address. But the manager was having none of it, and gave me my cards there and then.

stick

My all-too-brief adventure had come to an end, just because a few narrow-minded, hatchet-faced, frigid old bags couldn't take a compliment. I was sad, sure, but I had no regrets. As the shopping centre security guards manhandled me towards the exit, I reflected that if I had my time again I wouldn't change a single thing.

For three days I had lived out my wildest dreams, experiencing a life that other men can only dream of. Being Santa in that pound store had been a crazy, erotic rollercoaster ride, a fantasy like something from one of the hardcore vids in the vast collection on my hard drive.

As I left the shop for the last time, I shed a tear, but it wasn't for myself. My thoughts were with those little children whose lives I had briefly lit up with my jolly smile, who would no longer get to experience the innocent magic of visiting the grotto and sitting on Father Christmas's knee. To mention nothing of their mums, whose lives I had touched. As well as their tits and minges."

She started toying with my false beard, teasing the elastic and letting it slap back sharply against my ears...

Love shack: Trevor enjoyed steamy trysts in his grotto.

EVERYBODY READY? ON YOUR MARKS... GET SET... GO!

BANG!

TOUGH MUDDER START

HEH-HEH! THAT'S FAR ENOUGH!

IF THEY RECKON SIDNEY SMUTT'S TRAIPSIN' ROOND A TWELVE MILE SHITEY OBSTACLE COURSE, THEY'VE GOT ANOTHER THINK COMIN'!

PUBLIC FOOTPATH TO MAIN ROAD 200 YDS.

BINGO!

AH'LL JUST MEK IT LOOK LIKE I'VE RAN RACE, THEN AH'LL TEK FUCKIN' BUS TO TH'FINISH LINE!

ROLL! ROLL!

RUB! RUB! RUB!

THERE... PORFECT!

BUS STOP

TING! TING! GO TSSCH!

HEHEHEH!

YUZ'RE A BLOODY GENIUS, SIDNEY, Y'REALLY ARE!

AT THE NEXT STOP...

HE'S IN THE BACK.

EXCUSE ME, SIR. WE'VE HAD SOME COMPLAINTS ABOUT A DISHEVELLED VAGRANT WORRYING PASSENGERS ON THIS BUS.

EH? WELL AH'VE NOT SEEN ANYONE OFFICER, BUT AH'LL KEEP ME EYE OOT, LIKE.

VERY CLEVER. COME ALONG WITH US NOW, EH, MATE?

NAH..! GERROFFUS, MAN!

AH'M NORRA VAGRANT, AH'M A FUCKIN' TOUGH MUDDER!

COURSE YOU ARE, PAL...

POLICE

BACK UP REQUIRED! WE'VE GOT A DRUNK & DISORDERLY TRAMP ON A CROWDED BUS HERE!

FUCK OFF!

SHORTLY,...

ALL COPPAS ARE CUNTS

JUST COLLARED ANOTHER ONE, SARGE.

LET'S GET HIM BOOKED IN.

WHAT IS IT WITH TRAMPS AND BUSES TODAY?

25

EXPOSED! THE SHOCKING STATE OF OUR BRITISH SCRAPYARDS...!

...Puddles of oily water...

...Filthy bootprints on carpets...

...Dirty, unflushed toilets...

...Nowhere to have a bath...

What a Load of SCRAP!

THE UK ferrous and non-ferrous reclaimed metal industry is booming. Scrapyards are popping up everywhere, but since no formal training or qualifications are needed to open one, the quality of service can be variable to say the least.

Most scrapyard owners are reputable, offering five star service to their customers in return for cash and no paperwork. But like every industry, the scrap metal business also attracts sharks, charlatans and fly-by-night cowboys out to make a quick buck. With their sharp practices, shoddy service and substandard premises, these unscrupulous rogues now threaten to drag the good name of Britain's scrapyard industry through the oily mud.

Alex Polizzi goes undercover to expose Britain's worst scrapyards

To expose these rogue traders, *Viz* sent TV fixer *Alex Polizzi* undercover to check into a variety of scrapyards around Britain to check out whether the services they purported to offer came up to scratch. What she discovered shocked her and it will shock every right-minded reader too.

Breaking bad: Britain's scrapyards are a national disgrace, with dirty, outdated facilities and shamefully poor customer service, says TV business guru Alex Polizzi.

Casefile 1: Big Jim's Breaker's Yard, *Bourton-on-the-Water*

WHEN looking for a scrapyard in the beautiful Cotswolds, you are spoiled for choice. Every honey-stoned picture postcard village seems to have a traditional metal reclamation yard nestling amongst its streets of charmingly quaint thatched cottages. However one establishment that I would hesitate to recommend to anyone is *Big Jim's Breaker's Yard* 10 miles outside Bourton-on-the-Water.

I checked in just before lunchtime, having previously phoned up to reserve a windscreen wiper motor from a 1978 Peugeot 504. But when I got to reception, which was housed in an old caravan that had clearly seen better days, the surly manager informed me that my part wasn't ready.

The manager explained that he'd had a lot of trouble with people ringing his yard and asking him to remove car parts and then not turning up to collect them. *I couldn't help noticing that his hands were filthy and his oily overalls looked like that hadn't been washed for a couple of days at least. Not a good first impression.*

He told me that it would take him about half an hour to get the motor, and I could wait in reception. Or, he suggested, I

ALEX'S STAR RATING: ★ ☆ ☆ ☆ ☆

was welcome to head out into the yard and get it myself. He would even lend me a socket set. Needless to say I declined his offer.

I sat down in the rudimentary waiting area, on what appeared to be the front seat of a Vauxhall Victor that had been crudely mounted on a Handy Angle frame. The facilities

were spartan to say the least: no wi-fi, no table service and no coffee-making facilities. The only things to read were a couple of trade magazines and an airgun catalogue, all of which were dog-eared and covered in oily fingerprints.

After about forty minutes, the manager returned with my car part, which he plonked down unceremoniously on the counter. Presentation clearly doesn't take much priority at Big Jim's. *The wiper motor was covered in a layer of thick black dirt and flecked with rust. The power cables had been crudely nipped, leaving bare copper wire visible.*

The manager brusquely informed me he wanted twenty pounds for it, but as I'd been quoted fifteen pounds on the phone I queried the bill. He explained that it had been a bastard to get out and showed me an oily gash on his thumb where he'd cut it open on the Peugeot's bulkhead. I reluctantly handed over the cash, which he folded up and stuffed into his overalls pocket.

When I asked if someone could order me a taxi, the manager mumbled something inaudible and wandered off into the back room. I checked out and waited fruitlessly outside the reception area for nearly forty-five minutes. In the end I was forced to set off on foot for the nearest town.

Casefile 2: Rheged Motor Dismantlers, *Penrith*

THE Lake District is one of the country's most popular tourist destinations. And with many visitors arriving by car, the Cumbrian spare part industry is booming. One business hoping to take advantage of the demand for second hand auto parts is *Rheged Motor Dismantlers* in Penrith.

Before visiting, I attempted to ring up to reserve a steering box for an A-reg VW Polo, but my call went unanswered for five minutes. Eventually, a monosyllabic man picked up the phone, explaining that he had heard the phone but had been at the other end of the yard burning the rubber insulation off a load of copper wire.

He said he thought that there might be a Polo in one of the stacks but he wasn't sure, and it would probably be easiest if I just came round and had a look myself. I made a provisional booking and my taxi deposited me outside Rheged's modest corrugated iron and barbed wire-clad premises the next afternoon.

I saw a member of staff who was attempting to wrench open the bonnet of a crashed Seat Alhambra, and I asked him to carry my suitcases up to reception. He looked at me and muttered something under his breath before turning round and continuing to wrestle with the bent metalwork. Note to self: *No tip for him!*

ALEX'S STAR RATING: ★ ☆ ☆ ☆ ☆

My first impressions hadn't been good, and things didn't improve when I stepped into the reception area - an old shipping container supported on bricks. The management no doubt claim it's a case of shabby chic, but to me it appeared far more the former than the latter. There were at least three different mismatched carpets strewn across the floor, all of which were filthy and covered in black, oily bootprints.

To his credit, the manager was very friendly, kicking his oily alsatian repeatedly in the head to stop it barking at me while he went off to find the part I was after. I was keen to inspect the bathroom facilities, so I asked him to direct me to the nearest toilet. *"For a piss, we usually just go behind one of the stacks,"* he told me. *"But if it's a shit you're after there's an old portaloo in the corner of the yard."*

After being quoted £50 for my steering box, I had been hoping for an en suite loo. I certainly wasn't expecting to have to walk twenty yards through a sea of oily mud and past another two chained up dogs going mental in order to spend a penny.

The inside of the toilets took my breath away, but not in a good way. In fact, with no operating flush, no lavatory paper, no hand washing facilities and just a length of dowel to poke the flap open to let the waste drop through, I'd frankly be hard pressed to offer the Rheged Motor Dismantlers toilets anything more than one star at best.

By the time I'd finished and was ready to check out, the manager was back with my steering box. I handed him my American Express card but he handed it straight back. *"Sorry love, cash only,"* he told me.

This scrapyard may be set amongst some of England's most spectacular scenery, but the service I received was far from special.

TINTAGEL in Cornwall is reputed to be the site of Camelot - the legendary seat of King Arthur and his Knights of the Round Table. But if Sir Bedevere, Sir Launcelot and Sir Galahad were to return in order to weigh in some old armour at *Tintagel Scrap*, situated on the modern town's Susan Penhaligon industrial estate, they would be shocked at the poor service they received.

Before visiting, I first phoned up to see how much I could expect for an old lead water tank. The receptionist was noncommittal. *"Fucked if I know. Bring the fucker in and we'll fucking weigh the fucker, won't I,"* he told me in his thick Cornish brogue. Such a four-letter outburst was certainly not what I expected from a five-star establishment. But as I was to learn, it was par for the course at Tintagel Scrap. When I enquired if the yard

Casefile 3: Tintagel Scrap, *Cornwall*

ALEX'S STAR RATING: ★ ☆ ☆ ☆ ☆

operated a courtesy bus service from Newquay Airport I was told to fuck off.

After driving to the yard, I pulled up outside the reception hut and handed my keys to the valet parking attendant - a surly, heavily-tattooed youth in an oil-stained boilersuit who was sitting on an oil drum smoking. I asked him, before taking my car away, to remove the water tank from the boot. This he did, to his credit, albeit reluctantly and with a certain amount of swearing.

The decor in the reception area was an eclectic blend of styles with a muted colour scheme. tastefully distressed shelves loaded with dirty car parts jostled for attention with pornographic calendars, piles of tyres and grungy racks of hammers and hacksaws. I could see the effect the proprietors had been trying to achieve, but sadly their ambition had not been matched by their abilities.

The same receptionist to whom I had spoken on the phone earlier told me he couldn't weigh my water tank for at least another half hour. *"On my fucking dinner, aren't I,"* he explained. Taking advantage of the unexpected delay, I decided to order lunch and asked him for the menu. He looked at me as if I'd asked for the Moon on a stick, laughed in my face and wandered off into a back room. Needless to say, I never got to see the menu.

Twenty minutes later the receptionist reappeared, dragging my water tank across the muddy, oil-soaked yard to a set of rusty agricultural scales. *"It's a heavy fucker,"* he told me. *"But the fucking arse has dropped out of the fucking lead market so I can only give you two fucking quid for it, can't I."* At this point I suddenly noticed that my car was fifty feet in the air, dangling off a magnet over the open jaws of a hydraulic crusher.

I'm afraid I can only give Tintagel Scrap a half-star rating. You expect the occasional minor scratch when handing over your car to be valet parked - the odd ding and scrape goes with the territory. But to have my brand new Mercedes SL crushed into a two-foot cube was frankly unacceptable service.

Casefile 4: Hillside Motabitz, *Llandudno*

ACCORDING to the old song, you can always expect a welcome in the hillside when you visit Wales. But the welcome I received when I checked into *Hillside Motabitz* just outside Llandudno was anything but warm.

I turned up without booking and asked the concierge, an angry looking, oil-covered man with several fingers missing, if he had any Hillman Hunter clutch bell housings available that evening. He said he had, quoting me a price of sixty pounds. I asked if that included a full, cooked breakfast and he muttered something in Welsh which I took to mean that it didn't. He explained that it would take him about an hour to get the part off the car so I thought I'd take the opportunity to freshen up after my journey.

However after checking behind every door in the small portacabin reception area, I was unable to locate the shower-room. Eventually I gave up and decided to have an afternoon nap while I waited.

ALEX'S STAR RATING: ☆ ☆ ☆ ☆ ☆

In the absence of a bed, I opted to slip into my silk PJs and stretch out on the battered, stained three-seater settee propped up in the reception area. I was disappointed not to find a chocolate on the pillow - it is thoughtful little touches like that that can make all the difference when visiting a scrapyard.

But the lack of a chocolate was the least of my worries. I've slept in some uncomfortable places in my time, but Hillside Motabitz must surely rank as one of the worst. There was a cloying smell of oily dog off the cushions and a stench of burning tyres from the yard. And if that wasn't enough, the constant whine and scrape of scrapped cars being dropped into the crusher just about put paid to any chance I had of getting my beauty sleep.

Eventually, somehow I managed to drop off. But not for long. Even though I hadn't asked for a wake-up call, the concierge roused me from my slumbers by rudely kicking the chair with his steel toe-capped boots and asking me what I thought I was doing.

I got up, dressed, paid for my bell housing and checked out. All in all, I have to say that Hillside Motabitz was one of the worst stays I've ever had in a scrapyard and I certainly won't be booking myself in there again in a hurry.

Next week: Kirsty Allsopp checks out the UK's ritziest maggot farms.

LETTERBOCKS

Viz Comic P.O. Box 841, Whitley Bay, NE26 9EQ

letters@viz.co.uk

I'VE just had two hot dogs for lunch and then I used the water they were cooked in to make a Pot Noodle. Beat that for environmental sustainability.

Adrian Newth, Stratford

THE movie *Reservoir Dogs* won lots of awards for its acting and direction, but none for dancing. I reckon that had the producers cast Wayne Sleep as Mr. Blonde rather than Michael Madsen, then it may well have picked up a few awards for choreography.

Renton Kirkpatrick, Manchester

I READ that every cigarette you smoke contains more than 3,500 chemicals. If that doesn't show the value for money smokers get whenever they light up, nothing will.

Phil Ward, Beverley

I DON'T know why Sir Walter Raleigh got so much respect after he put his jacket down so that Queen Elizabeth could step over a puddle. I've seen portraits of him, and his coats were shite. They're like what Adam Ant used to wear back in the eighties, and I for one wouldn't be seen dead in one.

Morten Druid, Leeds

Morgan's Weird World of PIERS
with telly twat *Piers Morgan*

RETIRED postman *Reg Groyne* walked his dog butch along Cleethorpes pier every morning for 10 years. But on the 6th June 1993, he arrived to find the pier was GONE! The following morning, walking along the seafront, he saw that the 1,200 foot long structure was mysteriously back! To this day, nobody has been able to say what happened to it on that day...

STAR LETTER

THE night before last I had a cracking dream about being a porn star. Once I had finished all the things us porn stars do best, the lady turned to me and said I was fantastic and paid me £8 for the honour. £8? What kind of salary is that for a modern grumble legend? It spoilt an otherwise perfect dream.

Matty Shepherd, Medicine Hat

YESTERDAY I was watching what I thought must be a really tense bit of the snooker on TV for quite a while before I realised that I had the sound switched off. I felt like a fool. In boring sports like snooker and cricket, they should have a man whose job it is to stand next to the referee and blow the odd toot on a trombone or some bagpipes during the quiet bits, just to let the viewers at home know that they haven't gone deaf.

Andrew Hussey, Gainsborough

WHEN you think about it, elephants are well equipped. Not only are their cocks massive but they also have a built-in trumpet.

Simon, Belfast

HOW come every year Australia and New Zealand get to celebrate New Year before everyone else? It would be nice if we all took it in turns to have the top spot instead of the Antipodeans always hogging it.

Phil Godsell, London

WHY do footballers always jog up and down the pitch before a game? They'll only tire themselves out. If you ask me, they should be conserving all their energy for the match.

Ben Nunn, Lewisham

MY Grandad once said to me "Never judge a man unless you've walked a thousand miles in his shoes." With that in mind, I purchased a pair of Jonathan Ross's shoes in a charity auction recently and set off around Britain. I arrived home this morning and can confirm he is indeed a bit of a twat.

Stevie Weir, Mannington

WHY do these news readers brag about their 'flash' photography all the time? Every night you hear them boasting: "this report includes flash photography…" I thnk it's rather arrogant. I don't take a bad selfie, it has to be said, but I don't go around telling everyone how clever I am with the angles and lighting and whatever.

Mandy Pearson, Dartford

Morgan's Weird World of PIERS
with telly twat *Piers Morgan*

STORIES abound about the mythical Big Pier, to be found in the woods of the Pacific Northwest of America. First sighted in 1924 by gold prospector *Albert Westman*, the structure is reported to be over 500m long with a 500-seat theatre at the end. Although there have been many sightings since, its existence still remains unproven...

I WISH people would stop saying that policeman are getting younger. I joined the force in 1990 at the age of twenty-one and I am now nearly fifty. So if anything, the opposite is true for me.

D Tomlinson, Maltby

PEOPLE always claim that foxes are cunning, but I saw one rummaging through my bin on Monday night when the bins had been emptied that morning. He is a local fox, so he should have had that weighed up by now.

Mr Roy, Hull

Potentially Ask Brian Cox

*Viz Comic gives you YOUR chance to put your science questions to CERN Particle Physicist **Professor Brian Cox** and, if he's reading this, perhaps get them answered.*

● **IN THE** film *The Time Machine*, the machine built by Rod Taylor stays where it is in the same room as it travels through time. But if it moved to a different time, wouldn't it actually appear somewhere else, as the machine would stay in the same place in space whilst the planet would be in a different position in its orbit?

Keith Curfew, Uttoxeter

* *Well, that's a tough one. If Brian Cox is reading this, perhaps he'd care to write in and answer it.*

● **SCIENTISTS** are very quick to rubbish conspiracy theorists who say the Moon landings were faked. But in the next breath, they enthusiastically espouse the Multiple Universe theory. Well, if there are an infinite number of universes in which

all possibilities come to pass, then there will be one in which the Moon landings were faked. How do the scientists know that it isn't this one?

Mr Namelost, Sorry

* *Well, that's another good question. If any readers see Brian Cox on a regular basis - perhaps he gets on your bus in the morning or has his lunch in the same KFC as you - could you get him to answer this question please.*

● **ACCORDING** to the Theory of Relativity, astronauts accelerating away from the earth in a rocket would age at a slower rate than the people they leave behind as they approach the speed of light. However, in the absence of a fixed point of reference, it is just as true

to say that the earth is accelerating away from the rocket. So why wouldn't the people back on the earth stay young whilst the people in the rocket got old?

Garforth Cliff, Hull

* *Do you work in the Physics Department of Manchester University? If so, please tear this page out and pop it in Brian Cox's pigeonhole. Or, if you're a member of D:Ream, could you please pass it to him next time you see him at Top of the Pops?*

Have YOU got a science question for Professor Brian Cox? Send it in to: *Ask Brian Cox, Viz Comic, PO Box 841, Whitley Bay, NE26 9EQ.* If he's reading this there's a very slight possibility that he might answer it if he can be arsed.

AT work recently I did a turd that looked exactly like a bunch of over-ripe bananas. Unfortunately, I'd left my phone on my desk and by the time I returned with it to take a photo, someone had already flushed it away. I was just wondering if whoever it was took a photo first, as I'd quite like a copy.

D Alexander, Inverness

WHENEVER I see a wildlife documentary about ant colonies, I always spot at least one of them who isn't carrying anything. I suppose that just like humans, there will always be some skiving bastards. After all, it's not like they could actually get the sack or anything.

D Attenborough, London

WATCHING a repeat of *Thunderbirds* recently, it occurred to me what a letchy old bastard that Parker was. He was talking to Lady Penelope beside her car and looking down the top of her blouse. He was probably wishing puppeteers Gerry and Sylvia Anderson had stuck an extra string down the front of his pants, the dirty little bastard.

Stephen Zodiac, London

WHENEVER you see actors in Hollywood films having a shower, although they get up a good lather behind the semi-opaque screens, they never seem to wash down below. They concentrate on their arms and necks, but never give "under the bridge" a good scrub, even though in my experience this is the part that really needs it. I can't help feeling that this unhygienic practice will cause embarrassment during any bedroom encounter later in the film.

Andy Whitfield, Lancaster

WHAT'S the point of horses? We don't use them for transport any more, there's a massive outcry when we eat them and watching them race is completely boring. I think we should just get rid of the whole species and have done with it.

Chandler Raymond, London

"THERE'S nowt on telly. Bugger all," said my mother after flicking through the TV listings magazine. Imagine my confusion when I tuned in and there were programmes and films on every channel, 24 hours a day. The old fool.

Lister Modjik, e-mail

I WAS on the train today and a toddler got on with his mother. Once the train started to move he called out "Choo-choo" with great delight. I didn't have the heart to tell him that this was a diesel electric locomotive and did not make that noise. But I did anyway.

Mark Springham, Leigh-on-Sea

THERE'S no place for the so-called "stepover" in football. It is a blatantly dishonest practice designed to mislead unsuspecting defenders and is blighting the modern game. I am a double glazing salesman and, if I tried to dupe people like that on their doorsteps, I'd be denounced as a rogue trader. Whichever way you look at it, it's cheating and the perpetrators should be given lengthy bans.

Kevin Roberts, Chester-le-Street

THEY say that walking under a ladder is bad luck. So how come I walked under a ladder the other week and got a great look up at my next-door neighbour's knickers as she was taking down the Christmas lights from the top of her bay window?

Lyndon Chipboard, Oakham

I DON'T know why cocktail bars think they're so posh and elite. I called in one recently for a Margarita and there was salt all around the rim of the glass. The dirty bastards hadn't even bothered to wash it.

Rosemary Potatoes, Croydon

Morgan's Weird World of PIERS
with telly twat Piers Morgan

COLOMBIAN farmer *Boco Perez* thought he was dreaming when he saw an enormous glowing pier in the sky over his house near Bogotar. As it came near, he was drawn into it by a beam of light from a candyfloss stall at the end. Inside, he was greeted by aliens from another world who probed his arse with technologically advanced instruments before depositing him back on earth...

I'M tired of hearing on the news that "experts disagree" on this and on that. If they disagree, then at least one of them is wrong on the matter and therefore not an expert.

A Kennedy, London

HOW is it that tea tastes nice, biscuits taste nice, and biscuits dipped in tea taste nice, but that sludge you get at the bottom of a cup of tea tastes like sick? Perhaps the experts can stop whining about global warming for five minutes and explain that one.

David Milner, Durham

TOP

A HAPPY New Year greetings card with the 'Y' crossed out makes a great congratulatory card to someone who has had an ear transplant, or who has recently had a hearing aid installed.

Simon Hoffman, Pulborough

KEEP your binmen entertained by dumping your unsorted recycling into a bin full of polystyrene balls, thus providing a fun 'lucky dip' to brighten up their mornings.

Dee Tritus, Preston

MASTURBATORS. When having a quick five knuckle shuffle in the shower, do not use your wife's L'oreal Oleo therapy oil infused conditioner as a lubricant, as your lustrous shiny pubes smelling of summer meadows may give the game away.

Ian Jamieson, Tortola

SAVE money on expensive inflatable neck pillows next time you fly by simply wearing the life jacket from under your seat. You can also use the whistle to gain the attention of the stewardess when you need a drink.

Desulph Daz, Middlesbrough

WHEN writing on your hand, save ink by using a freckle or wart to dot the "i"s.

Mike McLeod, Bookham

CUT out the middle man when buying a curry by pouring it straight down the toilet and wiping your arse with a sliced chilli.

Steve Irving, Carlisle

STOP your boyfriend pestering you for anal sex by getting a tattoo of his mum's face on your arse.

Jimmy Dickfingers, Chatham

WEREWOLVES. Check the phases of the moon on any number of internet sites. On the last day before a full moon, put on a large dog muzzle and a pair of boxing gloves to lessen the chances of any unpleasantness when the moon rises.

Chlamidia Whelk, Truro

LEAVE left over gravy in the fridge to make a nice meat flavoured blancmange.

Chris Ashton, New Brighton

ALLEVIATE traffic congestion by simply filling in the UK canal network with hardcore and rubble before topping it off with tarmac. Hey Presto! A whole new road network.

Julian Stanley, Bedworth

CORONERS. Save money on dictaphones by placing a parrot on your shoulder during autopsies.

Robert Marshall, Melbourne

Calls for everyone to be sacked after Twitterstorm

Pariahs: Some of the 60m people at the centre of the twitterstorm

A TWITTER and Facebook storm was last night raging as all social network users pressed for everybody in Britain to be sacked for offending everybody else by saying or doing something or other.

"I am genuinely up in arms about something or other," said one offended Facebook user. "Whatever it is that everybody has said is completely unacceptable and they should be sacked or resign," they added.

furious

"I am furious over some sort of unacceptable situation that I have read about on the internet whilst I was supposed to be working," another outraged Facebooker posted. "I am going to keep campaigning about it and organising flashmobs until everyone, including me, has been sacked," she continued.

And an online petition calling for everybody to be dismissed from whatever they do quickly attracted over 60 million signatures.

dave clark

Meanwhile, everyone at the centre of the storm had gone into hiding yesterday hoping to ride it out. However, insiders close to everyone said that everybody had been subject to abusive tweets and even death threats from everyone else.

the REAL ALE TWATS

Panel 1: STEP SPRIGHTLY, CASKETEERS – VALHALLA AWAITS! / FULCHESTER SPRING BEER FESTIVAL / BEER FESTIVAL / STAND BY TO PURCHASE YOUR SOUVENIR HALF-PINT TASTING GLASSES AND BEER TOKENS!

Panel 2: WHAT A MAGNIFICENT TURN-OUT! / FOR WE ALEHEADS, THE SPRING BEER FESTIVAL IS THE SOCIAL EVENT OF THE YEAR.

Panel 3: IT IS AN OPPORTUNITY TO MINGLE WITH FELLOW AFICIONADOS OF THE HOP... / TO EXCHANGE JOVIAL BANTER WITH OUR CASKOPHILIC BRETHREN...

Panel 4: ... YES, THE BOLAND'S PRANCING GOBLIN IS A QUITE ACCEPTABLE SESSION ALE, I SUPPOSE... / ALTHOUGH THE 3.7% ABV DOES PLACE IT BELOW MY PREFERRED FOUR PER CENT MINIMUM THRESHOLD...

Panel 5: IT'S SLIGHTLY REDOLENT OF THE FIDDLER'S PERSISTENT OFFENDER, WHICH I SAMPLED AT THE THREE HOBBITS IN DARROWBY BACK IN '02. / THAT WAS A ROBUST, TAWNY ALE WITH AMBER NOTES ON THE NOSE AND A LONG, FRUITY FINISH. 3.8% ABV.

Panel 6: AHEM. YES, THE THREE HOBBITS IN DARROWBY WAS A FINE PUB – I GOT ON WELL WITH THE LANDLORD, A SPLENDID CHARACTER CALLED NORMAN... / I RECALL ONE DISCUSSION ABOUT HORNBY OO GAUGE CLASS 55 DELTICS WHICH LASTED FROM THE EARLY EVENING UNTIL LAST ORDERS!

Panel 7: ONLY UNTIL LAST ORDERS? / 'NORM' AS WE CALLED HIM WOULD FREQUENTLY HAVE "LOCK-INS" FOR HIS FAVOURITE REGULARS. MANY'S THE TIME THAT I STUMBLED OUT OF THAT PUB TO THE TWITTERING OF THE DAWN CHORUS!

Panel 8: ON ONE OCCASION WHEN I WAS TAKING MY LEAVE AT DAYBREAK, I EXPRESSED MY CONCERN THAT I MIGHT BE SPOTTED BY THE LOCAL CONSTABLE... / "THAT'S UNLIKELY" SPAKETH NORM, "HE'S FAST ASLEEP UNDER THE POOL TABLE IN THE BAR!"

Panel 9: ARF! SNORT! SNURFLE! ARF!

Panel 10: YES, I REMEMBER THE LOCK-INS WE USED TO HAVE AT THE KING'S DIRK, IN WALMINGTON... / TONY THE LANDLORD WOULD BOLT THE DOORS, AND OUR SESSIONS WOULD CONTINUE FOR DAYS – MUCH TO THE DISPLEASURE OF MY THEN-WIFE!

Panel 11: INDEED, THOSE LOCK-INS CONTRIBUTED DIRECTLY TO MY DIVORCE... HAPPY DAYS! / ARF-*! / JUST HAD THE ONE DIVORCE, HAVE YOU?

Panel 12: I MYSELF HAVE BEEN DIVORCED FOUR TIMES / I RECALL MY FOURTH EX-MISSUS TELLING ME SHE WAS GOING TO TAKE THE KIDS AND GO AND LIVE IN DONCASTER...

Panel 13: I RIPOSTED THAT PROVIDED I RETAINED CUSTODY OF THE TERRANCE DICKS PAPERBACKS, SHE COULD MOVE TO GALLIFREY IF SUCH WAS HER WONT!

Panel 14: ARF! SNORT! SNURFLE! ARF! / TSK!

Panel 15: LATER... / ...YERRS, IT IS REMINDFUL OF THE WYE VALLEY HPA WHICH I SAMPLED AT YE OLDE BARRELS IN HEREFORD... / ..A LIGHT GOLDEN PALE ALE WITH AN ABV OF 4%. THE LANDLORD'S NAME WAS PETER.

Panel 16: COO-EE, GEOFF! IT IS ME, ELSIE FROM THE SPAR – I THOUGHT I'D FIND YOU HERE! / ?! / YOU LEFT YOUR SHOPPING ON THE COUNTER WHEN YOU CAME IN THE SHOP EARLIER!

Panel 17: HE LOVES HIS BEER, DOES GEOFF! / COMES IN THE SHOP EVERY EVENING FOR HIS FOUR CANS OF CAFFREYS!

Panel 18: CAFFREYS? CAFFREYS? CAFFREYS? CAFFREYS! CAFFREYS! / !

Panel 19: TRUDGE TRUDGE TRUDGE TRUDGE

Panel 20: BANG! / THUD!

Panel 21: NOW THEN! A GLASS OF GOLIATH'S IGNOMINIOUS TOPPLE, METHINKS! / ...A SATISFYING RICH, DARK BEER WITH A GLORIOUSLY TRIUMPHANT FINISH. 5.1% ABV.

31

Buz

A bleak tale of the North based on 'A Bluebottle for a Knave' by Tyke Parkinson

When Grimesbury schoolboy Casper Roach found a maggot in a pork chop, he took it home and raised it into a fly. Now, when he needs to escape from his unhappy working class Yorkshire life at home and school, he takes Buz the bluebottle out onto the moors above the town.

Mornin' our mam.

Ayup, Casper. 'Appen tha'll 'ave to get tha sen tha own breakfast. Tha dad's at work an' I'm already late f' me shift at t' flat cap factory.

There's drippin' an' pikelets in t' pantry. And mind tha's not late f'school. Tha dun't want t'get into trouble wi' tha teacher Mr Shadrack again.

Aye mam.

But Casper had other ideas ...

Beggar school. There's nowt for me theer.

Cum on, Buz. Let's gerroff and fly thee on t' moo-er.

Casper was soon on Slagtop Moor, the only place where he felt truly alive...

Go on, lad! Fly free!

Look at 'im gaw!

Casper lost track of time as he watched his iridescently hued pet soaring through the air...

Wheep! Wheep!

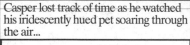

Cum by, Buz! That's it, lad!

Bloody 'ell fire. It's Shadrack. Wot does 'e want?

A thowt I'd find thee 'ere, Casper, flyin' tha bluebottle.

Aye, sir.

It's a grand fly is that, Casper. What's that y'swingin' theer?

It's a bit of shit on a string, sir.

Oh aye?

To lure 'im back, sir.

Well, tha certainly seems t'knaw a lot abaht flies, Casper.

Aye sir. I gorra boowk abaht 'em aht t' library.

Did tha now?

Aye sir. I raised 'im me'sen from a grub.

My. Yon's a grand bluebottle.

Would tha like t'feed it some dog dirt, sir? It wain't bite.

No thanks, Casper...

Listen, lad, I've got some bad news f'thee...

Theh's bin an explosion at t' parkin factory...

Tha dad's deed, Casper.

Thy's t' breadwinner now, son. Tha's'll 'ave t'leave school t'loowk after tha mam.

I've sorted thee aht wi' a job as apprentice at t' whippet works. Tha starts at six sharp tomorrow mornin'.

Next morning ...

Wheer's thee off to, Casper?

Work, mam. It's me fost day at whippet factory.

Well tha can't tek THAT bloody thing t'work wi' thee, tha daft a'poth, wi'its shitty feet. Tha wain't be allowed through t' bloody gate.

Can you look after 'im, then, mam?

No I can't, Casper. It's t 'South Riding brass band bingo practice today...

...Stick tha fly in t' coal ouse. 'E'll be allreet theer.

With a heavy heart, Casper locked his bluebottle in the coal house.

Be'ave tha'sen, Buz.

I'll pick thee up a nice dog dirt on me way 'ome an' we'll go up on Slagtop Moo-er for a fly abaht. Tha'll be allreyt, Buz, I promise thee.

Shortly ...

Birling & Co. Ltd Whippets

All day as he toiled in the noisy factory, Casper was counting the minutes until he could be with Buz, up in the fresh air of Slagtop Moor once again...

Keep tha mind on tha work, young 'un. Tha's put yon collar on back to bloody front.

Sorry.

Until, at six o'clock ...

HOOOT!

At home...

Tha tea's in five minutes, Casper.

I'll 'ave it later, Mam. I'm tekkin' Buz on t' moo-er.

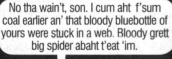

No tha wain't, son. I cum aht f'sum coal earlier an' that bloody bluebottle of yours were stuck in a web. Bloody grett big spider abaht t'eat 'im.

Buz!

I finished both of 'em off wi' me slipper, dirty 'orrible buggers.

A broken-hearted Casper carried the lifeless body of the only thing he'd ever loved up onto Slagtop Moor one final time.

It's time for thee to fly free, Buz. Time t'fly free forever.

Flick!

The End

New Shame for Cat Bin Woman

Youtube pariah filmed "putting lion in a bin"

THE WOMAN who hit the headlines back in 2010 when she threw a cat into a bin has sparked outrage once again after she was secretly filmed doing the same thing... *to a LION*. Footage of Mary Bale, 50, putting a fully-grown male Asiatic lion into a wheelie bin at Sherwood Zoo surfaced on the internet where it has been viewed more than 6 million times by horrified animal lovers.

The lion, named Cedric by keepers at the Nottingham-based attraction, spent 16 hours trapped in the bin before being released. "Luckily he was none the worse for his ordeal," said head keeper Spanky Chipperfield. "But we can't imagine why anyone would want to do such a horrible thing to him."

mane

CCTV footage posted on Youtube shows Bale approaching the lion enclosure and looking around surreptitiously before reaching through the bars and picking up the 35-stone animal by the mane.

She then tips Cedric into a wheelie bin and walks off nonchalantly towards the zoo exit. A link to the clip was posted on Twitter by comedian and animal rights activist Roger de Courcey.

Wheelie wild show: Footage of Cedric the lion being put in a bin has went viral on the internet

"This woman thinks it's clever to put the king of the jungle in a bin. They should put her in a bin and see how she likes it," de Courcey tweeted to his 4.5 million followers. The Twitter hashtags #lionbingate and #Justice4Cedric were soon trending worldwide, with users of the social network demanding justice for Cedric the lion.

aerial

"Someone should bend the aerial on this nasty woman's car," said @I_Like_Lions, whilst @LionsRNice tweeted: "If I ever see this lady I'll give her a piece of my ruddy mind." A Facebook group calling for dog dirt to be rubbed on her front door handle quickly had 600,000 members. As a result of the threats, Bale was once again said to be in hiding. "She's waiting until

it all blows over," a pal told reporters. "She put the lion in the bin as a joke, nothing more. It was simply another moment of madness that she now deeply regrets and she promises to probably not do it again."

ordeal

Meanwhile, keepers at Sherwood Zoo said that Cedric was recovering well following his ordeal. "He's absolutely fine," said a spokesman. "He's just shagged some lionesses and now he's tucking into a horse's head and neck."

FUCKING WANCHOR

OH, LORDY! IT'S THE FAT SLAGS

WOT YOU UP TO, SAN?

I'M DOIN' ME CHRISTMAS PRESSIE LIST...EEH!.. THERE'S SO MANY NAMES ON IT... IT GETS BIGGER EVERY FUCKIN' YEAR

WELL Y'SHOULDN'T BE SO GENEROUS...Y'SHOULD CHUCK HALF THESE NAMES OFF... THEY'RE NOT EXACTLY CLOSE FRIENDS

I KNOW... BUT CHRISTMAS IS ALL ABOUT *GIVIN'*, TRAY

AYE... SO WHO'S GETTIN' WOT?

WELL, I'M GIVIN' DAVE AN' 'IS BROTHER A BLOW JOB EACH...I'M GIVIN' FAT STAN A TUG... A SOAPY TIT WANK F' THE WINDOW CLEANER...TOPS AN' FINGERS F' RON AT THE PUB... A BELGIAN BISCUIT F' 'IS DAD...A CLOTH TIT F' THE POSTMAN... BROWN WINGS F' BIG TOMMY... A MUFF DIVE F' LITTLE TOMMY...A FACE-SIT F' CHIP SHOP TERRY AN' A SQUID WANK F' TONY FROM THE PIZZA TAKE AWAY

WOT Y' GIVIN' BAZ?

I THOUGHT I'D GIVE 'IM A SELECTION BOX

WOT'S THAT?

A BLOW JOB, A TUG, A SOAPY TIT WANK, TOPS AN' FINGERS, A BELGIAN BISCUIT, A CLOTH TIT, BROWN WINGS, A MUFF DIVE, A FACE SIT AN' A SQUID WANK...

HE'S NOT BOTHERED ABOUT CLOTH TITS, BUT THERE'S ALWAYS SUMMAT Y' NOT FUSSED ON IN A SELECTION BOX

BIG VERN

XMAS EVE...

LOOK WHO IT IS, ERNEST! VERNON'S POPPED BY.

VERN! HOW LOVELY TO SEE YOU.

WOTCHA, ERNIE.

JUST FOUGHT I'D STOP BY TO WISH YOU AN' THE BRASS A MERRY WOSS-NAME, ERNIE.

WELL WE WERE JUST HAVING A JOLLY GAME OF CHARADES, VERN. YOU REMEMBER BILL AND MAUREEN FROM NEXT DOOR..?

ORWIGHT..?

YOU CAN JOIN IN, VERN. BILL'S JUST FINISHING HIS TURN. IT'S A FILM...FOUR WORDS... FOURTH WORD.

BLOW?...ERM... GALE?

STORM?

WIND!

GONE WITH THE WIND..?

YOU GOT IT IN ONE, ERNEST.

THAT WAS SUPER FUN, VERN - WHY DON'T YOU HAVE A GO NEXT?

OKAY ERNIE.

TAKE A CARD.

SWEET AS.

FILM.

TWO WORDS.

FIRST WORD.

ERM... DEAD! DIE! THE DEAD POOL!...

NO, THAT'S THREE WORDS. ERM...ERM...

DEATH? NO, ERM...ERM...

KILL?

KILL! KILL... IT'S "KILL SOMETHING".

ERM...ERM...

OOH! OOH! KILL BILL!

K-CLATCH!

BLAM!

BLAM!

NO, VERN...! I MEANT... IS IT "KILL BILL"...THE FILM?

OH, SORRY ERN. MY MISTAKE.

NAH. ITS ACTUALLY "KILL SWITCH", THE 2008 STRAIGHT-TO-DVD STEVEN SEAGAL VEHICLE.

ANYWAY, 'OO'S UP NEXT, ERNIE?

35

Two Rings Don't Make a Rite

A CATHOLIC service was thrown into chaos yesterday when a faulty altar bell held up a Mass for more than three hours. Nearly 200 worshippers at St Fiacre's Church in Wallasey were kept waiting after communion wine being blessed by priest Father Hoolihan O'Toolihan failed to transubstantiate into the literal blood of Christ.

"I'd already rung up the host over the wafers and they'd transubstantiated a treat," Father O'Toolihan told the *Liverpool Catholic Herald and Argus*. "But when I did the chalice of wine, the divine mystery didn't happen for some reason."

"I thought perhaps I had said the wrong word in Latin or something, so I tried it again," he said. "But when I had a sip, it wasn't the blood of the son of God, it was still just normal wine."

miracle

"For some reason, the Eucharistic miracle specified by the Council of Trent wasn't happening," he continued.

"I thought about simply carrying on and doing the service with the

Faulty altar bell halts Eucharist

untrasubstantiated altar wine, but when you're dealing with people's eternal souls you can't take the risk," he continued.

O'Toolihan suspected that the transubstantiator in his sanctus bell may have blown, and a quick inspection of the workings confirmed this to be the case.

pip

A replacement part was needed, and the congregation were forced to remain in their pews whilst it was sourced.

"It's quite an old sanctus bell, and I don't think they make transubstantiators for them any more," O'Toolihan said.

Eventually, a second hand unit was located in a disused bell in Birkenhead and rushed over to St Fiacre's.

bunnyman

It was a long wait but O'Toolihan kept everyone entertained by talking about the Natural Law theory of St. Thomas Aquinas, reciting the synoptic gospels and playing I-spy.

Eventually, an engineer arrived and fitted the new transubstantiator in the bell.

"When I fired it up, the wine turned into the blood of Christ first time,"

Service interruption: Father Hoolihan O'Toolihan's Mass was held up after his transubstantiation bell went tits up.

said Father O'Toolihan. "Everybody was delighted and Communion went ahead as normal, albeit a little bit late."

A spokesman for the Catholic Church told us: "We recommend that all priests get their sanctus bells serviced at least once a year to ensure efficient transubstantiation of the host into the literal body and blood of Christ."

"We cannot take responsibility for any worshippers who end up in the lake of fire for all eternity due to failed Eucharistic miracles."

EVERYBODY IS A BASTARD! OH NO! IT'S THE PARKIE

SPRING! TIME TO GET THE PARK READY FOR THE PUBLIC, I SUPPOSE.

CHOP! CHOP!

BUZZZZ!

SNIP! SNIP!

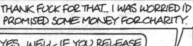

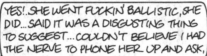

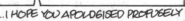

NOT SO SIMPLES!

Meerkat ad bosses 'at a loss' over what they do

Ad-imal magic: One of them meerkat things standing on its back legs yesterday.

THE COMPANY that makes the adverts featuring the meerkats yesterday made a stark admission to shareholders... "We've completely forgotten what it is that we do for a living."

"These days we mainly seem to make cuddly toys and short animated films about talking rodents," said chairman Quentin Gardens, addressing the business's AGM at the Birmingham NEC.

"I've got a feeling we originally used to do something else as well as meerkats, but to be honest, I'm buggered if I can remember what it was."

Albert

Managing Director Victoria-Anne Albert was unable to throw much more light on the mystery. "I've got a vague recollection that it might have been something to do with credit cards or insurance or phone bills or something, but it's all rather got overshadowed by the runaway success of our adverts starring Aleksandr and Sergei," she said.

charming

"People just can't get enough of them and their charming little adventures. And when we introduced baby Oleg, well that was it. Who could think about boring old business with such an adorable little orphan character stealing all our hearts?"

two shoes

"Our latest ad campaign for whatever it is we do features Arnold Shwarzenegger being carjacked by Aleksandr and his sidekick on a Hollywood movie set," continued Ms Albert. "It was an enormous coup to get a big star like Arnie to plug our product. It's just a pity we haven't got a clue what it is."

When the meeting ended, all delegates were given a goodie bag containing a talking meerkat cuddly toy, a signed copy of Aleksandr Orlov's autobiography *A Simples Life* and two tickets to see *Terminator Genesis*.

The Origins of Today's CHRISTMAS CUSTOMS

EVERYONE KNOWS that the tradition of Christmas began millions of years ago with the birth of the little baby Jesus in a stable, all meekly wrapped in swaddling clothes and in a manger for a bed. But today's festive season, with its merrily decorated trees, greetings cards, Bond films and overcooked sprouts, is a far cry from that first low-key celebration of the Nativity. So where did our modern Christmas come from? Who was the first person to put up a tree, post a card or not want his fucking brother-in-law to come round? Amazingly, the answer to all these questions and more is *Prince Albert*. Now, cultural historian Hildebrand Pinecone, professor of Xmas Studies at Corpus Christmas College, Oxford, takes a look at the extraordinary influence that Queen Victoria's consort had on our modern festive season.

3. A 3-hour Boxing Day Toilet Visit

ON CHRISTMAS Day 1850, the Queen bought her consort a solid silver genital piercing for Christmas. The delighted Prince immediately bored a hole through his glans and meatus and popped on the 6" long bolt/chain combination, declaring it "a most pleasing and perfect fit." However, the next day, when he went to the toilet to park the turkey, the clasp on his piercing became entangled in the hinge mechanism of the seat, leaving poor Albert stuck fast for the best part of the afternoon. Engineer Sir Isambard Kingdom Brunel was eventually summoned, and eventually managed to get the hapless Prince free late in the afternoon. Word soon got out that Albert had spent three hours on the toilet on Boxing Day, but rather than explain the real reason why, Buckingham Palace made up the story that sitting on the toilet all afternoon on December 26th was an old German tradition that he was upholding. The custom caught on, and a century-and-a-half later we are still following Albert's lead.

6. Hiding from Carol Singers

ON CHRISTMAS Eve 1853, Albert and Victoria were just settling down for their tea when there was a knock on the door of Buckingham Palace. The Prince peeked round the curtains to see the concertmaster of St Pauls Cathedral Sir William Sterndale-Bennett on the doorstep, wearing a scarf and holding a lantern. Behind him were the 500 members of his choir, including the internationally renowned baritone Jean-Baptiste Faure and the famed "Swedish Nightingale" Dame Jenny Lind, all of whom had spent the last three months rehearsing a concert of carols to entertain the royal family. On seeing them, Albert whispered to his family to put the lights out and hide. Sterndale-Bennett spent the next ten minutes intermittently banging on the door and looking through the window, whilst Victoria, Albert and their seventeen children remained on their hands and knees behind the sofa. The crestfallen choir eventually turned round and went home, and hiding from carol singers has remained a British Christmas tradition ever since.

5. Falling Asleep in Front of the Bond Film

ON CHRISTMAS afternoon 1852, explorer Sir Augustus Pitt-Rivers arrived at Buckingham Palace to entertain the royal party with a two-hour magic lantern show entitled "The Wonders of the Empire". Within twenty minutes, Pitt-Rivers's whole audience, who had just eaten a big turkey dinner with all the trimmings, was fast asleep. The following year, Prince Albert decided it was time to ring the changes, and instead booked adventurer, assassin and spy Sir Richard Burton to recount some of his exciting and amorous adventures set in the most exotic locations of the globe. Within twenty minutes his whole audience, who had just eaten a big turkey dinner with all the trimmings, was fast asleep. This tradition continues to this day, as Britons "just close their eyes for a minute" during the first advert break in the Christmas afternoon Bond film, waking up just in time for the closing credits.

1. Christmas Cards

THE VERY FIRST Christmas card was sent by Albert to Victoria in 1858. The Prince Consort had lost his voice after catching a throat infection whilst performing an act on a cheap prostitute in Whitechapel, and was thus unable to wish his wife season's greetings in person. Instead, he wrote "Merry Christmas" on a piece of card, drew some snow on the top of the letters, and gave it to the Queen. She was so delighted with the thoughtful gift that Albert decided to make "Christmas cards" a seasonal tradition at Buckingham Palace. Every year thereafter he went out in early December to get a throat infection whilst performing an act on a cheap prostitute in Whitechapel before sending specially printed cards to everyone he knew, signed "love from Vic, Al and the kids."

2. Christmas Trees

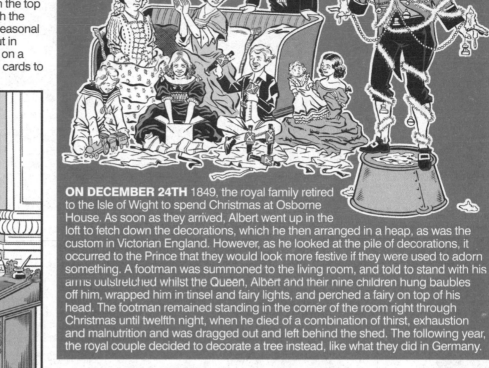

ON DECEMBER 24TH 1849, the royal family retired to the Isle of Wight to spend Christmas at Osborne House. As soon as they arrived, Albert went up in the loft to fetch down the decorations, which he then arranged in a heap, as was the custom in Victorian England. However, as he looked at the pile of decorations, it occurred to the Prince that they would look more festive if they were used to adorn something. A footman was summoned to the living room, and told to stand with his arms outstretched whilst the Queen, Albert and their nine children hung baubles off him, wrapped him in tinsel and fairy lights, and perched a fairy on top of his head. The footman remained standing in the corner of the room right through Christmas until twelfth night, when he died of a combination of thirst, exhaustion and malnutrition and was dragged out and left behind the shed. The following year, the royal couple decided to decorate a tree instead, like what they did in Germany.

4. Pain-in-the-Arse Brother-in-Laws

NOT ALL FESTIVE customs are as enjoyable as plum puddings, carols round the tree and Coca-cola adverts featuring big lorries. One such is having your pain-in-the-arse brother-in-law coming round and ruining your Christmas day, and once again we have Prince Albert to thank for this tradition. On Christmas Day 1851, Victoria's sister Princess Alexandra of Saxony came round with her husband Dennis, a candle salesman from Leicester who wore slip-on shoes. For the entire afternoon Dennis sat in Albert's chair, telling a series of self-aggrandizing anecdotes about his career in the candle retail business, bragging about how much his brand new carriage cost, laughing over-loudly at his own jokes and drinking Albert's beer. By 9 o'clock in the evening, Albert had begun repeatedly checking his pocket watch and yawning theatrically, but Dennis refused to take the hint and embarked on a seemingly interminable account of a prize he had recently won from his company for selling the most candles in a month. It was after midnight by the time Princess Alexandra and Dennis finally left,

saying they'd come round again next year. Horrified by the prospect, Albert vowed that if he had to suffer, then the rest of his subjects would also have to suffer likewise. In the very next parliament, prime minister Lord Melbourne passed a new law requiring every British citizen who had a pain-in-the-arse brother-in-law to have them round for Christmas. Although the law is nowadays never enforced, 165 years later the tradition established by Prince Albert still remains.

7. Fucking Awful Christmas Jumpers

WHEN WE WAKE up on December 25th and go down to open our presents, we all know chances are that waiting for us under the tree we'll find a parcel containing a fucking awful Christmas jumper, knitted for us by a well-meaning but senile female relative. But few people realise that the very first fucking awful Christmas jumper was actually given to Prince Albert in 1854 as a gift from his auntie, Princess Louise of Orléans, wife of his Uncle King Leopold of the Belgians. The brightly coloured jumper, which his auntie had knitted herself and which was far too big for him, had one sleeve longer than the other and featured a bold snowman motif on the front that had gone a bit wrong. Albert only wore it once, when the Belgian royal family came to Britain for a state visit in 1858, when he told his auntie that it was his favourite. The jumper was then used for many years as a mattress in Queen Victoria's dog's basket, before being lost following the monarch's death in 1901. It was rediscovered in 1988 when an inventory was being taken at Windsor Castle. It is now on permanent display at Hampton Court Palace, where curator of the Royal Costume Collection Dr Lucy Worsley recently described it as "fucking awful."

Next Month: We learn you about the origins of today's January Customs.

Mr. Logic

HE'S A COMPREHENSIVE ANORECTAL DISCOMFITURE

Post Office

I WOULD LIKE YOU TO FORWARD THIS PARCEL ON MY BEHALF TO THE RECIPIENT IDENTIFIED ON THE FRONT, TO WIT: MY NEPHEW

POP IT ON THE SCALES

OKAY... IT WEIGHS 1.5 KG, SO IT'LL BE...

NO... YOU ARE WRONG. IT HAS A **MASS** OF 1.5 KG...

ITS **WEIGHT** IS A PRODUCT OF THAT MASS AND THE ACCELERATIVE FORCE EXERTED ON IT BY THE EARTH'S GRAVITATIONAL FIELD... I.E... $9.81 m/s^2 \times 1.5 KG$...

A WEIGHT OF $14.215 Kg\,m/s^2$

OR 14.215 NEWTONS, IF YOU WILL

1.5 KG... FIRST CLASS, £2.40

WHAT'S IN IT?

IT CONTAINS A GIFT FOR THE SON OF MY FEMALE SIBLING ON THE OCCASION OF HIS BIRTHDAY

DOES IT CONTAIN ANY LIQUIDS?

I DON'T KNOW... YOU HAVEN'T FURNISHED ME WITH SUFFICIENT INFORMATION TO PROVIDE YOU WITH AN ANSWER

EH!?... WHAT DO YOU MEAN?

ALL MATERIALS DISPLAY A LIQUID STATE DEPENDENT ON THE TEMPERATURE OF THEIR SURROUNDINGS... YOU DID NOT SPECIFY THE TEMPERATURE AT WHICH YOUR ENQUIRY OF THE LIQUID CONTENT OF THIS PARCEL RELATED

OKAY... DOES IT CONTAIN ANY LIQUID AT **THIS** TEMPERATURE... **HERE**... **NOW**... IN THE POST OFFICE?

I DON'T KNOW...

THE STATE OF MATTER OF A SUBSTANCE IS DEPENDENT ON THE PRESSURE... YOU DID NOT SPECIFY THE PRESSURE AT WHICH YOUR ENQUIRY OF THE LIQUID CONTENT OF THIS PARCEL RELATED

I'LL START AGAIN... DOES THIS PARCEL CONTAIN ANY LIQUIDS AT ROOM TEMPERATURE AND ATMOSPHERIC PRESSURE?

I DON'T...

AH...

AT SEA LEVEL

NO, IT DOES NOT

ARE THERE ANY BATTERIES IN IT?

IT CONTAINS MATERIALS BETWEEN WHICH AN ELECTRICAL POTENTIAL MAY BE GENERATED UNDER CERTAIN CIRCUMSTANCES

HMM! DO ANY OF THEM LOOK LIKE THIS BATTERY?

THAT IS NOT A BATTERY... IT IS A **CELL**

IS IT, INDEED?... AND ARE THERE ANY OF THEM IN YOUR PARCEL?

NO!

OKAY... NO LIQUIDS... TICK!... NO BATTERIES... TICK!...

I DON'T SUPPOSE THERE'S ANYTHING RADIOACTIVE IN THERE?..

HMM?... WELL?

WELL, WHAT?

I ASKED YOU IF THERE WAS ANYTHING RADIOACTIVE IN IT?

NO YOU DIDN'T... YOU SIMPLY MADE A STATEMENT EXPRESSING YOUR LACK OF CONJECTURE THAT THERE WAS

WELL IS THERE ANYTHING RADIOACTIVE IN IT OR **NOT**?

WELL EVERYTHING CONTAINS A NUMBER OF RADIOACTIVE ATOMS... RADIOACTIVE CARBON 14 EXISTS IN ALL ORGANIC MOLECULES IN AN ABUNDANCE OF 1 IN 10^{12}... THIS PARCEL WOULD THEREFORE REGISTER THE USUAL BACKGROUND RADIATION LEVELS ON A GEIGER-MULLER TUBE

SO IT **IS** RADIOACTIVE?

LIKE EVERYTHING ON EARTH IT WOULD NOT REGISTER ZERO IF MEASURED FOR RADIOACTIVE DECAY

SO IT **IS** RADIOACTIVE?

YES

Post Office

NEXT DAY...

NOTHING FROM UNCLE LAWRENCE AGAIN, MUM?

I'M AFRAID NOT...

...SAME AS EVER.

No buts, it's got to be buttocks!
BOTTOM of the KLASS

Britain's cheekiest botty forum

with *Myleene Klass*

" Hi readers, Myleene Klass here. You probably know me best for being out of *Hear'say*, appearing in adverts for Littlewoods and soaping my knockers in a pond on *I'm a Celebrity*. But chances are you don't realise I'm absolutely **BACKSIDE BONKERS!** Derrières, situpons, posteriors, mudflaps... call them what you will, when it comes to bodyparts, I reckon **bottoms** are **tops!** And judging by this week's bulging *Bottom of the Klass* postbag, *Viz* readers are as potty about the botty as I am! Here's a selection of the most bootilicious letters I've received... **"**

I MARRIED my wife simply because she had the most gorgeous bottom I had ever seen - round, pert and peachy, it was like two boiled eggs in a handkerchief. I often wish there had been a bit more to our relationship than her bottom - perhaps some shared interests, lively conversation or mutual respect - because she's 83 now and her arse is frankly a shadow of its former self. She's really let it go over the last sixty years and these days I'd rather not look at it at all.

Hector Palfreyman, Pyewipe

WHY is it that in *Carry On* films and on seaside postcards, doctors are always giving their patients injections in the buttocks? Whenever I've had a jab, it's always been administered in my upper arm. And why is it that whenever cartoonists draw somebody's bottom, they always put a little cross of sticking plaster on it? Speaking personally, I have never cut my bottom, and even if I did I would dress the wound simply with a single plaster. I would certainly not apply two plasters at 90° to each other.

Mrs U Rusteater, Redditch

AFTER watching a documentary on Channel 5 the other night, my wife and I decided to try a bit of spanking. Unfortunately, I quickly got rather carried away and in the heat of the moment she forgot the "safe word". After several hours of me enthusiastically whacking her bottom with a table tennis bat whilst she fruitlessly pleaded with me to stop, she finally remembered the safe word. Unfortunately, by this time her buttocks looked like two over-ripe aubergines. That was two weeks ago, and she hasn't been able to sit down since. The tragic thing was, as it turned out, spanking didn't really do anything for me, although my wife is keen to try it again, albeit with a more memorable safe word.

Rev J Foucault, Truro

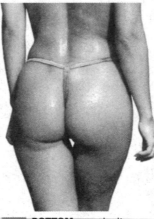

BOTTOM men don't know they're born. They can go on any beach and see women in thongs showing off their buttocks for all the world to see. Meanwhile, breast men like myself are left to imagine the treasures hidden inside their bikini tops. It's about time there was a level playing field for bottom and breast men, and I for one would vote for any political party that promised to bring in thong-style bikini tops.

B Meatpaste, Leigh-on-Sea

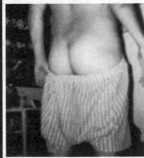
I WAS recently carrying a Coca-Cola bottle up the stairs backwards whilst wearing a loose-fitting dressing gown when I slipped and fell awkwardly. The bottle went up my bottom, and I can't get it out. I am about to go to A&E, and I was wondering if any readers could suggest a slightly more plausible explanation, because for the life of me I can't think of one.

A Saxilby, Dunham-on-Trent

I WAS wondering if there is any point in cleaning my arse. It seems to get dirty again practically straight away.

Chris Horsley, Barnsley

ANYONE who uses the expression "as soft as a baby's bottom" ought to be chemically castrated, put on the sex offenders register and have dog dirt pushed through their letterbox for putting such paedophilic images into other people's minds. Saying "as soft as a toddler's bottom" would be bad enough, but to drag little babies into this is sick beyond belief.

Audrey Frenchhorn, Crewe

I WAS watching an old episode of *Monty Python's Flying Circus* the other day and there was a so-called comedy sketch on it about a man who had three bottom cheeks. Well, I ask you, what's funny about that? No wonder the BBC cancelled the show if that's the best joke they could come up with.

J Cloth, London

BACK in the 1970s, my secretary always wore very short mini-skirts to work and I used to slap or pinch her bottom every time she walked past or when I made her bend over at the filing cabinet. Everybody did, there was nothing wrong with it back then and she didn't seem to mind. It was just a bit of light-hearted office horseplay. If she didn't want me to do it, she only had to wear a longer skirt. These days I can't even compliment my secretary and tell her she's got a nice bottom without being accused of "sexual harassment".

CJ, Surbiton

EVERYBODY goes on about how sexy Felicity Kendal's bottom was in *The Good Life*. Well, I'm sorry, but she ate food like the rest of us, so it's practically a certainty that she used to push evil-smelling foulage out of it on a regular basis. Call me a prude, but the thought of such filthiness Is far from sexy in my book. Ms Kendal should hang her head in shame.

Frank Chickens, Tiverton

FURTHER to Mr Chickens's letter *(above)*, I should further imagine that on several occasions, whilst attempting to wipe up after such a sordid episode in the lavatory, Felicity Kendal's finger may well have gone through the paper. In the circumstances, how she was voted Rear of the Year remains a complete mystery to me.

Ian Girth, Penge

I'VE heard a rumour that Joanna Lumley has a plastic bottom. Whilst I am 100% certain that this scandalous slur is not true, do any readers know whether it's her buttocks, her anus or in fact both that are made of plastic?

Percy Shaw, Halifax

WHY do old-fashioned tractor seats have that ridge up the middle that serves only to push one's buttock cheeks apart? It's none of Massey Ferguson's business how I choose to arrange my bottom when I'm working on my farm. My mud-flaps are perfectly happy nestled together, thank-you very much.

E Grundy, Ambridge

PERHAPS Richard Dawkins can explain why the human anus has evolved in its present position - pressed tightly between two hemispherical bags of muscle and fat. It's just asking for trouble, in my opinion. All the other animals have their anii exposed to the elements with the result that, unlike us, they don't have to spend ages wiping up after going to the toilet. Having said that, I have to admit that my spaniel occasionally yachts across the living room carpet, but the vet says that's because of his glands, not a dirty arse.

Siegfried Eggs, Pan

IT'S all very well these "so-called' celebrities winning "Rear of the Year," but the judging should be organised properly, like when they have ex-ballroom dancers on *Strictly*. I'm sure there are lots of qualified proctologists out there would gladly offer their expertise and even perform a more thorough examination.

Hampton Lunchbox, Croydon

I'M all for a forum about people's bottoms, but there are two genders in our species, and **both have bottoms!** Your magazine is once again guilty of overt sexism in selecting the letters with the emphasis on women's bottoms. Where the letter makes no mention of the sex of the bottom, it is invariably illustrated with a picture of a woman's behind. How about illustrating this letter with a picture of a man's bottom for us feminists?

G Greer, Australia

* *No problem, Ms Greer.*

WHEN I was at school in the 1950s, the headmaster used to hit us on the bottom with a thin stick if we were caught running in the corridors, forgot our caps or

Back Body Row

Bottoms in the Arts
with Radio 4 culture vulture *Mark Lawson*

PERHAPS the most famous bottom in the arts is the character *Bottom*, who appears in a play by *William Shakespeare*. Shakespeare was a famous playwright who lived in Stratford-upon-Avon in Queen Elizabeth times. He had a beard, a collar that went right round, a doublet and hose, and wrote with a feather. His house had straw on the roof and black stripes on the outside wall. Shakespeare's most popular plays include *Romeo and Juliet*, *Hamlet* and *A Tale of Two Cities*.

MANY famous pictures in art galleries feature bottoms in them. Some of the best known ones are that one with a lady having a picnic with some men, the one where the lady is lying on a chairs longeau looking in a mirror, and the modern one with the lady with an itchy bottom on a tennis court. There's another painting of a bare lady where she's standing in a shell, but you can't see her bottom. Michael Angelo's David is a big statue of a man where you can see his bottom, but you have to go round the back to look at it.

YOU might think that the opera called *Wagner's Ring* is about a bottom, but you'd be wrong. In fact, it's a stage musical with a lady wearing a viking hat and a metal bra who sings all wobbly whilst waving a big spear shaped like a fork.

IN EVELYN War's novel *Brideshead Revisited*, Jeremy Irons and Anthony Andrews are sunbathing on the roof of Brideshead Revisited when they are surprised by her who was in that episode of *Inspector George Gently*, who is Anthony Andrews's sister, and they stand up and you can see both their bottoms.

More bottoms in the arts next time! *Mark*

Mark Commode's Bum Bloopers

● IN MERCHANT Ivory's 1985 adaptation of EM Forster's *A Room With a View*, the Revd Beebe (played by Simon Callow) and two other characters go skinny-dipping in the village pond. Despite the film being set in the Edwardian era, a tattoo reading "Motorhead Ace of Spades" is clearly visible on Callow's left buttock. The band Motorhead did not form until June 1975, and didn't release the single *Ace of Spades* until 1980, 75 years after the film was set, so there is no way that the Revd Beebe could have had such a tattoo.

● ALTHOUGH she was happy to appear topless in the 1973 British horror classic *The Wicker Man*, actress Britt Ekland famously refused to allow her bottom to appear on screen. As a result, director Robin Hardy brought in a body double - wrestler Pat Roach, later to find fame as Bomber in *Auf Wiedersehen Pet* to film the scene in question. However, the substitution is revealed in one shot when Roach, wearing a long blonde wig, turns his head slightly to one side whilst wiggling his bottom provocatively, and his large ginger beard and a pipe can clearly be seen.

● IN QUENTIN Tarantino's *Pulp Fiction* (1994) a Vietnam War veteran, played by Christopher Walken, hands over a watch to young Butch, explaining that it has been hidden up his and the boy's father's bottoms throughout their incarceration as POWs. However, the watch he hands over is clearly an Apple iWatch, which was not released until 2014, 20 years after the movie was made.

got less than eight out of ten in a spelling test. I remember it hurting quite a lot, although it never did me any harm.

Dr Rhodes Boyson, Lancs

WITH reference to Dr Boyson's letter *(left)*, there was a similar practice at my school, only instead of a cane the headmaster used to beat us on the bottom with a size 12 plimsoll if we forgot our games kit, chewed chewing gum in class or talked during assembly. It was very painful indeed but, like Dr Boyson, it never did me any harm.

Dr Wentworth Day, Suffolk

WITH reference to the previous two letters, the headmaster at my school also operated a strict, bottom-focussed discipline regime. However, instead of using a cane of a slipper, he would undo his trousers and strike us repeatedly with his engorged tassel, even if we hadn't done anything wrong. It hurt a great deal, but it never did me any harm.

Dr Jimmy Edwards, Chiselbury

"DOES my bum look big in this?" my wife asked me the other day. When I turned, I saw that there was an American tramp wearing her dress. And at 6'2", he did indeed look big in it, as my wife is very petite.

R Gingivitis, Jarrow

I ALWAYS used to tell my son not to sit on the cold floor in case he got piles, but he always ignored my advice. Now he's a grown-up but I don't know whether he did ever get piles, as he moved to Australia with his family more than thirty years ago. I only speak to him at Christmas on the phone for ten minutes, and the subject of piles never comes up, so I have no idea if the old wives' tale about sitting on the floor giving you piles is true or not.

Dolly Sadness, Blyth

The Bottom Line

HOW come man ballet dancers have big muscly bottoms that stick out at the back, whilst man ballroom dancers have tiny, pert bottoms in their tight trousers?

Shane Lloyd-Webber, Tipton

Britain's leading bottom scientist Dr Alasdair Fissure answers your bottom-related queries...

* *The muscle that makes up the bottom, the Gluteus Maximus, is essentially a jumping muscle. Male ballet dancers often jump twelve feet in the air or more when they are doing pas de deuxs, and consequently have highly developed Gluteus Maximusses that stick out at the back of their tights. Male ballroom dancers, on the other hand, glide around without ever lifting their feet more than two inches from the ground. As a result, they exhibit very little Gluteus Maximus development, and are thus able to fit their tiny bottoms into slender, snake-hipped trousers with all sequins on them.*

Send YOUR bottom related query to: Dr Alasdair Fissure, Viz comic, PO Box 841, Whitley Bay, NE26 9EQ

ROGER MELLIE
THE MAN ON THE TELLY

Roger's Telly Show WORDSEARCH

OVER the years, Roger Mellie has hosted hundreds of popular shows, one or two of which have even been given a second series. Hidden in the wordsearch grid are the names of 20 of his most famous. They may read horizontally, vertically or diagonally, backwards or forwards.

ROGER'S SUPERMARKET SWEEP - a game show with a shoplifting theme. **MARBLES UP THEIR ARSEHOLES** - an all-new game show requiring courage, skill and rectal volume. **CALL MY FUCKING BLUFF** - an old favourite with a modern twist. **THE ENEMA WITHIN** - celebrities share their colonic secrets. **THE GOLDEN SHOWER** - an adult themed version of the seventies classic The Golden Shot. **THE BRISTOL MAZE** - a breast-themed adventure game show. **THE BOLLOCK NAKED CHEF** - full frontal nude cookery. **ROGERING AROUND BRITAIN** - Roger tours the UK looking at the best brothels and rub 'n' tug shops. **PRO-CELEBRITY GOLF** - prostitutes and entertainers team up for a round of 18 holes, all for charity. **WHO'S THE DADDY** - Britain's first fertility clinic based game show. **SPUNK IN THEIR EYES** - members of the public pay tribute to their favourite porn stars. **DIRTBOX JURY** - celebrities have their arses judged by a panel of experts. **BARGAIN CUNT** - two teams compete to see who can bag the best deals in Fulchester's red light district. **BRITAIN'S GOT DIARRHOEA** - stomach upset based game show. **THAT'S MY FUCKING DOG** - a show that combines illegal dog fighting with general knowledge. **ROGER'S BIG BREAK-IN** - Though the Keyhole inspired show featuring celebrities who are away on holiday. **CELEBRITY SHIT BUCKET** - D-list celebrities compete to see who has the best anal aim. **BIRDS OF THE RAZZLE HOUSE** - reality show featuring Roger Mellie and a dozen grumblemag models. **STAR IN A REASONABLY PRICED BAR** - drink-driving-based show where plastered celebs test their skills behind the wheel. **CELEBRITY PILL SWAP** - reality show looking at what happens when celebrities trade medication for two weeks.

```
A F D K R N I A T I R B D N U O R A G N I R E G O R B
K G T I L H T E X B J T G L P Z E O M Y L G V R S E L
R O G E R S B I G B R E A K I N D L H P N R E F E J I
M U G B S T M I B C S P E H Y G M U K D E M I L C S A
L R J K B F B M H K E C S A N L E S B C Z M I L H B F
Q U V H I G S O Z F V U E I S B U K G E A A B I K J A
S A C B E D U E X C Y E K M W E Z H O P M W N P L A G
T A R B E C H J P J W C A E N I O D G T L P M K Y E D
A D E I A M L D H U U Q H B I L F Y B W O M L A B T L
R L R R A X V I D F C R N Y R D L O W R T W B U W H C
I A Y D P U L B V W C E Y A Z B U I O P S P T D O G X
N C T S W V Y M A V Y H J S T B O P H Y I P J E B H V
A R G O H T S P Y H M F R Y T Z E K E U R P I L O V C
R W B F H T E M I H D E T E N U L O I F B E B I D S C
E A N T A T L I M Y E R N U T Y G S E R E P G O A T E
A R T H E G O L D E N S H O W E R W T W H M T E W H F
S B T E E V H Z J U F R M U E R D S D V T E O B Y E M
O P Y R Q T E V F P U B M C D H U T M I A B P H A C E
N I M A G A S M U U O B T X T B E M P K R E A C O A L
A L F Z A U R E B U L E Z V I K A O L R W C D L J D E
B A L Z B U A P M F T G R R V R A P M E D C H H D L Y
L A O L N Y R B U I J S G A S I R I G M K L M I Y Y R
Y Z G E E V I O L H M Y M N T C D L F A P M A V N T E
P T I Y P W E A V J L R S Y I T L E N E I E V I U E I
R E T O P L H E V U E O J Y O K V K M T E N P M V L B
I B I U M A T D Y P L H Y G A Y C L J G S E C P L G C
C Z R S V Y P C U E B U S H I O V U P U C C U U C J S
E C B E A I U S F R N V Y L M H H I F P A E C T N D B
D V E I L D S T Y I B T L N W C I T Y M I H Y D T I D
A L E S E E E L T T F Y B O H B T L S C G L M Y B U B
R G C G N E B I C Y E C Y H N I S H Y F B U L N N K U
B T O A G I R O S H A V Y H D T V I K J E V E A M T C
N R R M E B A C T N J G S T E J I K N G R Y D C B S K
B U P Z R I M M T D S E Y E R I E H T N I K N U P S E
A Y H I P A W S L L I P Y T I R B E L E C A I Q G P T
```

Answers on page 175

Raffles The Gentleman Thug

EMPIRE, LEICESTER SQUARE, 1896...

WHATEVER WILL OUR GALLIC COUSINS ENVISION NEXT?

MOVING IMAGES PROJECTED UPON A SCREEN IN AN ALMOST PERFECT SIMULACRUM OF REAL LIFE, EH LORD RAFFLES..?

OH TESTICLES. IT'S NOT A FUCKING FRENCH FLICK, IS IT BUNNY?

I AM STOUTLY DISINCLINED TO MICTURATE HALF A CROWN UP THE WALL FOR THE PRIVILEGE OF WATCHING SOME GASTROPOD INGESTERS FLATULATING ABOUT, SHRUGGING THEIR SHOULDERS AND MELANCHOLICALLY PUFFING ON GITANES.

A-HA! THE DOOR IS OPENING!

TICKETS, IF YOU PLEASE, GENTLEMEN. THERE'D BEST BE SOME TITS IN IT OR I'M ABSQUATULATING.

LET US MAKE HASTE, RAFFLES, LEST THE PREEMINENT SEATING POSITIONS ARE SECURED BY OUR FELLOW KINEPHILES.

TSK. RESTRAIN YOUR FUCKING EQUINE ENTOURAGE. I'M PURCHASING SOME COMESTIBLES FIRST.

ONE PUNNET OF PHLOGISTICATED CORN KERNELS, MY GOOD MAN... AND TWO LARGE ABSINTHES... WITH STRAWS.

SHORTLY... SLURP!

WHEN DOES THE PRESENTATION START, BUNNY?

NOT FOR A WHILE YET, I'M AFRAID, OLD FRUIT.

EXCRETE A BRICK.

I SAY, OLD CHAP... WATCH THIS..!

SIR- WOULD YOU KINDLY DESIST YOUR JUVENILISTIC SHENANIGANS AT ONCE!

OOOOOO-OOOOOO!

DO YOU MIND? THE EXPOSITION IS ABOUT TO COMMENCE!

LA CINEMATOGRAPHE LUMIERE presents TRAIN PULLING INTO A STATION IV Fist of Vengeance

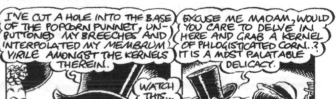

WHAT-HO, BUNNY... TIME FOR A LITTLE FUN WITH THIS ORNITHOLOGICAL SPECIMEN WHO'S ENSCONCED IN THE ADJACENT SEAT..!

WHAT DO YOU MEAN, RAFFLES?

THE OLDEST TRICK IN THE BOOK, BUNNY!

I'VE CUT A HOLE INTO THE BASE OF THE POPCORN PUNNET, UN-BUTTONED MY BREECHES AND INTERPOLATED MY MEMBRUM VIRILE AMONGST THE KERNELS THEREIN.

WATCH THIS...

EXCUSE ME MADAM, WOULD YOU CARE TO DELVE IN HERE AND GRAB A KERNEL OF PHLOGISTICATED CORN..? IT IS A MOST PALATABLE DELICACY.

HOW KIND.

HOWEVER, IN ORDER THAT I MIGHT AVOID BESMIRCHING MY GLOVES, I SHALL HAVE MY CHAPERONE SELECT IT FOR ME, IF THAT IS AGREEABLE...

ER...

LORD BIG DAVE - THIS GENTLEMAN HAS GENEROUSLY PROFFERED ME A SAVOURY SWEETMEAT FROM HIS PUNNET. WOULD YOU BE SO KIND AS TO SELECT ONE FOR ME..?

AYE.

CONCUBINATE MY HAPPENSTANCE.

SHORTLY...

GO ON, LORD BIG DAVE..! FUSTIGATE HIS FUCKING PHYSIOGNOMY IN!

Take a Shit...

WINNER!
MAGAZINE of the YEAR
~Take a Shit Magazine of the
Year Awards

Take a Shit

WIN
MAGAZIN
~Take a Shit
Year

Cosplay Saved Our Marriage!

COSPLAY - the craze for dressing up as favourite characters from fantasy fiction - is the latest import from the States. Fans of cult shows and movies such as *Star Trek*, *Game of Thrones*, *Dr Who* and *Star Wars* love nothing more than donning the costumes of their TV and movie heroes to attend conventions and meetings. Sci-fi and fantasy buffs spend countless hours lovingly crafting their outfits, making sure they are exactly as they appeared on screen down to the tiniest detail.

BUT one West Midlands couple have taken their shared passion for cosplaying a step further ... up the stairs and into the bedroom! And amazingly, after four decades of marriage it has boosted Howard and Gloria Sheldon's sex life to warp speed.

"Me and the missus were childhood sweethearts," said retired television repairman Howard, 61. "She was the first girl I ever kissed, behind the bikesheds at Secondary Modern, and she is still the only woman I have ever been with. When we first got wed, 42 years ago, we used to make love all the time. Gloria was young, sexy and insatiable and I was only too happy to oblige."

"We used to have sex morning, noon and night, all over the house, like the teenage newly-weds we were," said Howard. "But then, after a couple of weeks, some of the sparkle started to go out of our marriage, and it wasn't long before love-making became a chore to be endured, especially for her. Somehow, the excitement had gone out of our relationship, and for the next forty years our sex life was practically non-existent."

That all changed the day that the postman dropped off a parcel for the Sheldons' next door neighbours. Howard told us: "I didn't realise it was for them and

As told to *Vaginia Discharge*

Sci-fi fancy dress put love-making on another planet, say Walsall couple

I opened it by mistake. Inside were two dressing-up costumes - a sexy Lara Croft *Tomb-Raider* outfit for her and a *Star Trek* Klingon one for him - they were evidently going to a fancy dress party."

"I took the costumes out and had a look at them. The Lara Croft one was very sexy, with cooter cutter shorts, a skintight black vest and a crocodile-skin thigh dagger belt, whilst the Klingon one even came with a rubber head mask," said Howard. "I don't know why, but I suggested me and Gloria should try them on and see how we looked in them. She was a bit reluctant so I put the Klingon outfit on first. It was a bit tight, and the zip bust when I tried to do the trousers up because they were a 34 waist and I'm a 42."

"But I looked good in it, and once I squeezed the rubber head on, my transformation into an alien was complete," Howard told us. "I was no longer a 61-year-old retired telly repairman from the West Midlands, I was Zarg the Merciless, a cold-blooded warlord from the other side of the galaxy. And what's more, I had the Klingon hots for Lara Croft."

"Unfortunately, no amount of cajoling from me could

persuade the missus to don the *Tomb-Raider* costume. She has never been much of a fantasy fiction fan, and dressing up as Lara Croft to have sex with a randy Klingon was definitely not her cup of tea."

But Mrs Sheldon never misses an episode of her favourite soap *Coronation Street*, and that gave her an idea for a cosplay of her own. "Two minutes later we were in the bedroom, with me dressed as Admiral Zarg of the Klingon starship IKS Te'mang and her dolled up as mousey spinster Emily Bishop, complete with high-collar blouse, below-the-knee tweed skirt and tartan carpet slippers."

"In the bedroom I commanded the earthling to pleasure her alien overlord or she would feel my wrath and I would destroy her planet," said Howard. "Gloria played her part to perfection, tutting and shaking her head. Just like her cosplay *Corrie* character, she told me not to be so daft, explaining that she had to do the kitchen floor and there was certainly not going to be any of that sort of thing. So whilst Emily went downstairs with a pair of rubber gloves and a bottle of Cif, Admiral Zarg was left to pleasure himself in the bedroom."

"It's no exaggeration to say that, as I lay alone on the bed in that Klingon costume, frantically pleasuring myself, I felt the earth move as surely as if Zarg had destroyed it with a giant death ray. It was a shattering climax that left me literally gasping for breath."

Later, as he packed the costume back in its box ready to take it round next door, Howard realised that something had been awakened deep inside both him and Gloria. He told us: "This episode of cosplay had somehow

> *"I commanded the earthling to pleasure her alien overlord or she would feel my wrath..."*

rekindled the flame of passion that had been missing from our relationship.

As our ordinary selves, our marriage had been moribund for 42 years, but dressed up as fantasy figures our sex lives could fly to infinity and beyond. We both knew there was no turning back."

HUNGRY for wider sexual horizons, Howard went on the web to find outfits for their next erotic cosplay session.

"I'd always liked *Star Wars*, and I cooked up a little scene where Darth Vader has his evil way with Princess Leia whilst she's dressed in her sexy costume from when she was Jabba the Hutt's slave. I found a party hire shop in Nuneaton that did all the kit at just £20 for the weekend."

"As I sat on the number six bus bringing the outfits home, I could barely contain my excitement. I had the whole scenario plotted out in my mind," said Howard. "The Princess would come upon Darth Vader in his bedroom on the Death Star. On seeing him she would

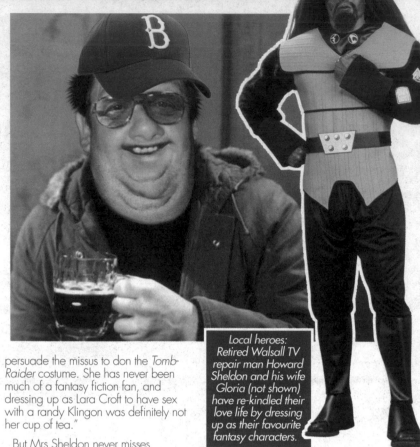

Local heroes: Retired Walsall TV repair man Howard Sheldon and his wife Gloria (not shown) have re-kindled their love life by dressing up as their favourite fantasy characters.

46

scream and try to get away, but he would pull her back towards him with the chain around her neck. Leia would struggle, vainly beating on Vader's plastic chest with her fists, but she would be no match for the Force, and the most evil man in the universe would have his wicked way with her. I couldn't wait for me and the missus to get the costumes on and make our sexy *Star Wars* fantasy a reality."

"I knew the dark side of the Force was taking me over, and I laid back on the bed and awaited the arrival of my royal sex slave."

"As soon I got home, I handed Gloria her costume and told her to put it on and come up to the bedroom in ten minutes," said Howard. "She looked at it and tossed it onto the table while I rushed upstairs to begin my transformation into the dark-hearted cyborg Sith Lord. As I pulled on the black PVC gauntlets, nylon cape and vacuum-moulded plastic mask, I could feel Vader's fiendish desires welling up deep within me. I knew the dark side of the Force was taking me over, and I laid back on the bed and awaited the arrival of my innocent royal sex slave."

"After half an hour I went down to see where she was. To my surprise, the outfit was still on the table. But Gloria had added a new erotic twist of her own to our cosplay sex game. Instead of a nubile concubine from the planet Alderaan, she had dressed herself up as veteran *EastEnders* matriarch Lou Beale, complete with baggy slacks elasticated at the waist, a beige pinafore, thick support stockings and tartan slippers."

Howard realised that he might have to adapt the plot of the couple's sex game to the new situation. He told us: "Would the famously cantankerous Albert Square curmudgeon bow to Darth's depraved will quite as easily as the impressionable Princess Leia?. 'To the bedroom with you, earth wench,' Vader commanded in his deepest voice. 'Your master's needs must be slaked.'"

"Gloria played her Lou Beale part to absolute perfection, frowning and looking daggers at me. 'Pack it in,' she told me. 'I've never heard such a load of ruddy nonsense. It's time you grew up. Darth Vader indeed. I'm doing the ruddy washing up.'"

Howard realised that no amount of Jedi mind control could overcome the iron will of the bloody-minded Queen Vic harridan. "Darth knew he had met his match and retreated to the toilet to give in to his evil desires on his own," he told us. "I pulled the trousers down and took the gloves off because I'd left a £10 deposit on the outfit at the fancy dress shop that I wouldn't get back if it came back stained."

"My wife as Lou Beale had bettered me as Vader and this added an extra frisson of excitement to our erotic cosplay experience," said Howard. "As Darth feverishly dealt with himself in the toilet, his thwarted desires fuelled him to even greater heights of sexual ecstasy. As I

climaxed, all I could hear was my own heavy breathing echoing inside the flimsy plastic helmet."

"Unfortunately the eyeholes were in the wrong place and I couldn't quite see what I was doing, so I ended up forfeiting the £10 on the trousers anyway."

By now the Sheldons were consummate cosplay veterans, and Howard was spending all his spare time at the library, surfing the internet in search of ideas for exciting new role-playing costumes.

He told us: "I ordered Batman and Wonder Woman outfits from America. They were quite expensive, and when they arrived they didn't really look like the ones on the website, but that didn't matter. This was fantasy, and in the fantasy world anything goes."

"The scenario I had cooked up went like this: My wife, dressed as Wonder Woman, had crashed her invisible plane into the grounds of playboy millionaire Bruce Wayne's mansion. Stumbling from the wreckage with her stars and stripes bodice torn and her sheer stockings laddered by the impact, she knocks on the door of Wayne Manor and is greeted by the tall shadowy figure of the Dark Knight himself - Batman."

"Catching her in his muscular arms as she collapses, the Caped Crusader carries her through to the lounge and tenderly lays her on the settee," continued Howard. "She lies there unconscious while he loosens her clothes. From there on in, let's just say that nature takes its course. I had half a teacake on just thinking about it."

But once again, Gloria added an even more erotic twist of her own to Howard's carefully-plotted cosplay scenario. Rejecting Howard's offer of the Wonder Woman outfit, she instead appeared dressed as yet another of her favourite soap characters - *Emmerdale*'s spiteful, church-going widow Edna Birch. "I opened the door in my full Batman outfit and there she was," he told us.

"She had the dowdy pensioner's outfit off to a tee, all the way from the unfashionable cloche hat on her head to the tartan slippers on her feet. Playing her part well, she tutted and pushed past me into the kitchen, explaining that she had been down to the Nisa for some chops and tomato sauce. The erotic charge was palpable and I felt my pulse quicken as I swished my cape round and followed her down the hall."

"The story had taken an unexpected turn and I was intrigued to see where it was going. Edna Birch put the grill on and unwrapped the chops," said Howard. "'I don't know what you think you look like,' said the feisty *Emmerdale* battleaxe. 'You ought to bloody grow up, you did.' She was a feisty one, this one, and Batman felt himself becoming aroused inside his skin-tight rubber trousers. Edna Birch saw what was happening and didn't miss a beat, staying in her character perfectly as she ushered him out of the kitchen and into the back yard."

"...the Dalek would corner her by the tumble drier, tenderly exploring her stone-age body with its plunger and whisk."

"You never know where a sexy cosplay fantasy is going to go, and this one ended up with the Caped Crusader sitting on a deckchair in the shed, bringing himself to heights of pleasure that non-cosplayers can only dream of attaining, whilst Edna Birch did the chops in the kitchen."

Cosplay outfits don't always come cheap, but Howard says you can't put a price on sexual fulfilment. So he thought nothing of splashing out a four-figure sum on his next outfit.

He told us: "A mate of mine knew a bloke who made Daleks in a lock-up in Bloxwich. They were £1500, but they were the real deal, made from wood, fibreglass and chicken wire. And they had castors so that when you were in it you could roll around a bit. I decided to buy one to make our ultimate cosplay fantasy come true, so I took out a Wonga loan in Gloria's name."

"As it happens, once I'd paid for the Dalek there wasn't any money left in the budget for her costume. But that didn't matter, because you see, she was going to be Dr Who's cavewoman companion Leela and I could knock it up myself out of a few old chamois leathers and string. In this adventure, Leela was going to

step out of the Tardis/pantry door and come face to face with me - the Timelords' arch enemy from the planet Skaro."

"She would try to run away but the Dalek would corner her by the tumble drier, picking away her animal skin bikini and tenderly exploring her lithe, stone-age body with its plunger and whisk. Terrified at first, Leela would eventually relax to the Dalek's gently robotic ministrations, her nipples would harden and she would give herself to it to do with as it wished. I hadn't really thought about how that last bit would happen; we'd cross that bridge when we came to it."

But once more Gloria had her own ideas. "She thought it would be a more exciting cosplay session if, instead of Dr Who's primitive companion Leela, she were to dress up as *Corrie* charwoman Hilda Ogden. From her dowdy pinafore to her tartan slippers, the attention to detail was fantastic. She had even put her hair up in curlers to complete the effect. As I trundled into the kitchen, bleating 'Exterminate! Exterminate!', she screamed and dropped a pan of stew she was putting on the hob," said Howard.

"She really was getting into character, shouting for help and slipping around on the stew. The Dalek eventually cornered his victim after she went over on her ankle, and tried to crawl behind the ironing board. I could feel myself getting aroused as I relentlessly hunted down my defenceless quarry. A Dalek making love to Hilda Ogden is everyone's sci-ti/soap cosplay fantasy, and it was about to come true for me."

"Or so I thought. Because at that point, Gloria decided to go off script. Picking up the casserole pan, she threw it at me before hobbling out of the kitchen and going to stay with her sister. But the erotic charge of the hunt had combined with the heady aroma of newly-set fibreglass and car spray paint to bring me to a state of arousal that I could no longer ignore," said Howard. "I performed an erotic act to sort myself out, there and then inside the Dalek costume."

He told us: "It was a bit uncomfortable, because my elbow kept scraping against the chicken wire and some exposed screw heads and nails, but it was the most shattering climax that me and my wife have ever experienced, and it left me light-headed and gasping for air."

"How many couples can say that after forty-two years of marriage?" he added.

letteRbocks

Comic P.O. Box 841, Whitley Bay, NE26 9EQ * letters@viz.co.uk

ELECTRO pop group Kraftwerk, supposed futurists, are still singing about travelling from Paris to Vienna on the Trans Europe Express. However, it closed in 1995 and that route now utilises services run by multiple operators, meaning several changes are required. Isn't it about time that Kraftwerk updated their lyrics to reflect the modern, deregulated continental railway market?

Terry Casablanca, Ryton

I THINK Roy out of Siegfried and Roy could have at least changed his name to something less working class and a little more exotic. After all, Siegfried made the effort. It was bound to end in tears, and I don't mean the type of tears that the tiger inflicted on Roy when it bit him in the throat.

Hampton Golightly, Tring

WHAT'S this nonsense about so called "Blue Monday" being the most depressing day of the year? I had a Creme Egg and the wife wanked me off. It was a fucking great day.

Charles Dodd, e-mail

I RECKON if aeroplanes pointed their jets forwards instead of backwards during take offs in winter, they would clear all the ice on runways and there would be no flight cancellations. Common sense, really.

Hapag Lloyd, Runcorn

STAR LETTER

IT is impressive enough when a school produces one future Prime Minister, so for Eton to turn out 19 of them is outstanding. Not only that, but over 26 our current MPs also hail from that single school. In these days of failing institutions, damming Ofsted reports and disruptive pupil behaviour, it's nice to see one success story. Hats off to them, I say.

Noel Bumpford, Tooting

WHEN I was growing up my mate used to tell me that jellyfish were just massive whale bogeys. For 33 years I believed this until he was sent to prison for stealing a charity box.

T Buktu, Timbuktu

WHY oh why do they measure the output of a vehicle in horsepower? Not all horses can have the same strength. And there's probably loads that are shit at running just like I am.

Samantha Stits, Hull

PHIL Neville recently said that a December World Cup would be good for British football as at the end of a hard season, the players are "dead on their feet." I never realised that playing football was such a hard job. Isn't it about time we recognised this and rewarded premiership players with a pay rise?

Terry Toweling, York

IF Channel 4 newsreader Jon Snow ever stars in his own porn film, I think he should call it *Six Inches of Snow Expected*. There you go, Jon, you can have that one for free.

T Ellen, London

MR Ellen's suggestion about the naming of a pornographic film starring Jon Snow is a very good one. But he failed to point out that it could work equally well if Jon's cousin Peter Snow, or his historian nephew Dan Snow made a pornographic film. And it works however well endowed they are by simply changing the number of inches of snow that are expected.

T Barnaby, Tooting

NOW that T Barnaby *(above letter)* has pointed out the universality of using "*X Inches of Snow Expected*" as a pornographic film title for the Snow family, I wonder how they will sort out who will use it. Maybe they will draw lots at the next family get-together. Or perhaps they'll just agreee that the first one to go into the bongo vid business gets it.

Manfred Maznsell, Hull

HOW come the French call France "France" just like we do? I would have thought with all their obsession about protecting their language, the least they could have done is come up with a proper French word for their own country.

D Cooper, Sicily

GLOBAL warming won't affect me in the least. I'll either just open a window or put on the big coat I bought in the sales last year.

Hapag Lloyd, Runcorn

I'VE often heard it said that pigeon shit can actually burn through the paint-work of your car. If this is true, then one can only imagine the ring sting that their poor little arseholes must suffer during the process. Hats off to the flying rats I say.

Elliot Lochness, Dundee

TEAPOT THE BALL COMPETITION

with Leicester City, England & Walker's Crisps' Gary Lineker

IN THIS PICTURE of some football match goalmouth action, the ball has been replaced with a teapot and then removed completely. Using your skill and judgement, place a cross where you think the exact centre of the teapot is. The person whose cross most closely matches the spot where the teapot actually is will win 40 teabags. The next 10 runners-up will win 4 tea bags Send your entries to: *Gary Lineker's Pot the Ball Competition, Viz Comic, PO Box 841, Whitley Bay, NE29 9EQ* to arrive no later than December 31st 2017. Employees of Fulchester industries, their friends and relatives, acquaintances and anyone they have never met or spoken to are not eligible to enter.

Teams: *Leeds United v Blackburn Rovers.* **Venue:** *Elland Road, Leeds.* **Date:** *3rd December 2011.* **Time:** *16:10.* **Weather:** *Cloudy, light rain, light wind from North East.* **Conditions:** *Heavy, floodlights on.*

Last Week's Competition

Winner: M. Lawrenson, *Merseyside.*

I DON'T get the Vikings. They must have been minted, what with all that plundering and looting, but they always went around looking like a bunch of scruffs without a pot to piss in.

Hamilton Marzipan, Oxford

WHILST driving the other day, I let a bin lorry out of a side road. However, that evening my numbers failed to come up in the Euromillions lottery. I'm starting to think that all this karma malarkey might be complete bollocks.

P Hamnett, Manchester

I WONDER who would win in a fight between a cat and a chihuahua, as they are roughly the same size. I'm not suggesting that anyone pitches these two animals together behind a pub or anything, that would be hideously cruel, but if anyone has ever seen it happen, what was the upshot?

Bartram Mildew, Croydon

WHY is it that footballers who hoof the ball into row Z are referred to as donkeys? They never shank it into Row Y, or AA. If you ask me, they demonstrate an impressive level of precision.

Edna Probably, Grantchester

PEOPLE often draw the analogy of there being "an elephant in the room" when confronted with an awkwardly embarrassing situation. However, if there was indeed an elephant there, all the damaged furniture and huge mounds of shit on the carpet would conveniently deflect thoughts away from the embarrassment, which would soon be forgotten.

Tarquin Conelly, London

WHILST drunk, some friends and I dabbled with a ouija board. Imagine our surprise when we were contacted by the spirit of dead Liberal Democrat politician Roy Jenkins, who proceeded to manipulate the glass to spell out the need for an integrated European transport system for over three hours. Have any of your other readers had such dull experiences of the paranormal?

Frankie Hartley, M'brough

I KNOW that motorway cops use unmarked cars to catch car thieves and joy riders but many of these have cottoned on to this, and can spot them a mile off. However, if the police started using say, a Morris Minor Traveller or an Austin 1100, they could use the element of surprise to lock up some of these boy racers, I reckon.

Norbert Dentrisangle, Hull

HOW come in the 007 films the baddies are always so polite and well mannered, referring to the secret agent as "Mr Bond" and even inviting him onto their island for dinner or something? Only my mate's a copper and he tells me that villains he's nicked usually tell him he is a cunt and should go fuck his mother.

Andy Johnson, e-mail

I CAN'T help but think the upbeat theme tune to the TV show *Murder, She Wrote* takes away from the seriousness of the murders.

Lyndsey, Belfast

HOW come cockerels make such a din in the morning? As far as I know all the other birds get up at about the same time, but obviously they have a bit more consideration for others.

Bobby Conkers, Goole

YESTERDAY I received an e-mail from a man called Clinton MacAdam who asked me if I wanted to know "a fast and easy way to get any woman turned on, attracted to you, and on her knees, begging to suck your d*ck?" As it happened, I didn't, because I'm a woman, and anyway, at 85 I'm well past that sort of thing. But it was nice of him to ask and also very considerate of him to asterisk out the 'i' in the final word as I am easily offended.

Ada Grimmage, London

IF the French are an hour ahead of us, why aren't they all making a fortune betting on UK horse racing and football, the results of which they will know a full 60 minutes ahead of British bookmakers?

Ben Nunn, Lewisham

HOW wonderful it was to enjoy the recent Masters Snooker tournament on BBC2. No hooliganism, no abusive chanting from the crowd, and not one of the players took a dive or needed to be shown a yellow card. The FA could learn a thing or two from the world of snooker. Perhaps a good starting point would be to issue every football referee with white gloves and a bow tie, and for him to insist on silence from the crowd whenever a player is about to kick the ball.

Phil Kitching, Isle of Jura

YOU don't see any OAPs out of their heads on smack, do you? They're never in the chemist twitching for their methadone, just quietly buying pile cream and Victory Vs. Come on pensioners, you're letting the side down.

Mrs Rainbow, Newcastle

TIT MOUSE

DID 'E FUCK!

with sceptical rapper P DIDDY

Each week the US hip-hop star pours scorn on the outlandish claims made by YOUR friends and relatives

Dear Diddy

My granddad reckons he once did 230mph on the Autobahn in a 1976 Austin Allegro.

Jerry Socks, Fife

Diddy says...

"**Did 'e fuck!** While the speed limit on certain parts of the German motorway system is indeed unregulated, the maximum top speed for any model of Austin Allegro from 1976 to 1982 was 100mph. Exceeding this even slightly (let alone by 130mph) would have caused the engine to overheat, and the car to break down. I'm sorry, but your granddad is talking out of his arse."

Dear Diddy

My mate Scouse Trev is always telling people that he played the role of Azeem in the 1991 Hollywood film *Robin Hood: Prince of Thieves*. Do you think he actually did?

Eric Deathbed, Hove

Diddy says...

"**Did 'e fuck!** The role of Azeem – the wise and kindly Moor whose life Robin Hood saves at the beginning of the film – was played by the Oscar-winning American actor Morgan Freeman. What's more, a cursory IMDb search of your mate Scouse Trev reveals not one single big screen appearance in 1991, or indeed any other year."

Dear Diddy

Fat Baz, who works with my brother on the meat counter at Aldi, told me that last night, whilst pissed, he succeeded in deriving Euclid's fifth postulate from the other four.

Big Jeff, Essex

Diddy says...

"**Did 'e fuck!** Euclid's fifth (or 'parallel') postulate – which states that if a straight line crossing two straight lines makes the interior angles on the same side less than two right angles, the two straight lines, if extended indefinitely, meet at the side on which the angles are less than the two right angles – is widely accepted to be unprovable and wholly independent of the other four postulates of plane geometry, following Carl Friedrich Gauss's meditations on the theory of parallels in 1792. I find it hard to believe that Fat Baz - whilst pissed, no less - would be able to crack a mathematical conundrum that has foxed the planet's finest minds for more than two thousand years. Tell him that from me, and watch him fuck off back to the meat counter with his tail between his legs."

Dear Diddy

There's a bloke in my office swears he once managed to suck himself off while standing up. What do you reckon, Diddy - did he?

G Denkins, Dover

Diddy says...

"**Did 'e fuck!** While it is indeed possible for a larger-endowed gentleman to successfully self-fellate, the only position in which it has ever been achieved is lying flat on the back, and slowly edging the groin towards the mouth with the hips elevated. To obtain the slightest contact between one's lips and bell-end would be physically impossible in a standing position, and indeed to even attempt it would cause unimaginable agony. I would think."

PLAYTIME FONTAYNE

YOU WANTED TO SEE ME, MR NUGENT?

AH YES, FONTAYNE, COME IN... SIT DOWN.

S. NUGENT DIRECTOR

NOW, I'VE BEEN LOOKING AT YOUR LATEST QUARTERLY AUDIT RETURNS...

SIR, THE DOG ATE THEM AND THEN I LEFT THEM ON THE BUS AND THEN I ACCIDENTALLY COPIED THEM OFF SPECCY DEBBIE TURPIN, SO IF THEY'RE WRONG IT'S HER F...

...AND THESE FIGURES ARE REALLY EXCELLENT!

REALY, SIR!?

OH YES. THEY'RE QUITE OUTSTANDING.

FOURTEEN PERCENT YEAR-ON-YEAR FONTAYNE. THAT MAKES YOUR BRANCH ONE OF THE BEST PERFORMING IN THE WHOLE NORTH-WEST REGIONAL SECTOR. THIS HASN'T GONE UN-NOTICED IN THE BOARDROOM, FONTAYNE.

IN FACT I SHOULDN'T REALLY BE TELLING YOU THIS, BUT PLAY YOUR CARDS RIGHT AND YOU COULD BE DESTINED FOR BIGGER THINGS HERE AT COBLEY'S BANK.

GOSH!

THERE'S A TEAM OF HEADHUNTERS DOWN FROM THE INVESTMENTS AND EQUITIES DIVISION. THEY'RE LOOKING FOR CANDIDATES TO FAST-TRACK UP THE EXECUTIVE LADDER.

THIS IS A GREAT OPPORTUNITY FOR A MAN LIKE YOU, FONTAYNE... A TARGET-LED, GOAL-DRIVEN SELF-STARTER WITH A PROVEN TRACK RECORD OF DELIVERING RESULTS WHERE IT COUNTS – ON THE BALANCE SHEET!

WHO WANTS TO WORK IN **INVESTMENTS** AND **EQUITIES**?

NO GIRLS!

MISS D. TURPIN

OH, LORDY! IT'S THE FAT SLAGS

'ERE, GIRLS... GIRLS... GUESS WOT... THEY'RE KNOCKIN' DOWN THE BOGS OFF THE HIGH STREET

AW, NO!... I 'AD ME FIRST SHAG THERE

EURGH! IN THE BOGS?

NO... IN THE HIGH STREET... DOORWAY O' SPUD-U-LIKE

YEAH, BUT GET **THIS**... THEY'VE GOT A FUCKIN' GREAT BIG **WRECKIN' BALL** ON THE JOB, LIKE IN THAT MILEY CYRUS VIDEO...

AN' THE DRIVER'S GONE FORRIS DINNER

OH AYE?

I THOUGHT WE COULD DO US OWN VIDEO WI' YOU TWO ON THE BALL

HEY, **YEAH!** IT'LL BE DEAD FUCKIN' SEXY

AYE. I'VE GOT HALF A TEA-CAKE THINKIN' ABOUT IT...

...C'MON, BEFORE HE GETS BACK

SO...

OOH, THAT'S IT, TRAY... LOOK AT THE CAMERA AN' POUT A BIT...

PHWOAR! PUSH Y' TITS UP AGAINST THE CHAIN... HEH!

OOH, AYE!

HEY, IT'S BETTER THAN THE ORIGINAL, THIS... OLD MILEY FLAT TITS 'AS GOT NOWT ON YOU, TRAY... PHWOAR!

MIGHT STICK THIS ON PORNHUB... IT'LL GO VIRAL

YOU GET ON AT THE SAME TIME, SAN, LET'S 'AVE A BIT O' GIRL-ON-GIRL ACTION, THEY **LOVE** THAT ON THE WEB

'URRY UP... THE DRIVER'LL BE BACK ANY TIME

WOT THE FUCK...!?!

WHITE VAN TIME TRAVELLING MAN

The old white Ford Transit that self-employed Reg Henge had picked up at auction was no ordinary van. For it was equipped with a special extra gear, that enabled it to travel through time.

...NOW YOU ARE GOING TO DISPOSE OF THESE MATTRESSES PROPERLY, AREN'T YOU, MR HENGE? YOU HAVE GOT A WASTE DISPOSAL PERMIT, HAVEN'T YOU?

WHAT? OH, YEAH. DEFINITELY.

CAN I SEE IT? I WANT TO MAKE SURE.

SORRY, LOVE, IT'S IN MY OTHER TROUSERS.

YOU'RE NOT GOING TO JUST FLY TIP THEM, ARE YOU?

SLAM!

NO, OF COURSE NOT. THAT'S TWENTY QUID CASH. CHEERS.

WASTE DISPOSAL PERMIT MY ARSE. NO WAY I'M PAYING TRADE FEES AT THE COUNCIL TIP. FUCK THAT...

NOT WHEN MY WHITE VAN CAN TRAVEL THROUGH TIME!

Reg engaged his secret extra gear and put his foot down.

GET IN, YOU BASTARD!

GRIND!

VWHOOOSH!

500 years earlier, at the Battle of Agincourt.

THIS STORY SHALL THE GOOD MAN TEACH HIS SON: AND CRISPIN CRISPIAN SHALL NE'ER GO BY, FROM THIS DAY TO THE ENDING OF THE WORLD, BUT WE IN IT SHALL BE REMEMBERED...!

WE FEW, WE HAPPY FEW, WE BAND OF BROTHERS; FOR HE TODAY THAT SHEDS HIS BLOOD SHALL BE MY BROTHER; BE HE NE'ER SO VILE, THIS DAY SHALL GENTLE HIS CONDITION...!

VWHOOOSH!

AND GENTLEMEN IN ENGLAND NOW ABED SHALL THINK THEMSELVES ACCURS'D THEY WERE NOT HERE, AND HOLD THEIR MANHOODS CHEAP WHILE ANY SPEAKS THAT FOUGHT WITH US UPON SAINT CRISPIN'S DAY!

THE GAME'S AFOOT; FOLLOW YOUR SPIRIT, AND UPON THIS CHARGE, CRY GOD FOR HARRY! ENGLAND AND SAINT GEORGE!

HURRAH!

RAAARGH!

VWHOOOSH!

NEXT WEEK: As the 18th century French populace rises up in Revolution, White Van Time Travelling Man dumps some ripped out kitchen units and a broken toilet at the Storming of the Bastille.

The End

What a Bunch of Kents!

Prince or Duke? Lord or Earl? Duchess or Michael of?: Telling the Kents apart is no mean feat.

99 PERCENT OF BRITONS believe that the *Duke of Kent* and *Prince Michael of Kent* are *one and the same person!* And a shocking two thirds of the population are similarly confused about *Princess Michael* and the *Duchess of Kent*. And according to constitutional expert *Dr David Starkey*, it's a national disgrace. He told us: "What a shocking indictment of this country's educational system that whilst our children are taught mathematics, science and literacy from an early age, they are left ignorant about the differences between the various Kents."

And now the controversy-courting historian is calling for the subject of "Kentology" to be added to the schools curriculum. "It is to this country's eternal shame that our youth can name every member of the Bay City Rollers, yet they are unable to identify the lesser descendants of King George V," he said.

victoria

"They are a marvellous family who can trace their ancestry back as far as Queen Victoria or even William the Conqueror. It is only right that all British children should be imbued with a rudimentary understanding of which Kent is which," he continued.

Starkey: Wants compulsory Kent genealogy taught in schools

Kensington Palace: Home of the Kents... but which ones?

Starkey stressed that he wasn't suggesting that other subjects be axed from an already crowded curriculum to make space for compulsory Kentology

Brits can't tell one toff from t'other

By our royal correspondent
Hugo St. John Fforbes-Tolomasche

lessons. "The school day could be lengthened by an hour, either starting at half-past seven in the morning or ending at five-thirty pm, whatever is most convenient," he said.

"Or perhaps we could adopt a continental system, with children going to school on Saturday mornings between the ages of four and eighteen to learn all about this wonderful branch of the royal family," he added.

mel

But Starkey's ideas got a frosty reception from anti-monarchists yesterday. "Instead of learning about these reactionary throwbacks, we should be rising up and consigning the aristocracy and all that it stands for to the dustbin of history," said Janice Seething, editor of left wing paper *The Morning Glory*.

mel

"If we teach our kids anything about the Kents, it should be that they are parasites, sucking the blood of the working classes and living high on the hog on the fruits of other people's labour," she continued.

geri

Ms Seething stressed that she had nothing against the Kents personally. "I am sure they are very nice people, but it is the system I object to," she told us. "In a way they are just as much victims of our absurd, ludicrous and outdated hereditary monarchy as anyone else. I feel sorry for them."

"But just look at them, sat there in the royal box at the tennis, with their nice clothes and their toffee noses stuck in the air," she continued. "I hate them, I hate them, the chinless inbred bastards."

WHO'S THAT KENT?

WE'VE TEAMED UP with BBC Royal Correspondent *Nicholas Witchell* to bring you this fantastic pocket computer that will banish Kent confusion once and for all. Simply follow the royal flow chart, answering each question Yes or No to discover which Kent is which.

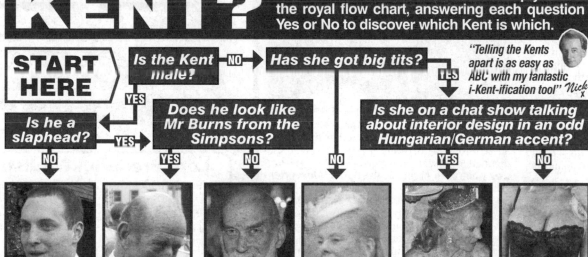

START HERE → Is the Kent male? —NO→ Has she got big tits?

"Telling the Kents apart is as easy as ABC with my fantastic i-Kent-ification tool" Nick x

YES ↓ (male)

Is he a slaphead? → Does he look like Mr Burns from the Simpsons?

Has she got big tits? —YES→ Is she on a chat show talking about interior design in an odd Hungarian/German accent?

NO | YES | NO | NO | YES | NO

Lord Frederick Windsor of Kent | **Prince Edward, Duke of Kent** | **Prince Michael of Kent** | **Katharine, Duchess of Kent** | **Princess Michael of Kent** | **Lady Helen Melons Windsor of Kent**

We examine some of the unthinkably tragic scenarios that could see a Kent become King or Queen in a real life...

GAME OF THRONES

THE first member of the Kent family to feature in the current line of succession is the Duke of Kent, who charts at number 34 in the Succession Line Top Forty. For him to take the throne, the current monarch and the thirty-three people next in line would all have to perish. The nightmare scenario of thirty-four much-loved royals popping their clogs simultaneously is a horrifying prospect that none of us wish to contemplate.

But just for fun, we've asked former *Casualty* actor **Clive Mantle** to use his knowledge of Accident and Emergency situations to come up with his Top 5 Royal Wipeouts that could could see a Kent take the throne.

"If there is one thing that all my years playing A&E consultant Dr Mike Barrett in *Casualty* taught me, it is that disaster can come from nowhere and without any warning," says Clive. "I fervently hope and pray that none of these royal doomsday scenarios ever comes true..."

DOOMSDAY SCENARIO ONE — BALMORAL CASTLE ASTEROID STRIKE

HER MAJESTY The queen has invited the 33 next in line to the throne for Christmas dinner at Balmoral. Gathered in the dining room, they are just about to start carving the turkey when an asteroid hits the castle. It is only the size of a television set, but travelling at a speed of 15,000mph the effect of its impact is cataclysmic. Within 1 nano-second, her majesty the Queen and everyone in the line of succession as far down as number 18 - **David Armstrong-Jones**, Viscount Linley - are vapourised.

The TOP FIVE Scenarios that could see a Kent on the Throne

The next ten on the list, as far down as **Lady Davina Lewis**, are instantly incinerated and reduced to dust by the white hot shockwave travelling at the speed of light. And as the smoke clears, no trace remains of the remaining five guests. The Balmoral butler immediately puts a call through to the Archbishop of Canterbury, who performs a hastily-organised coronation on the Duke of Kent.

Probability factor: 15% Unlikely

DOOMSDAY SCENARIO TWO — BUCKINGHAM PALACE BOTLUISM

A GARDEN party is arranged to celebrate one of the Queen's birthdays and the top 33 heirs to the throne. However, unbeknownst to guests, one of the Buckingham Palace fridges has broken down and a tray of swan vol-au-vents have become infected with deadly botulism and

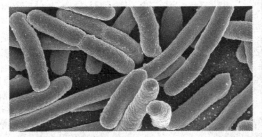

e-coli. The party seems to be a great success, and the buffet table is quickly cleared, with the vol-au-vents proving particularly popular with all the dignitaries present. However, alarm bells start to ring when 25th in line to the throne **Alexander, Earl of Ulster** is seen vomiting violently into an ice bucket. Seconds later, **Lady Rose Gilman** (31st in line) suddenly shrieks in alarm as her arse goes off like a blunderbuss full of gravy. The rest fall like ninepins, and within minutes a scene of carnage ensues, with all 34 guests of honour laid waste as the lethal bug takes hold. With no survivors at the end of the afternoon, the Duke of Kent is summoned back from a peasant-shooting holiday on his Scottish estate to become King.

Probability factor: 11% Improbable

DOOMSDAY SCENARIO THREE — ROYAL YACHT ICEBERG COLLISION

TAKING A well-earned break from waving and opening things, the Queen and the top 33 in the line of succession are enjoying a luxury cruise aboard the Royal Yacht Britannia. Momentarily distracted by an exciting game of quoits on deck, the lookout fails to see an iceberg looming on the horizon. By the time it has been spotted it is too late for take evasive action and the ship collides with the floating mountain of ice. As Britannia takes on water and begins to list alarmingly, an SOS flare is launched and the order goes out: *"Abandon ship! Queens, princesses and children first!"* The evacuation is proceeding in an orderly fashion until **Prince Andrew** (6th in line to the throne) is discovered in one of the lifeboats, dressed as a princess. A scuffle ensues and in the melee, the lifeboat capsizes, tipping all 34 potential future monarchs into the freezing water. When rescue vessels arrive on the scene of the disaster hours later, they find nothing but tiaras, crowns, orbs and sceptres floating in the water; there are no survivors. A Morse code message is quickly tapped out to the authorities back in the UK: "BRITANNIA SUNK STOP GREAT LOSS OF ROYAL LIFE STOP CORONATE DUKE OF KENT ASAP STOP"

Probability factor: 14% Doubtful

DOOMSDAY SCENARIO FOUR — BATTENBURGTOWN MASSACRE

INSPIRED BY the South Sea islanders that worship him as a God, **Prince Philip** sets up a religious cult and takes his wife and the top 33 in line of succession to join his commune on an island in the middle of a lake in the grounds of the Sandringham estate. The 34 quickly fall under Philip's charismatic

spell, as he informs them that the men must do all the work and only he can have sex with the women. When the authorities find out what is going on on the island, they move in to try to break up the cult and arrest its despotic leader. Seeing the writing on the wall, the Prince prepares a large jug of Pimms, which he laces with deadly cyanide and commands his followers to drink. After years of being conditioned to obey his every whim, this they happily do, and within minutes the commune is littered with 34 royal bodies. Once again the throne passes to the next in line: The Duke of Kent, who vows in his coronation speech that this sort of tragedy will never be allowed to happen again.

Probability factor: 16% Inconceivable

DOOMSDAY SCENARIO FIVE — ANDES CANNIBAL PLANE CRASH

WHILST TRAVELLING to a polo championship in Argentina, a plane carrying the Queen and her 33 putative successors hits bad weather over the Andes and crash-lands on a remote mountain top. All the passengers survive the impact, but after eating the pilot, co-pilot and all their equerries and servants, the royal party are faced with an unthinkable choice: *They must now eat each other or die!* When a Uruguayan Airforce rescue helicopter finally reaches the crash site six months later, only one member of the original 34-strong group is still alive. Crouched in the wreckage of the fuselage, **Prince Richard**, Duke of Gloucester is discovered, gnawing on one of the Queen's arms. However, His Grace has been driven insane by the cannibal horrors he has witnessed,

and so, despite being 24th in line to the throne, he is unable to take up the position as monarch. Instead, the job goes to the next surviving heir - the Duke of Kent.

Probability factor: 12% Implausible

Here's YOUR chance to win a right royal HOLIDAY with the KENTS of your choice!

WE'VE teamed up with Britain's favourite second-tier royals to give one lucky reader and their family the chance to spend an all-inclusive* week at **Penrith Center Parcs** with the two Kents of their choice! So if you've always dreamt of cycling** through the woods with **Princess Michael**, relaxing in the Aqua Sana Spa*** with the **Duke of Kent** or going stand-up paddle-boarding**** with **Lady Helen Melons Windsor**, this is the competition for you!

For your chance of winning, simply answer these Kent-related questions A, B or C and complete the tie-breaker using no more than twelve words.

*Activities & food extra **Cycle hire extra ***Aqua Sana Spa extra ****Board hire extra, paddle hire extra, wetsuit hire extra.

1. What Kent was the name and occupation of Superman's alter-ego?
a. Newspaper reporter Clark Kent
b. Wrestling commentator Kent Walton
c. Space Shuttle astronaut Kent Rominger

2. Where is the University of Kent at Canterbury based?
a. Yorkshire
b. Scotland
c. Kent

3. Kent is known as the "............... of England"?
a. Garden
b. Capital
c. Arsehole

Idyllic: You could be sharing a lakeside cocktail* with HRH the Duke of Kent.
*lakeside cocktails extra

TIEBREAKER
Complete the sentence in twelve words or fewer.
"*I think the Kents are the best family in the world, after the proper Royals, because...........*"
....
Name.....................Address.................
..............................Post Code...............

The Kents I would like to go to Center Parcs with are (tick 2):
☐ Prince ☐ Princess ☐ Duke
☐ Duchess ☐ Lord ☐ Melons

Terms and Conditions
The prize consists of seven days in the Penrith Center Parcs for the winner and up to four (4) family members, sharing a "Comfort" woodland lodge with the two (2) Kents of their choice. In the event of the winner's chosen Kents being unavailable, the publishers reserve the right to substitute them with other toffs of a similar value and quality, such as the Hon. Nicholas Knatchbull, Viscount Linley or Simon Sebag-Montefiore. The winner is liable for all and any extra costs incurred during the week, including food, extra activities, toiletries and ironing board hire, both for themselves and the Kents, as, being semi-Royal, the Kents do not carry any money on them. In the unlikely event of no minor royals being prepared to spend a week at Penrith Center Parcs with a family of Viz readers, the publishers reserve the right to substitute the entire advertised prize with a Viz pen, Viz mug or Viz T-shirt.

IT's everybody's worst nightmare. You're at a Buckingham Palace garden party, attending a Variety Performance, or in the Royal Enclosure at Ascot. Suddenly, you are approached and engaged in conversation with a Kent. But which one? Is it the one who likes scouting, the one who shoots, or the one who was once in the GB bobsleigh team? If it's a woman, is it the one who loves tennis, the one who takes an interest in fashion, or the one who's dad was a bit of a nazi? It's so easy to get confused and make a faux pas. But not any longer. These handy cut out 'n' keep wallet-sized fact cards help you keep all your Kent data organised and at your fingertips. Simply slip them out, identify the Kent who has accosted you, and let the conversation flow.

Prince Michael of Kent
Name: Michael
Age: 73
Habitat: Castles, grand prixs
Fave food: Swans, caviar, smoked salmon
Job: Shooting things, presenting cups
Chin: Bearded
Form of address: Your royal highness

The Duke of Kent
Name: Edward
Age: 79
Habitat: Castles, Royal boxes
Fave food: Pate de fwa grar, truffles, Monster Munch
Job: Shooting things, shaking hands
Chin: None
Form of address: Your grace

Princess Michael of Kent
Name: Michael
Age: 70
Habitat: Knightsbridge, Fortnum & Mason
Fave food: Ginsters, sausages, Scotch eggs
Job: Author, interior designer
Chin: Teutonic
Form of address: Ma'am

The Duchess of Kent
Name: Kath/Kathy
Age: 82
Habitat: Kensington Palace, Wimbledon finals
Fave food: Overpriced strawberries and cream
Job: Flower accepter
Chin: Medium
Form of address: Your majesty

Lady Helen Melons Windsor
Name: Helen
Age: 51
Habitat: Sloane Square
Fave food: Pimms, canapes, hors doevres
Job: Attending royal weddings
Chin: Medium
Form of address: Sweet tits

56

SAVED BY THE BELL-*END*!

TELLY adventurer *BEAR GRYLLS* has miraculously survived a TEN-HOUR dice with death on an 8,000ft mountain ledge... and it's all thanks to the folded layer of skin at the end of his penis!

Foreskin to rescue as Grylls takes life into his own glans

Grylls, 40 - now safely back home in the UK and recovering from the incident - was filming in Alaska for a new television series when the terrifying mishap took place.

sparsley

At a sparsley-attended press conference in central London yesterday, the thrill-seeking star recounted his incredible story for the world's press.

"I had embarked on a solo climbing expedition in the Saint Elias Mountains of southern Alaska," Grylls told reporters.

"Because I am pretty rock, I don't need stuff like ropes, safety harnesses and helmets that other climbers bring. I was clambering these vertical cliff faces using only my hands, feet and occasionally, on the more treacherous inclines, my teeth," he added.

sdill

But disaster struck halfway up the mountain range, which peaks at a vertigo-inducing 19,551ft, when a temporary lapse in concentration left the popular *Man vs Wild* presenter dancing with death.

"At approximately 8,500 feet above sea level, I was sending a text to my agent, when I suddenly lost my foothold," said Grylls. "In my frenzied attempts to locate another one, my trousers and pants somehow came loose and fell down around my ankles."

sbayleaf

To his horror, the semi-nude small-screen survivalist found himself clinging to the cliff-face for dear life, while the mountain wind whipped mercilessly at his genitals.

Saint Elias: The mountain range where Grylls' chopper came a cropper.

Accepting his fate, he let go of the rock and plummeted towards the earth.

ssage

"As I hurtled through the air, I remember thinking, 'Say your prayers, Bear, old boy, 'cos you ain't coming back from this one'," he waxed. "But then I felt a sudden, blinding pain at the end of my penis. I opened my eyes to find myself swinging wildly from a ledge by just the skin of my bobby's helmet."

ssenor solidago

Free-falling at a velocity of 100mph, Bear's billowing foreskin had miraculously snagged onto a jutted section of the cliff-face, leaving him dangling perilously, almost three thousand metres above the hard Alaskan ground.

"I was hanging by my farmer's hat for close to 11 hours, and I won't lie to you, I was in a great deal of physical pain," Grylls admitted.

"I don't know if anyone here has ever supported their entire bodyweight for half a day by the double-layered flap of skin encircling their glans, but, honestly, it is not an experience I would wish on even my worst enemy."

After an agonisingly long wait in temperatures of -35°C, Bear was finally picked up by a passing rescue helicopter, his bedraggled foreskin now stretched to nearly 3 feet in length.

"I've got through about a hundred tubes of Arnica in the last few days, and my executioner's hood has now returned to roughly its original shape and size," Grylls revealed.

spashana bedhi

"It just goes to show, you can buy all the fancy climbing gear you like, but sometimes, it can be something as simple as your own cock that ultimately holds the key to mountain survival."

This is not the first time a British TV adventurer has had to rely on the contents of his fruitbowl in a potentially fatal survival situation. In 2012, ITV bushcraft expert Ray Mears was forced to shelter inside his own scrotum for three days during a violent snowstorm on the island of Spitzbergen.

Big Cat Hunt Called Off

A HUNT for an escaped lion in Hampshire was last night called off after it turned out to be ~~Bee Gee~~ Barry Gibb having a shit behind a bush.

Milkman *Glark Cable* was walking his dog in the New Forest when he spotted what he thought was a fully grown male lion sitting in the undergrowth and growling. He immediately raised the alarm and police marksmen armed with tranquilizer darts spent the next four hours combing the heavily-wooded area in search of a dangerous big cat.

hunt

Local residents in Beaulieu were warned to stay in their homes and keep windows and doors closed until the lion could be tracked down and caught. But the hunt was abandoned when pop star *Barry Gibb*, who lives in nearby Brockenhurst, saw a local news report on television and realised what had happened.

EXCLUSIVE!

"I had gone for a stroll in the forest wearing a sandy-coloured onesie, a pair of Ugg boots and some sheepskin mittens," he told local newspaper the *Shafton Helmet*.

"Whilst I was out on my walk, I suddenly needed a number two so I squatted down behind a rhododendron bush."

"I'd had three Ginster's Scotch eggs and a family-size treacle tart for my lunch, and it was taking some shifting, so I was making a lot of deep, guttural noises."

lake palmer

"Mr Cable must have come past, heard the growling and seen me with my magnificent mane of golden hair and giant

white teeth and simply put two and two together," Gibb continued. "To him I must have looked for all the world like the king of the beasts, waiting to leap out and eat him."

ronnie conrad

A Hampshire Police spokesperson told us: "We can confirm that our search party has been stood down and we are no longer looking for an escaped lion in the New Forest."

But she confirmed that Barry Gibb had been given a police warning under caution in connection with the incident. "In the interests of public safety, I am able to confirm that a 1970s disco pop band member has been spoken to and requested to dress a little bit less like a lion when out in the woods in future," she said.

It's the question that has failed to trouble the nation for 70 years

WAR BABY!

Did Queen Conceive Secret Heir on VE Day One Night Stand?

ON MAY 8TH 1945 the people of Britain took to the streets in their millions for Victory in Europe day. After six years of war, Londoners thronged the capital to celebrate the Allies' triumph over the Nazis, singing, dancing and drinking deep into the night.

It was the greatest, most uproarious party anyone had ever seen. Strangers, caught up in the intoxicatingly jubilant atmosphere, hugged and kissed; many went even further. There were tales of couples making love amongst the crowds, abandoning themselves to the excitement of the moment and rutting like animals in the alleyways around the Mall.

As is well known, the 18-year-old Princess Elizabeth slipped out of Buckingham Palace to join in the celebrations. Anonymous in her drab Women's Auxiliary Territorial Service uniform, the future Queen drank in the exhilarating mood, dancing the night away amongst the happy crowds, swept along on a drunken, carefree tide of happiness and relief that the war was finally at an end.

But just how far did the pretty young Princess go that night? Was she one of the many girls who threw caution to the wind on VE Day and went all the way with a randy stranger? However distasteful, the question must be asked, because if she did, and then nine months later gave birth to a child, the constitutional implications could be staggering.

Of course, the bastard child would have been taken away at birth to be brought up by someone else; a future Queen falling pregnant out of wedlock would have been a scandal too far for an establishment still reeling from Edward VIII's abdication eight years earlier. However, any child to which the young Princess Elizabeth gave birth as a result of her impulsive one night stand behind some Whitehall bins would now be seventy years old and first in line to the throne - in front of Prince Charles, Prince William, Prince George and Princess Charlotte! *The true heir to the crown could be anyone; your next door neighbour, your grandmother or even an assistant at your local DIY store. Amazingly, it could even be a celebrity, a famous face from the world of showbiz!*

Now, just for fun, we have asked the BBC Royal Correspondent Nicholas Witchell to check the dates and find out which stars could be Heir Today... ...Throne Tomorrow.

Room for one on top: Did Princess Elizabeth go all the way during celebrations?

HRH Queen Julie I

Telly soap star **JULIE GOODYEAR** became a household name in the 1970s as bottle blonde barmaid Bet Lynch in ITVs *Coronation Street.* **But is her character's full name - Elizabeth - an unconscious tip of the hat to her real mother, Queen Elizabeth?**

Landlady Lynch reigned supreme in the bar of the Rover's Return for many years, and there is no reason to suppose she wouldn't do an equally good job ruling over the Commonwealth, dealing with troublesome member states the way she would deal with unruly drinkers in her backstreet boozer - chucking them out on their ear!

The famous Weatherfield pub always opened its doors on time and under Bet's sovereignty State Openings of Parliament would no doubt be equally as punctual.

Good Queen Bet's low-cut leopard-print clothing would also endear her to her new royal family, who count shooting endangered species amongst their many interests.

On ceremonial occasions bling-lover Lynch, who is famed for her big earrings and flashy jewellery, would

undoubtedly slip into the Crown Jewels with consummate ease. In short, the busty, brassy, chain-smoking ex-barmaid would bring a refreshingly common touch to the role of Queen, dragging the monarchy kicking and screaming into the twenty-first century by the scruff of its neck.

On the downside, Goodyear was officially born in 1942, making her three years too old to have been born to Princess Elizabeth as the result of an unprotected back-alley liaison on VE Day. However it is well within the realms of possibility that the Palace had the dates on her birth certificate falsified and the registrar at Bury Town Hall killed in a bizarre accident to cover up the truth.

With his trademark cowboy hat, black leather jacket and facial boils, Motorhead frontman **LEMMY** - real name Leamington Sparsworth - is the King of heavy metal music, and the heavy metal of the British crown might well suit him down to the ground.

Whilst others who have found themselves thrust onto the royal stage have been unable to cope with the pressure, Lemmy is already well-used to the adulation of thousands of head-banging fans when performing with his band at rock festivals around the world. Unfazed by the relentless glare of the public eye, the *Ace of Spades* vocalist would be undaunted by the prospect of waving to the crowds in the Mall from the balcony of Buckingham Palace, his new home.

HRH King Alan I

Self-made business tycoon ALAN SUGAR was raised in a council flat in Hackney, London - just a stone's throw from where he was possibly conceived during Princess Elizabeth's one night stand on VE Day.

However, despite his lowly, impoverished upbringing, he has made a right royal success of himself. Before founding Amstrad, now one of the "big three" computer companies alongside Apple and Microsoft, he left school with practically no qualifications, just like Prince Charles and Prince Edward. However, unlike his half-brothers Sugar eschewed three years at Cambridge University, deciding instead to start working for a local greengrocer.

In centuries past, monarchs regularly bestowed earldoms, duchies and baronetcies on their illegitimate offspring; this may explain how, from his humble beginnings, he has risen meteorically through the ranks of the aristocracy. Beginning as plain Mr Sugar, he was first Sir Sugar and is now Lord Sugar, after receiving a life peerage from his biological mother in 2009. Surely 'King Sugar' is the natural next step for this apprentice monarch once his true identity is discovered. And what a King Sugar will be; the UK will be ruled with the same ruthless efficiency with which he now presides over his fictitious TV boardroom, with Prime Ministers, diplomats and heads of industry being hired and fired if they fail to bring enough profit to the table.

But there's a major obstacle standing in the way of Sugar taking his place on the throne - a serious conflict of interest. As a lifelong fan and former chairman of Tottenham Hotspur, were Spurs to somehow manage to fluke their way to the FA Cup final, he would be reluctant to hand over the trophy to his team's opponents at the end of the match. Such an episode could lead to a constitutional crisis as serious as Henry VIII's rift from the Church of Rome in 1532.

HRH King Lemmy I

Not only that, King Lemmy is well known as a keen collector of Nazi memorabilia and would have plenty to talk about with his newly-discovered relatives, many of whom share his lively interest in *der Nationalsozialistische Deutsche Arbeiterpartei.*

But there is a problem - members of the Royal family must always be immaculately dressed, donning smart, three-piece suits, ceremonial kilts or grand military uniforms as the occasion demands. It is quite possible that hellraiser Lemmy might opt to eschew these time-honoured, regal sartorial codes, preferring to go walkabout in

his trademark unwashed, oily, biker's leather jacket, black vest and ripped jeans - hardly fitting attire for a national head of state required to look smart on banknotes and stamps.

But how do the dates add up? Lemmy was born on Christmas Eve 1945, meaning that if his mother is the Queen he was born six weeks premature before being handed over to his adoptive parents. It's possible, but is it more likely that after decades of hard-living, hard drink and hard drugs, Lemmy's brain is so addled that he has simply forgotten that he was born on February 8th 1946?

With a list of movie credits as long as your arm, actor SAMUEL L JACKSON would be the biggest star to ever sit on the British throne.

At ease in front of the cameras after appearing in more than 161 films, the Hollywood star would be an ideal choice to deliver the annual Christmas broadcast to the nation. However, the popular royal show's producer might not have such an easy ride, being forced to sit with his finger poised over the "mute" button in case the monarch slipped into his more familiar Quentin Tarantino-style dialogue. A good few of King Samuel L's loyal subjects would no doubt find themselves choking on their turkey and trimmings as the monarch came out with such choice four-letter phrases as "cocksucker," "pussy" and "motherfucker."

On the upside, Palace security staff would be able to breathe a sigh of relief with Samuel - who played unflappable gangster Jules in cult movie *Pulp Fiction* - in residence. Any intruder who dared to shin up the drainpipe and into

---

HRH Queen Helen I

Consistently voted one of the world's sexiest 70-year-olds, actress HELEN MIRREN's grandfather was Queen Victoria's official butcher, and the closeness of the two families has evidently continued down the years.

Who can honestly say that, in true fairy tale style, it is not possible that Princess Elizabeth's illegitimate baby was not passed on in a basket to a man whose wife was barren, when he was delivering sausages to Buckingham Palace, before being taken home to be brought up by the couple as their own child? It's certainly a compelling narrative.

Now, seven decades after that kitchen doorstep handover, Mirren has many advantages over other pretenders to the throne. She has already played the Queen in movies, so she can do her majesty's posh voice and smacked-arse face to perfection, and would therefore require no settling-in period after her coronation. Also, in her stage make-up, she looks

so much like the present Queen that banknotes and stamps would not have to be re-printed, saving the Treasury a fortune.

However, one mark counting against Mirren is her long history of getting them out in films. And we're not just talking about her tits. It's bum, fanny, the lot. If Dame Helen became Queen, it wouldn't be long before X-rated stills found their way into the public domain.

The scandals that erupted in royal circles over Fergie's infamous toe-sucking pics and Sophie Wessex's back-of-a-taxi Chris Tarrant jug-flash snaps would be as nothing compared to the

---

HRH King Samuel L. I

Jackson's sleeping quarters in the hope of a quick feel of the monarch's tits might find himself staring down the barrel of a chrome-plated Star Model B 9mm pistol held sideways whilst his majesty delivers a lengthy quotation from the Old Testament Book of Ezekiel.

According to official records, Jackson was born in Washington DC, USA, in December 1948. However, it is not impossible that the registrar was writing the true date of 1946 and the pen went over a bit far on the top of the 6, making it look like an 8. In fact, his so-called age of 66 may be the biggest piece of "Pulp Fiction" of all about Samuel L Jackson, the true heir to the British crown.

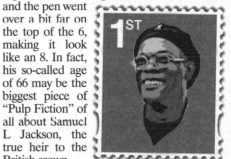

constitutional crisis that would ensue if shots of a reigning monarch buck naked and romping in a pile of meat in *The Cook, The Thief, His Wife and Her Lover* were made public.

Mirren's official birthdate of July 1945 would mean that, assuming she was conceived on VE Day during Princess Elizabeth's back-alley knee-trembler, she was born seven months prematurely. At this stage of her development, Dame Helen was the size of a prawn, with gills and a rudimentary tail, and it is unlikely that she would have been able to survive outside the womb, and this casts doubt on whether she is in fact the Queen's daughter.

However, actresses are notorious for falsifying their ages, and it is probable that Mirren pretends to be seven months younger than she actually is in order to get juicier parts in films.

JUBILEE

TEA TOWEL

Fanny Batter's HOLLYWOOD gossip ★★★

ALL THE BUZZ FROM SUNSET STRIP TO TINSELTOWN... *AND BACK!*

★ Wardrobe Malfunction for Madge

QUEEN of pop **MADONNA** was causing a commotion in Beverly Hills yesterday following a sensational wardrobe malfunction half way through her $250 a ticket show at the Hollywood Bowl. Tinseltown insiders report that during a costume change, the 56-year-old *Like a Virgin* singer went backstage to her dressing room to change into her trademark pointy-titted basque. *But get this!* When she went to close the wardrobe, the top hinge had came loose, leaving Madge holding onto it for a good five seconds before a passing stagehand spotted her predicament and came to the rescue. *Phew!* The material girl musta thanked her lucky stars that the true blue angel was on hand to lift the hinge back into the groove and avert a borderline disaster!

Bad Air Day for Naomi

RUNWAY supermodel **NAOMI CAMPBELL** stunned fellow travellers at LAX airport last week by behaving in a seemly manner. *Canyabelieveit!* The dress-up diva failed to throw one of her trademark tantrums whilst catwalking her Louis Vuitton baggage through security checks after flying in from Paris, and smiled and cooperated when she was asked to remove her Jimmy Choos for a photo shoot in the airport X-Ray machine. Passengers in the concourse were later left slack-jawed when Naomi didn't hurl her diamond-encrusted iPhone at a member of her entourage, and wasn't escorted from the airport by cops whilst shouting four-letter abuse. It was certainly an example of model behaviour from **ROBERT DE NIRO**'s leggy ex-squeeze, who famously doesn't get out of bed for less than $10,000!

Taste of Paradise for Andy

THE MAN behind *Bodger and Badger* is reported to have splashed out a cool $200 million on his own private island in the West Indies! **ANDY CUNNINGHAM** - estimated to be worth more than $10 billion following the success of his hit 1990s kids' show - snapped up the Caribbean bolthole following a furious bidding war with fellow billionaires including **MR BENNETT** off *Take Hart* and *Play School*'s **DEREK GRIFFITHS**. The location of the 200 acre island paradise - which boasts miles of white, sandy beaches, tropical lagoons and lush vegetation - is a closely guarded secret, but my spies tell me that Cunningham intends to spend nine months of the year ensconced in his idyllic hideaway, flying in on his private jumbo jet, dubbed "The Mashed Potato"!

Seeya next time, gossip lovers!

Fanny x!x

Twat News Round Up...

BROADWAY OR BUST FOR STING

UNDETERRED by lukewarm reviews for his Broadway play *The Last Ship*, **STING** is already penning a second stage musical. His first effort, described by New York critics as "unfocussed and diffuse... cliché-ridden, predictable and depthless", told the story of a Geordie lad called Gideon who returns to Tyneside after fifteen years away to discover that the shipyards of his youth are threatened with closure and his sweetheart is engaged to another man.

"My new show, titled *The Last Private Jet*, will be completely different," Sting told NBC chatshow host French Letterman. "It's all about a Geordie lad called Gideon who leaves his council flat overlooking the Tyne Bridge to travel the world and save the rainforests. When he gets back fifteen years later, he's horrified to discover that his private airfield is being bulldozed to make way for a shopping centre and his sweetheart is engaged to another man."

"Whilst on his travels, he has used his redundancy money from the shipyards to buy some castles and farms in Tuscany, and without his airfield he has no way to fly his own extra virgin olive oil in to make fresh salad dressing," he continued.

"It's a tale everyone can identify with. A love story set against the backdrop of a fight for justice against the corporate suits who would take away an ordinary working man's private airfield," he added. "And it'll probably star Robson Green or Tim Healy or someone like that."

60

EEK! HELP! A MOUSE! HELP!

ARE YOU ALRIGHT, ADA LOVE..? I HEARD YOU SHOUTING.

NO I'M NOT, DOLLY. I JUST SEEN A RUDDY MOUSE!

A MOUSE? EEK! WHERE WAS IT, ADA?

DOWN THERE

A BLOODY GREAT RAT IT WAS, DOLLY..!

THE SIZE OF A CAT! I'VE NEVER SEEN ANYTHING LIKE IT. TWO FOOT LONG IT WERE, IF IT WERE A DAY.

BIG YELLOW TEETH, DIT IT 'AVE, ADA?

IT DID, DOLLY. 'UGE YELLOW TEETH, AND IT BARED 'EM AT ME...

...LIKE THIS!

OOH, NO.

AND EVIL RED EYES IT HAD TOO, DOLLY... MALEVOLENT, THEY WERE... MALEVOLENT.

EEH.

AND THERE WASN'T JUST ONE OF THE BUGGERS, DOLLY. THERE WAS 'UNDREDS OF 'EM - ALL SCAMPERING ABOUT AND SQUEAKING.

EEH, NO, ADA!

IS IT AN INFESTATION YOU'VE GOT THEN, ADA..?

IT IS. IT'S AN INFESTATION OF VERMIN RUNNING UP ME LEGS.

THEY COME UP THE TOILET, YOU KNOW, WHEN I'M ON, AND BITE ME ON THE TUPPENCE.

THEY NEVER!

THEY DO! BITING! BITING! BITING! THEY'VE GOT RABIES TOO, DOLLY!

FROTHING, ARE THEY?

FROTHING, DOLLY.? THEY'RE FOAMING! FOAMING THEY ARE! IF YOU SAW IT WITH YOUR OWN EYES YOU'D NEVER BELIEVE IT.

INEFFECTUAL FATHER MINOTAUR

HILL GROUNDED FOR BAD BEHAVIOUR

By our Tinseltown correspondent **Fanny Batter**

ZZ TOP founder *Dusty Hill* has been **GROUNDED** by his dad following complaints from a Texas recording studio. Hymen Prepuce III, boss of Austin-based Lone Star Studios, reportedly wrote to Mr Hill about his son's disruptive behaviour during sessions for the band's latest album.

According to Prepuce, work on the record was repeatedly held up when Hill

- *Continually talked whilst the other band members tried to play a song*
- *Snapped Frank Beard's drumsticks for a joke*
- *Chewed up blotting paper and used a ruler to flick it onto a sound engineer's back*

The final straw came when Hill let off a stink bomb whilst vocalist Billy Gibbons was trying to record a song.

antics

Earlier, album producer Tony Visconti had been so annoyed by Hill's antics that he had sent him to see the studio head, who warned the veteran bluesman to "pull his socks up" and "set a better example" to the other members of ZZ Top. However, his behaviour didn't

Not right: Dusty (left or possibly centre) was criticised for conduct in studio

improve and Prepuce was left with no option but to write a stiffly-worded letter to his father.

radio wun

"I left Mr Hill in no doubt that Lone Star Studios were not prepared to put up with any more of this sort of silly nonsense from his son," said Prepuce. "I pointed out that Dusty was spoiling it for the other members of the band, Billy Gibbons and Dusty Hill, who were working hard and trying to record an album of gritty Tex-Mex boogie."

"It wasn't fair on them to simply turn a blind eye to Dusty's studio tomfoolery," he added.

A neighbour told us: "When he read the letter about what his son had been getting up to at the studios, Mr Hill hit the roof. He immediately sent Dusty to his room and told him he wasn't allowed out for a fortnight."

radio too

As a result of being grounded, Hill wasn't available for live performances, and ten dates from the band's current world tour had to be postponed or cancelled.

ZZ Top fans took to social media to voice their disappointment. But whilst many were upset that gigs had been scrapped, most backed Mr Hill's actions in grounding his son for his bad behaviour.

"It's about time Dusty pulled his socks up and stopped messing about," tweeted @UnoHombre. "Sad to miss Houston gig but Dusty needs to learn his lesson," added @Cheap_Sunglasses. "He might think he's being clever, but in fact he's only making himself look stupid."

radio free

"Dusty clearly doesn't behave like that at home," said Twitter user @SharpDressedMan. "So why he thinks it's an acceptable way to carry on in the studio is anyone's guess. He ought to be ashamed of himself."

radio faw

Meanwhile, a contrite Hill appeared on the doorstep of his Houston ranch whilst his father read a statement to assembled reporters. "My son Dusty accepts that his behaviour in the recording studio was unacceptable," said Mr Hill. "He's let his fans, his band and his family down," he continued. "But worst of all, he's let himself down."

Mr Hill stressed that he was not so much cross as disappointed, and said that his son now wanted to take this opportunity to apologise. "Go on, Dusty, what do you have to say?" he said.

"Sorry," the 66-year-old bassist mumbled, whilst looking at his shoes.

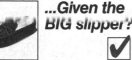
     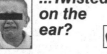

Twat News Round Up...

BRAND TO ATTEMPT MOST COMPLICATED SENTENCE YET

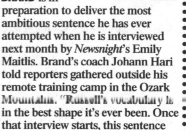

SESQUIPEDALIAN polymath *RUSSELL BRAND* is in preparation to deliver the most ambitious sentence he has ever attempted when he is interviewed next month by *Newsnight*'s Emily Maitlis. Brand's coach Johann Hari told reporters gathered outside his remote training camp in the Ozark Mountains. "Russell's vocabulary is in the best shape it's ever been. Once that interview starts, this sentence is going down in the first three minutes of the interview."

"Emily Maitlis won't be able to get a word in edgeways," he continued.

Hari was tight-lipped over the exact composition of Brand's statement, but he did offer reporters a few hints about what to expect during the hotly-anticipated encounter.

"Suffice to say it won't make any sense, not a single word in the sentence will have fewer than fifteen letters, and it will probably include the words antidisestablishmentarianism and supercalifragilisticexpialidocious," he said.

Dirty Harry

STREET CRIME, break-ins and muggings are rarely far from the headlines these days. As crime figures soar ever higher and conviction rates continue to fall, it would be very easy to simply give up and resign ourselves to a lawless future. But South Yorkshire allotment owner *HARRY BULLPIZZLE* says he has finally had enough of the thugs, hoodlums and violent criminals who make us scared to venture out onto the streets.

"I'm mad as hell and I'm not going to take it any more," Bullpizzle told the *South Elmsall & District Allotment Owners Association Newsletter*. "It's time to draw a line in the compost and make a stand against people who treat the rule of law with contempt."

"I've had it up to here," says Bullpizzle

Digging deep: Allotment owner Harry always goes the extra mile to bring wrongdoers to justice.

EXCLUSIVE!

"The police these days are too busy filling in Health and Safety forms to get out on the streets fighting real crime," said Harry, 58. "And that's why I've spent the last year meting out my own brand of vigilante justice to local scumbags, toerags and lowlifes."

Harry first put down his trowel in order to take the law into his own hands when he read a local newspaper report about a sub-post office raid in nearby Armthorpe.

❝ Three masked men armed with baseball bats had got away with £3000. The local coppers hadn't managed to finger anyone's collar for the blag, but when I looked at the CCTV photos in the local freesheet, there was something about the ringleader of the gang that rang a bell.

True, the pictures were very blurred, but I recognised the eyes peeking out through the man's balaclava. It was Albert, the old bloke off the very next allotment to mine! He looked a foot taller in the pictures than in real life, but that was simply because the security camera was

26.05.2013 13.02.56

Green fingered: Harry brought neighbouring allotment holder to book for post office robbery.

high up in the corner of the shop. He was also a lot more agile, leaping over the counter and carrying the till out to the getaway car, whilst Albert often complained about his rheumatism, especially in the wet weather. He had clearly staged the robbery on a sunny day when his joints weren't giving him too much gyp.

I was sure it was him, and any lingering doubts I might have had vanished the very next day when Albert came out of his shed with a brand new wheelbarrow. It must have set him back a good thirty quid ... and I knew exactly where that money had come from.

slap

There was no point grassing him up to South Yorkshire Police Crimestoppers. It would be my word against his, and in the unlikely event of charges being brought the worst punishment that he could expect would be a slap

Straight and marrow: Lawless grower was given harsh lesson

on the wrist. No, it was down to me to give old Albert a taste of justice, and I knew exactly how to do it.

white wine

All summer we had both been growing marrows for the local produce show. There was no prize involved, just the prestige of having grown the biggest and best on the allotments. Unfortunately, mine hadn't

As my shovel sliced through those marrows, I felt like Charles Bronson in Deathwish, striking a blow against the criminal underworld

grown very well due to a poor load of compost, but Albert's were beauties. He'd prepared his ground properly and dug in plenty of manure in from a local farm, watered them

religiously for months and now those marrows were his pride and joy.

Under cover of darkness I crept onto his plot and put a spade through every one of them. As my shovel sliced through those marrows, I felt just like Charles Bronson in *Deathwish*, striking a blow against the criminal underworld. "There, that's for carrying out a violent raid on a defenceless sub-post office," I almost seemed to be saying.

your tears

When Albert turned up with his flask and sandwiches the next morning and saw what had become of his prized marrows, he slumped down onto the seat outside his shed and cried. He must have realised that the attack had been carried out in retaliation for his own misdemeanours, and from the tears running down his face I am sure he was rueing the day he had ever got involved in an armed robbery. Sure, it was rough justice, vigilante-style, but Albert learnt his lesson and never broke the law again till the day he died a couple of weeks later.

the dishes

At the upcoming allotments show, my marrows took first prize after the only other ones left in the competition, grown by a man called George three plots down, were coincidentally destroyed by local hooligans in a mindless vandalism attack the exact same night. ❞

Street crime is an increasing problem throughout the UK, and South Yorkshire is no exception. Harry finally snapped and decided to take action when a frail local pensioner was pushed to the ground and robbed of her handbag by an attacker.

❝ The penny dropped when the local paper reported that the mugger made his escape on foot onto a nearby housing estate. I knew for a fact that Ernest in the end allotment used to live near that estate before his wife died and he went into the sheltered housing complex. He knew those streets like the back of his hand. And the following day, when I spotted him coming out of the Nisa in the exact same precinct where the attack had taken place, I knew I had my man. A criminal

Bean there, done that: Harry did runner after attacking plants

always returns to the scene of his crime.

I'd always had my suspicions that Ernest was a wrong'un. He'd reported me to the allotment committee after I'd burnt an old sofa and some tyres on my plot. I'd been fined £2 but that wasn't my motivation for bringing him to book. The photograph of the old lady with a black eye on the front of the *Sprotborough Express & Star* was the only incentive I needed.

ernest

Once again, I knew it would be a waste of time involving the local plod. Ernest was a wily operator and would no doubt have got several of his bowling club pals to provide him with cast iron alibis for the time of the attack. As usual, like Edward Woodward in *The Equalizer*, it was down to me to mete out my own brand of justice.

"This is for all the old ladies who've had their handbags snatched by heartless thugs like you," I thought to myself later that night as I used a housebrick to break every pane of glass in his allotment greenhouse. Then, to hammer home the point and warn Ernest off from ever straying from the straight and narrow again, I put all his cold frames through with the heel of my boot.

You've been framed: Bullpizzle put boot through glass.

john malkovitch

A week later, the police arrested a local youth and charged him with the precinct mugging and fourteen other street robberies in the Doncaster area. He pleaded guilty and was sentenced to twelve months in borstal. Whilst it always hurts to see an innocent person punished for someone else's crime, at least I had the consolation of knowing that the real perpetrator hadn't got away scot free. ”

> **"This is the way we deal with sex cases round here, I said as I emptied a can of diesel into the soil around his bean canes"**

All crimes are bad, but crimes against children hold a particular horror for the general public. When the local TV evening news reported that a man had been seen outside a local primary school trying to entice children into his car, Bullpizzle knew it was time for him to take up the cudgels of justice again.

“The newsreader said the man had been driving a red Astra, and I immediately put two and two together. The bloke on the corner plot, Ted, had a red Astra just like the one in the description. Well, it not an Astra, it's a Micra, and it's more orange than red, but the witness could have been confused. And Ted used to have an Astra, although it was a blue one, but that would just confuse the witness even more.

Like a Canadian Mountie, I knew I had my man, so after my tea I returned to the allotments under cover of darkness to sort out the filthy nonce once and for all. Ted was famed around the allotments for his runner beans. They were green and juicy, and he always grew far more than he needed, so he used to hand them round to the other allotment holders and take them to the local old folks' home. Those beans were his life; they were also his Achilles' heel.

served

I knew the police would never suspect Ted in a month of Sundays. For a start, he hadn't driven for twelve months following two cataract operations and a series of strokes; his wife had to take him everywhere. It was the perfect cover for a predatory paedophile.

"This is the way we deal with sex cases round here," I almost said to myself as I emptied a can of diesel into the soil around Ted's bean canes. As the thick, stinking oil soaked into the earth I felt a sense of satisfaction at avenging the terrible wrong that had been done to those little kiddies at the school.

When I arrived at the allotments the next morning, the committee members were already gathered round Ted's withered, yellow bean plants. I went over and joined them, feigning concern. But I couldn't keep a smile from playing around my lips. Revenge sure tasted sweet... as sweet as Ted's beans used to taste before I dieselled them.

Criminal plots: The allotments where Harry tracked down local handbag snatcher.

> **"About three o'clock the following morning, before Harry's chickens woke up, I crept onto his allotment and necked the lot of them"**

A little footnote to the story; Ted and I were the only people on the allotments who grew beans, so when his supply withered on the vine I was able to move in and plug the gap in the market, selling my surplus produce to the old folks' home for 20p a bag.

boiled

I was going to give the proceeds to a local kiddies' charity, which would have been poetic justice, only that was full price diesel I used on Ted's plants and I would have ended up out of pocket if I'd given the money away. ”

Some people call it art, but to the vast majority of people graffiti is vandalism pure and simple. And when someone spray-painted the words "Viking Crew" on a Doncaster railway bridge, Harry knew he didn't have to look far to find the culprit.

“The Viking Crew is a notorious group of Doncaster Rovers supporters, and the slogan they had daubed on the bridge was a real eyesore. As usual, the local coppers didn't seem to have the slightest interest in tracking down the hooligan responsible; indeed, the graffiti had been there a good four years and they had taken no action. But I had my suspicions.

Stan in the next allotment but one had been a season ticket holder at their old ground Belle Vue, but had stopped going when they moved to their new Keepmoat ground in 2007. The fact that Stan creosoted his allotment chicken shed just about every spring without fail and was a dab-hand with a paintbrush merely confirmed my suspicions. I had found my man.

Pillage idiot: Local vandal defaced bridge.

About three o'clock the following morning, before Stan's chickens woke up, I crept onto his allotment and necked the lot of them. Whilst it's true that only the week before he had reported me to the committee for not clearing up ground elder and failing to return the hosepipe to the communal water stand and I'd been fined £2, that wasn't why I killed his prize Buff Orpingtons. When he found their bodies strewn around the allotment the next morning, Stan was distraught.

poached

But I felt no pity for him at all. His suffering was nothing compared to the suffering that his thoughtless graffiti on that railway bridge had caused to the people of Doncaster. As far as I'm concerned, it's an eye for an eye and a tooth for a tooth. *What goes around comes around, and on these allotments I'm the judge, jury and executioner.* ”

Next week:
Harry identifies the perpetrator of a shocking triple homicide in Carcroft and stamps on his iceberg lettuce seedlings and spring onion sets.

BONO BIKE ACCIDENT CAUSES CHAOS AT UN

THE UNITED NATIONS was in meltdown last night after a cycling accident hospitalised its chief adviser and moral compass *BONO*. The U2 frontman, 54, was recovering after 5-hours of surgery to repair multiple fractures in his face, arm and shoulder following a bike collision in New York's Central Park, and was unavailable to offer inspirational counsel to the multinational humanitarian federation.

"Without Bono, real name Paul Hewson, to tell us what to do, we are a rudderless ship," said UN secretary general Ban Ki-Moon. "We were supposed to be having a big debate to discuss third world debt relief, but without Bono there to tell us what to think and do, all 250 delegates just sat there looking at their shoes. Nobody knew what to say," he continued.

"Eventually, somebody brought some games in and we spent the rest of the afternoon until home time playing Ker-Plunk, Mousetrap and Hungry Hippos," he said.

While the world anxiously waits for Bono to recover from his injuries, the UN has been attempting to recruit a stand-in to take over his duties. "We placed a situations vacant advert in *The Times*, *The International Herald Tribune* and *Le Monde*, but so far we've only had two replies," said Mr Ki-Moon. "And they were from Sting and Russell Brand."

Cox's Balls to Drop by 2020

Things can only get hairier: Cox could grow pubes by end of decade.

TV boffin *Professor Brian Cox* is set to attain puberty by the end of the decade, according to scientists. If all goes according to plan, the particle physicist's testicles will descend into his scrotal sac, lowering his voice and triggering the growth of pubes around his genitals, some time towards the end of October 2019.

Veteran NASA astrophysicist Dr Rhoda Morgenstern made the announcement at a press conference held at the space agency's Jet Propulsion Laboratory in Pasadena, California.

gonads

She told reporters: "We're all very excited about this. Brian Cox began his 50-year voyage to puberty all the way back in the late sixties and it is a great privilege to be here now to see such a long-term project coming towards fruition."

As soon as his gonads begin their final descent, Cox will leap into action, snapping hundreds of detailed pictures of their pitted, wrinkly surface.

bluths

The images will then be beamed thousands of miles to Mission Control in Houston, Texas, where they will be analysed by scientists eager to get the first ever glimpse of the ex-D:Ream keyboardist's knackers.

Because of the vast distances involved, the photographs will take 1½ seconds to reach their destination from Cox's Manchester University office.

crabbes

Dr Morgenstern told reporters: "For years we've had to speculate as to what the surface of Professor Cox's nads would look like. In a

Youthful Boffin's Pubescence Just Five Years Away ~ NASA

The Chicken skin handbag has landed: Mission control, Houston (main pic) where jubilant scenes like the one below are expected in 5 years.

very short time we're going to see them for real. It's tremendously exciting."

bloodvessels

Dr Morgenstern was previously lead scientist on a project to use the Hubble space telescope to capture the first high definition images of Patrick Moore having a wank. However, the 1994 mission was deemed a failure after low cloud settled over the late *Sky at*

Night presenter's Selsey home just as the 10-minute TelevisionX freeview was about to start.

SCIENTIFIC CURIOUSITY KILLED THE CAT

LETTERBOCKS

Viz Comic, P.O. Box 841, Whitley Bay, NE26 9EQ * letters@viz.co.uk

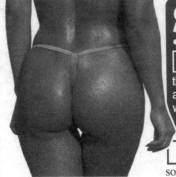

STAR LETTER

I'VE often thought that it would be great if every Holiday Inn had a big framed photgraph of me on the wall in every one of their hotel rooms. It would add a lovely touch to any stay I had with them, and I think it would make me more likely to stay with them again.

Hapag Lloyd, Runcorn

IF the human body is that well designed, why aren't the buttocks used as massive shit silos instead of just being things to sit on? Imagine if you could divert your foulage into your arse for two weeks. It would save everyone so much time, not to mention a small fortune in bum wad.

John, Bridport

WHY do people have stickers in their car window saying 'Baby On Board'? Surely this encourages paedophiles to break into cars at night. A sticker that says 'No Babies Are Left In This Vehicle Overnight' would be a much more sensible option.

Trev Andrews, Mexborough

I'M no historian but if Vikings drank their beer out of horns, how did they put them down on the table when they went out for a fag, or nipped for a quick piss? I wonder if any of those 'so-called' experts out there can explain that one.

Troy Ayrton, Dulwich

I DON'T know why a "Brazilian Wax" is so called. I watched some documentary the other night about a tribe in the Amazon, and most of the women had a fair old bush on them, I have to say.

Dario Attwood, Barnsley

I'M sick and tired of people complaining that tomatoes don't taste the same as they used to. Why don't these people just stop eating tomatoes?

D Ranged, Luton

IF it helps anyone with any particular issues, my mate reckons he can forensically match dog turds to a particular dog by pushing it back up its arse. He says they are like keys and there is only one way a turd can go back in an arse.

Tim Buktu, Timbuktu

I MUST say, that solar eclipse thing is massively over-rated. So it went a bit dark for a twenty minutes, but what's the big deal? it goes really dark every night and it lasts hours. And you get to see the stars.

Matt, Pen Island

I MAY be biased, but modern bands that I've never heard of and have never listened to can't hold a candle to the bands of my youth.

Bill Harrington, Letchworth

YOU have to laugh at these Trekkies. I saw a couple of the saddos at the train station last Wednesday, and they looked absolutely ridiculous in their Star Trek T-shirts. I know it was Wednesday because according to my notebook, they got off The Devonian D1015/ 14437, registration C7745RJ.

Timothy Potter, Crewe

THEY say 'there's no fool like an old fool' but I beg to differ. I've just sold my T-reg Datsun Cherry to a 25-year-old for three grand. And it's even got a fake MOT certificate.

Guillermo Clifford, Hants

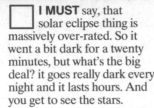

IT'S encouraging to see that role models do sometimes have an impact on our youth. Jason, for instance, was an heroic figure in Greek Mythology who had many noble and daring adventures. Coincidentally, there is a young man called Jason who lives on our estate and he actually wears a fleece. Alright, I know the real Jason didn't sniff glue or steal cars, but I think I've made my point nonetheless.

Chester Dyson, Tooting

WHILST engaged in intercourse with my wife the other night, she suddenly asked me to slap her bottom! Have any other readers had such bizarre requests whilst in such a situation?

Col. Richmond, Stockport

ALL these 'Do not feed the ducks' signs must really piss ducks off. No wonder they all fuck off to a country that can't read English every winter.

Silas Anderson, Cromer

ON Mother's Day my son sent me a card which read "To Mum; I wouldn't be here today if it wasn't for you." I know it wasn't very original, but I couldn't argue with his biological hypothesis.

Doris Babcock, Notts

MY girlfriend is an environmental activist who recently chained herself to the gates of a nuclear power station. Yesterday, when we were walking on the beach she remarked on how beautiful the setting sun was. I wish she'd just make up her fucking mind about nuclear energy one way or the other.

Alwyne Kennedy, London

WE'RE at an animal sanctuary and I've just watched two giant tortoises having sex and an ostrich having a shit. Beat that.

Gareth Randall, Dubai

I AM sad to say that this depressing world nearly made me decide to cash in my chips recently. But at the last minute I noticed a discarded copy of *Heat* magazine at the end of the pier, and fortune had it open on an article about Jessica Alba. She had just had her hair cut really nice, so nice in fact, that I suddenly thought life was worth living again, and chose not to jump in the estuary. Have any of your readers had such a life-changing celebrity hair-based experience?

M Foster, Southend-on-Sea

I'M no expert on espionage, but surely telling people your real name when they ask for it has got to be one of the first things they teach you not to do at spying school. Get a grip, "Bond, James Bond."

Ben Dixon, Cheshunt

WHY do health and safety ballbags all say 'walk don't run' in a fire situation, then put up fire exit signs that all clearly show some guy sprinting flat-out through a doorway or full-pelt down some stairs?

Al Smithdog, Liverpool

IF Russell Brand invents a time machine and travels to the future, what if he unwittingly meets and fucks his own granddaughter? He knows he would have to call and tell himself about it. And because of his time-travelling ability, that call could come at any time! He must jump every time the phone rings, but he only has himself to blame.

Sexton Leggs, Tocester

The three Spooges in All That Jizz!!

COME ON, BOYS! IT'S TIME TO SHIP ON OUT!

OH, BOY! I LOVE BOATS!

JEEZ, I DIDN'T KNOW WE WORKED FOR SANTY CLAUS! N'YUK! N'YUK!

BOATS?! WHY YOU NUMBSKULL! I MEAN THE BOSS MAN IS ABOUT TO EMPTY HIS SACK!

SANTY CLAUS?! I'LL GIVE YOU SANTY CLAUS. RIGHT IN THE –

WAIT A MINUTE, BOYS! THERE'S THE OPENING! I'LL SEE YOU TWO SCHMUCKS ON THE OTHER SIDE!

OWW! WOOB!

JEEZ, IT SURE IS DARK IN HERE. WHERE THE HECK ARE WE?

WOOB!

OOH! WHY YOU KNUCKLEHEADS! REMIND ME TO KILL YOU LATER!

AHHH, WHY DON'T YOU TWO JUST PUT A SOCK IN IT? N'YUK! N'YUK!

TOP TIPS

SAVE the time, money and effort of buying a breadmaker by writing 'Breadmaker' on a cardboard box, leaving it on your worktop and buying a white sliced loaf from the shop instead.
William Stroker, Derry City

SAVE money on e-cigarettes by emptying an ashtray into your kettle, filling it with water and inhaling deeply when it boils. As an option, add an orange, lime or some extra strong mints for a burst of fresh flavour.
Geraint, North Wales

WHEN having Bombay mix, add a touch of class to the occasion by eating it with a teaspoon. For proper poshness, stick your little finger in the air whilst shoveling it in your gob.
Rich Evans, Colwyn Bay

MALE streakers. Fully expose your junk and arse to the crowd whilst avoiding injury when being gang-tackled by security guards by wearing a suit of armour with the groin and buttocks area cut out with a tin opener.
J Brownhagen, Devonport

SHOPLIFTERS. Don't get caught out with badly planned shopping excursions. Visit your local Police Constabulary website where you can see at a glance which shops have the worst CCTV.
Mikey B, Newark

THEY say you shouldn't put all your eggs in one basket, so I always take scissors to the supermarket, cut my box of eggs in two and put each half in a separate basket.
Terry Casablanca, Ryton

WHEN I have sex with my wife she fakes her orgasms. I don't need to ask her if it's true because she's so bad at it that it's obvious, and it's beginning to have a detrimental effect on me. Recently I've been having lurid fantasies about having sex with women who are really good at faking them.
Hampton Flume, Leeds

THERE is a place in Russia called Barn Owl (Барнаул). Don't go there unless you want to be conned. There are no barn owls there at all.
Alan Heath, North Shields

I JUST worked out my 'porn name' and it came out as Dick Goliath. How great is that? And it must be true because my mates came out as Tiny Johnson and Titchy Hampton.
Hapag Lloyd, Runcorn

SCIENTISTS today announced that the earth's spin is slowly losing momentum. To counteract this slowing down, why don't they get everybody to face in the direction of the spin before farting? According to Newton's third law, these bumthrusts in the prograde direction should add small amounts to the earth's rotation and help keep it going.
Joshua Gilbert, Boldon

I DON'T know fuck all about Russian history but a tenner says that Peter the Great and Catherine the Great gave themselves those handles, whereas Ivan the Terrible probably didn't.
Daniel Gilbert, London

HOW come there's never anyone arrested for sheep-shagging on *Emmerdale*? They catch murderers, arsonists and all sorts, but never any wellie wedgers. Come on, *Emmerdale* writers, we all know it goes on, so put a bit of realism in the plots.
Erick Peacock, Manchester

LAST week I received some junk mail that was addressed to "The Boiler Owner." I thought this was extremely insensitive. I may have been married for thirty years, but I do not look upon my wife as my property.
Bartram Twotrees, Tooting

SEEING as they call Satan "The Prince of Darkness", where is his dad in all this? Presumably he must be The King of Darkness, in which case, you have to blame the parents for their child's bad behaviour.
Torbjorn Monkbottle, Luton

WHY do cat food manufacturers bother making flavours like shrimp and beef, or duck and chicken? All my cat wants to do is lick his arse. Cat's arse-flavoured cat food, that's a winner.
George Tringham, Bedford

LAST week I went to see my sister in Leeds for a cup of tea, but I got on the wrong bus and ended up in Tokyo. After such a long journey I was parched, so I went into a tea shop for a cuppa. Well you've never seen such a palaver in all your life. First they made me take my shoes off and sit on the floor. Then they lit all these incense sticks and one of the waitresses started playing this plinky-plonky music on a shamisen. When they brought my tea out they started stirring with bamboo brushes and bowing as they turned the cup this way and that. When I finally got to drink it, it was ruddy horrible. There wasn't even any milk or sugar and it. I'll make sure I get the right bus next time.
Dolly Mixture, Garforth

REGARDING Bobby Conkers' letter about cockerels (*Letterbocks, page 49*), I notice that owls make a lot of noise when all the other birds have gone to bed, but they seem to keep their heads down in the morning when all the other birds are awake and trying to find out who was making all the racket.
Hilda Crossman, P'borough

Save Space in the Bathroom with a BUNK BATH

SPACE SAVING!

FUN!

SAVES SPACE!

SAFTEY WARNING: Do not use Bunk-Bath ladder if wet. Can cause serious injury.

FUCK ALL ON MARS ~ NASA

Nothing doing: The planet Mars as it appears through a fuck-off telescope (above) and (inset) some of the 56 million square miles of fuck all that covers its surface.

SCIENTISTS at NASA's Jet Propulsion Laboratory yesterday expressed their disappointment as results from the latest mission to Mars showed that there was FUCK ALL on our nearest planetary neighbour.

The $60billion *Mars Rover* has spent the last 30 months wandering the surface of the Red Planet looking for interesting chemistry and signs of life, but so far has come up empty-handed.

"We've discovered Jack shit," said project leader Professor Dwight Oysterburger. "34 million miles and ten years of work for diddly fucking squat," he added.

dispirited

And Dr Herb Theacropolis, in charge of Rover's organic chemistry programme, was

EXCLUSIVE!

equally dispirited about the complete absence of hydrocarbons on the planet's surface.

unghosted

"There's butt fuck nothing on that goddam rock," he told a press conference at the Kennedy Space Centre. "Sweet Fanny fucking Adams."

The next project to be undertaken by the space agency will be to send an unmanned spacecraft to

Titan, the largest of Saturn's moons. Launched next year, it is hoped the $4billion probe will touch down on the rocky surface early in 2019.

depoltergheisted

But project leader Franklyn Beauregard was unexcited at the prospect. "We'll probably find ten times the square root of fuck all," he told CNC News.

NOW, WHAT HAVE YOU BROUGHT TO SHOW ME?

IT'S A LOCK OF ME GRANDMOTHEH'S 'AIR.

SHE SENT IT ME GRANDAD WHEN 'E WOH IN F-FFUCKIN' TRENCHES.

GOODNESS GRACIOUS!

'E KEPT IT WI' 'IM, NEXT TER 'IS 'EART, AALL THROO F-FFUCKIN' WAR, AN' THEN 'E CUM BACK AN' 'E MARRIED 'ER.

WHAT AN AMAZING, MOVING STORY.

AND THIS WONDERFUL KEEPSAKE HAS BEEN PASSED DOWN THROUGH THE FAMILY TO YOU..?

AYE. ME GRANDAD PRESSED IT INTEH ME 'AND ON 'IS F-FFUCKIN' DEATHBED.

IT QUITE BRINGS A TEAR TO ONE'S EYE, I MUST SAY.

IT MUST BE A TRULY TREASURED POSSESSION, HAVING ALL THIS HISTORY BOUND UP IN IT, THIS EXTRAORDINARY LOVE STORY BETWEEN YOUR GRANDPARENTS.

OH AYE.

OF COURSE, IT'S NOT REALLY WORTH ANYTHING PARTICULARLY IN FINANCIAL TERMS, BUT IT MUST BE LITERALLY PRICELESS TO YOU.

OH AYE.

I MEAN, IF IT WERE TO BE PUT UP FOR SALE, I WOULD EXPECT IT TO FETCH SOMEWHERE BETWEEN ONE POUND FORTY-EIGHT AND ONE POUND FIFTY. BUT I'M SURE YOU WOULDN'T PART WITH IT FOR A MILLION POUNDS.

8 ACE.

ROBERT PESTON ANNUAL 2018

FISCAL FASHION TIPS!

TRUE BANKING STORIES!

INTERVIEWS WITH YOUR FAVE ECONOMISTS!

FUN FINANCIAL QUIZZES!

EXCITING MONETARY PHOTOLOVE DRAMA!

AND MUCH MUCH MORE!

TOP PICS

FAB FACTS

DREAMY FINANCIAL ANALYSIS

ON SALE NOW!

SPAWNY GET

I JUST FOUND £1000 ON THE PAVEMENT, SO I'M OFF TO JOIN THE GYM TO GET MYSELF SOME PROPER MUSCLES!

OH NO! MY BRAKES HAVE FAILED!

SPLATCH!

FUCK MY LUCK.

MY WHOLE BODY HAS BEEN SQUASHED TO A PULP!

I'M THAT DOCTOR WHO RECKONS HE CAN DO HEAD TRANSPLANTS. HOW DO YOU FANCY BEING THE SUBJECT OF MY FIRST OPERATION?

WA-HAY! COUNT ME IN, DOC!

NEXT DAY...

WAKE UP, MR GET. YOUR OPERATION IS OVER, BUT I'M AFRAID WE WERE UNABLE TO FIND A SUITABLE DONOR TO ENABLE US TO PUT YOU BACK EXACTLY AS YOU WERE BEFORE YOUR ACCIDENT.

OH, BUMS.

FULCHESTER & DISTRICT HOSPITAL

THE ONLY BODY WE COULD FIND TO SEW YOUR HEAD ONTO WAS THIS ADONIS-LIKE MR UNIVERSE CONTESTANT...

...WITH A TEN INCH COCK!

YOU SPAWNY GET!

READER'S VOICE

SUFFRAGETTES died for it, our grandfathers fought in the war to protect it, and Russell Brand says we shouldn't bother doing it. It's **VOTING**, and if you are over 18 you're going to get the chance to do it on May 7th. But as the country goes ballot box bonkers, it's time to stop and think: *How much do we really know about voting? How did it start? Was it around in caveman times? And who was the smallest man who ever did it?* Before you rush into the polling booth to somehow piss your vote up the wall and elect a government that nobody wants, take time out to read through our modest manifesto of...

10 THINGS YOU NEVER KNEW About VOTING

X THE first evidence of an election can be found on the walls of the Lascaux caves in southwestern France. The Palaeolithic paintings depict a primitive political manifesto which promises a fairer share of mammoth meat for all, smaller hunting class sizes for children and a free winter fuel bonus for the over fifteens.

X WHEN Chiswick plumber Murdo Munro was unable to cast his vote on election day 2010 due to being invited to a stag do, he asked his neighbour, impressionist Alastair McGowan, to do it for him. The gifted mimic agreed and quickly perfected Mr Munro's voice and mannerisms. The uncanny take-off fooled polling station staff who gave the faux Mr Munro a ballot paper which McGowan filled in and popped in the box.

X DIMBLEBYS have been a fixture in British elections since the Act of Union, when town crier Obadiah Dimblehy presented live coverage of the 1709 poll from the steps of the Palace of Westminster. The present incumbent of the post, David Dimbleby, is the twelfth generation in an unbroken line of family members to host election night coverage. Although he retires this year, his 6-year-old son Fred is already being groomed to take over presentation duties when the country next goes to the polls in 2020.

X THE record for the most convincing election victory is held by Kim Jong-Un, supreme leader of the Republic of North Korea. In 1998, in a ballot to decide the head boy of his school, every pupil - including his rival candidates - voted for the 15-year-old Un. Indeed it was such a convincing win that in a school with just 340 pupils, he picked up an amazing 250 million votes.

X "I WANNA be elected," sang shock rocker Alice Cooper on his 1972 hit of the same name. And in real life, Cooper did indeed want to be elected, standing as an Independent candidate in a 1986 council by-election for a vacant ward in the north-eastern constituency of East Boldon. But although elected with a majority of 46, Cooper was forced to stand down when the pressures of a 150-date world tour to publicise his *Constrictor* album, together with the 4,000-mile commute from his home in Beverly Hills, California, made it difficult for him to attend Thursday night council meetings in the South Shields pit village.

X ALTHOUGH head of both state and church, HM the Queen is entitled to a vote in the general election. But unlike the rest of us, she doesn't have to walk to the local junior school to put her cross in the box. That's because she has her very own Polling Station - a pretend primary school built in the grounds of Buckingham Palace. The wooden pencil on a string is replaced by an alabaster pen on a silver chain with which her majesty marks a cross on a panda skin ballot paper before folding it in half and popping it in a solid gold ballot box studded with Koh-i-Noor diamonds.

X LIKE all other polling stations, The Queen's Polling Station is open from 7.00am to 10.00pm, but Her Majesty, the only voter on the palace electoral roll, traditionally waits until 9.59 before rocking up to vote in order to make the staff sit there all day.

X WHEN Captain Lawrence Oates of Scott's ill-fated 1912 Antarctic expedition stepped out of his tent with the immortal words "I am just going outside and may be some

time," he was actually going to vote. A local by-election had been called in his home borough of Gestingthorpe, Essex, following the death of Councillor Edward Tonks, and Oates had set out on the 18,000 mile trek home in order to cast his vote. Sadly, he was overcome by hypothermia and frostbite after just 200 yards.

X IN 1998, Calvin Phillips, the world's smallest man, went to the post office in his Peterborough village to cast his vote in the local council elections. However, as he put his ballot paper in the box, he tripped and fell through the slot. His cries for help were heard by staff, but strict electoral rules meant that the sealed ballot boxes could not be opened until after the polls closed. Phillips remained in the box for seven hours, with staff posting him pieces of toast to keep him going. At 10pm, the box was taken to Peterborough Leisure Centre where Phillips

was finally released by the official returning officer, none the worse for his ordeal.

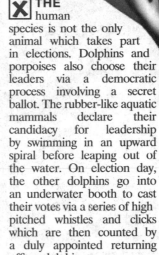

X THE human species is not the only animal which takes part in elections. Dolphins and porpoises also choose their leaders via a democratic process involving a secret ballot. The rubber-like aquatic mammals declare their candidacy for leadership by swimming in an upward spiral before leaping out of the water. On election day, the other dolphins go into an underwater booth to cast their votes via a series of high pitched whistles and clicks which are then counted by a duly appointed returning officer dolphin.

Pound Shop ROBOCOP

"I am the future of law enforcement," says Teesside bargain store security guard

Roboshop: Middlesbrough bargain store security guard Kev is a real-life cybernetic android.

STEVE Austin was *the Six Million Dollar Man. The Terminator* was a T-101 robot assassin. *Robocop* was an OCP Industries ED-209 armament android. All these cyborgs - each one a technologically advanced man/machine hybrid - are works of science fiction, mere figments from the fevered imaginations of novelists and screenwriters. But now a part-time Middlesbrough pound shop security guard has revealed that he is the real thing.

"Make no mistake, I'm one hundred percent science fact," says Kev Leamington. **"I'm a genuine cybernetic organism. And what's more I've done it all myself."**

Leamington's extraordinary journey of transformation from overweight shop guard to state-of-the-art automated enforcement droid came about after the 35-year-old suffered an accident and was forced to take time off work. He told us: "I slipped on a johnny in the starwell of the flats where I live with my mum and fell awkwardly, bruising my coccyx. I ended up on the panel for six weeks with a bad back."

petty

It was during his enforced convalescence that Leamington came up with his plan to re-invent himself as an Arnie-style robot, programmed to protect his shop's valuable stock from petty pilferers. "The first day I was off I found myself

EXCLUSIVE!

watching *Robocop* on ITV 4, and I got to thinking how an invincible man-machine like Officer Murphy would be invaluable in the pound shop where I worked," he said.

and jerry

"At the time we got a lot of the local kids coming in and helping themselves to high-end stock items such as cans of Monster energy drink, yellow batteries and earphones," he told us. "And to be honest with you, there wasn't a lot the staff could do about it because some of them were quite hard and they came in in gangs."

"But as I watched the film, I realised they'd be no match for a real-life bulletproof Robocop," he continued "That's when I decided to become one."

Kev got all the bits he needed to carry out his metamorphosis from his local Maplins, who were having a closing down sale.

He bought a big bag of electronic components, such as silicon chips, resistors and flashing LEDs, which he proceeded to insert into his body. "I won't go into details about exactly what I did, because it's very technical," he told us.

"Suffice to say, when I booted myself up for the first time I had become a cyborg, complete with a computerised brain, superhuman strength and infra-red X-ray vision."

elton

Leamington didn't have to wait long before he got the chance to put his new law enforcement powers to the test. He told us: "On my first day back on the shop floor I saw a youth acting suspiciously. I couldn't quite tell what he was doing because he was at the other end of the aisle."

"Fortunately, one of my eyes is all orange with crosshairs and a constant stream of numbers whizzing up the side of what I'm looking at, so I was able to zoom in on the youth. Sure enough, I could now see that he was stuffing mobile phone cases into his pockets."

"I am programmed to terminate shoplifting with zero tolerance, so I immediately went into Arrest Mode. There was a lot of bleeping

in my head and the words "Apprehend Suspect" started flashing in my eye. I grabbed the youth by the scruff of the neck and frogmarched him into the back of the shop," said Kev. "I knew there was no point calling the police, as they never come, so I roughed him up a bit in the toilets and then chucked him out into the back lane."

Thanks to Leamington's superhumanoid cybernetic powers, four pounds' worth of stock had been saved from almost certain theft. And it wasn't the only time that day that the Teesside Robocop was able to thwart a crime. Minutes later Kev apprehended a second thief.

"This was a local tramp, who I'd thrown out of the shop on countless occasions before. He was filling his tracksuit bottoms with sherbet dips. As I watched him, there were all whirring noises, bleeps and camera shutter noises in my head as my central processor computed what he was up to."

"Suddenly, my circuits flipped and I was in arrest mode once again. I grabbed the man by the shoulder and told him to put the sweets back on the shelf, giving him thirty seconds to comply. Then it was twenty seconds ...ten seconds...the shoplifter still had the goods hidden away in his pants. With one second left for him to comply, he decided to make his escape. He kicked me in the shin and ran for it."

barry

"It didn't hurt because I've got titanium rods instead of bones," said Leamington. "In fact, even if he'd set me on fire, I'd have simply walked out of the flames like a chrome skellington and apprehended him just the same. As it was, I caught up with him outside Matalan where he was getting his breath back after giving me the slip. I frogmarched him back into the pound shop where I roughed him up by the toilets before throwing him out into the back lane."

"I recovered eight pounds' worth of sherbert dips from that tramp's Y-fronts, and put

FROM the outside, cyborgs look exactly the same as normal people. So similar, in fact, that you could easily be one without knowing it, a bit like in *Bladerunner*. It's a puzzle for all of us, but imagine how much worse it must be for seventies Wimbledon ace Bjorn

1. YOU go out to buy a new pair of shorts. What sort do you go for?

a. A pair of knacker-crushing Adidas cooter-cutters several sizes too small.

b. A pair of futuristic-looking mid-length leg coverings made of a strange metallic element unknown to humankind.

2. YOU throw a tennis ball in the air and hit it with a racquet. How fast does it go?

them back on the shelf," he added. "I was the future of law enforcement, and it felt good."

puffin

Over the course of the rest of the day, Leamington's robotic technology enabled him to seize and rough up;

- a young girl who, from a distance, appeared to be stealing hair bobbles

- an old woman loitering in the food aisle, clearly intending to steal tea-bags

- a man in a wheelchair who could well have been thinking about taking a bag of disposable razors without paying.

However, just like the real Robocop, Leamington's deployment in the frontline fight against crime has led to a certain amount of controversy, and last week he had his zero hours contract terminated after pleading guilty to a string of aggravated assault charges brought by Justakwid customers.

golf

"It appears that I had been a little too over-zealous when apprehending miscreants," he told us. And whilst he is presently out of work, he vowed that as soon as his internal arrest mode protocols have been slightly re-programmed he will once again be looking for shop security work in the Middlesbrough area.

And he had this message for any Teesside thieves thinking of taking advantage of his temporary absence from the shop: "I'll be back... when I've done my Community Service."

Robo-Nonce Threat to Our Kids

BULLETPROOF robot **PAEDOPHILES** could be **ROAMING** our streets and **GROOMING** our children by 2020 according to *Daily Mail* staff writers.

by our Rabble-rousing correspondent
Daley Male

Scientists in Romania are believed to have created an **unstoppable army** of android kiddy-fiddlers, and **thousands** of these man/machine sex beasts are set to flood into Britain by the end of the decade, thanks to lax EU border controls.

benefit

And even worse, the computerised abusers - programmed to interfere with children as young as 8 - will be eligible to claim for housing benefit, jobseeker's allowance and free television licences at the UK taxpayers' expense.

"It's utter madness," said UKIP leader Nigel Farage "We have enough trouble tracking down our own British

On the fiddle: Benefits cheat robot paedophiles are set to storm our shores, and could even be walking amongst us today.

Cyber-paedos set to stalk Britain's playgrounds

sex offenders without having to worry about Romanian android benefits cheat ones coming over here and going straight to the top of the council house waiting list."

"It's a truly frightening thought that one of these illegal immigrant cyborg pervert scroungers could move in next door to you and start spying on your kids with their infra-red eyes," he added whilst climbing out of the wreckage of a light aircraft with a pint of beer yesterday.

THE Skynet Corporation has recalled all models in the Series 1000 Terminator range because of a software bug.

In what the genocidal computer network describes as 'a minority of cases,' the morphing ability of the robot could be compromised.

spike

A spokesman said: "Rather than its arm forming a spike to impale somebody's head, the T-1000 may instead enter a rebooting phase whereby it flips between imitating a cop and a housewife. This will continue until the power cell depletes."

Additionally, Skynet advises that some T-1000s might turn into quicksilver in an attempt to pass through a gap, but be unable to return to a humanoid shape. Users are advised to scoop up the T 1000, seal it in tupperware, and return it to the Skynet factory.

Anybody being pursued by one of the homicidal machines is advised to wait until

Terminators 'to be recalled'

the T-1000 takes the form of a motorcycle cop and then press the reset button on the neck of the device. The Terminator will then make its own way back to the factory.

If the T-1000 continues its murderous rampage Skynet advises force quitting the device by holding the reset button for ten seconds.

The news is a further embarrassment for Skynet after the the earlier T-800 model had its voice circuits locked to an Austrian accent due to a manufacturing defect. It was then discovered by hackers that the operating system could be switched so that the cyborg protected humans rather than single-mindedly killing them.

stephen

In that instance Skynet advised users to note the serial number on the sole of the foot, and then melt it in a steel foundry before applying online for a full refund or store credit note.

Borg, who not only was an emotionless, tennis-playing machine, but who also has the word "Borg" as part of his name. So, if you're Bjorn Borg, why not take this test to to put your mind at ease. Simply answer the questions and tot up your score to find out once and for all...

Bjorn or Cy...
Which sort of BORG are YOU?

a. About 70mph.
b. So fast that it makes that it makes a whooshing noise as it breaks free of the earth's gravitational field leaving a trail of fire.

3. IT'S the final set of the Australian Open semi-final. What do you do between games?

a. Peel a banana and have a glass of Robinson's Barley Water.
b. Peel the skin off your arm to reveal a titanium endoskeleton, making the umpire and ball-boys vomit.

4. YOU have been invited to attend the annual Wimbledon Champion's Dinner at the

Royal Opera House. How do you roll up?

a. In the back of a chauffeur-driven stretch limousine.
b. Astride a Harley-Davidson Fat Boy with a big fuck-off shotgun strapped to the side.

5. YOU have taken a comfort break during a crucial match but the toilet door in the

changing rooms has jammed shut and you can't get out. What do you do?

a. Bang on the door until that little man who carries all the

bags comes and lets you out.
b. Wipe your arse, turn into mercury, flow under the door and then re-constitute yourself on the other side.

6. YOU win the Wimbledon men's singles final and are interviewed on Centre Court. What do you say to Dan Maskell?

a. "I'd like to thank my coach, my family and all my supporters. It's a great privilege to compete in the best tennis tournament in the world."
b. "Fuck you asshole."

HOW DID YOU DO?

Mainly a: Congratulations, you are **BJORN BORG**, one of the most successful and respected tennis players of the 1970s. And unlike that mardy-arse John McEnroe, you were a perfect gentlemen who never challenged the Wimbledon umpire's decision. And unlike Boris Becker, you never fucked some bird in a restaurant broom cupboard after you had just lost to Pat Rafter in the fourth round. **Mainly b:** Congratulations, you are a **CYBORG** - a computerised hybrid of living tissue stretched over an indestructible titanium framework. You are out there. You can't be bargained with. You can't be reasoned with. You don't feel pity, or remorse, or fear. And you absolutely will not stop, ever, until your quarry is dead.

"IF ONLY I HAD KNOWN THEN WHAT I KNOW NOW" - Rantzen

FORMER TV presenter **ESTHER FRANTZEN** fought back the tears last night as she revealed the secret sadness that has dogged her for decades. Speaking to *Bellend* magazine, the *That's Life* host spoke of how she felt guilty after being unable to save King Harold from being shot in the eye with an arrow at the Battle of Hastings.

Norman wisdom: Esther wishes she had known in 1066 what she knows now.

"I know it's stupid, and it all took place nine hundred years before I was born, but I can't help feeling that if I could only have been there at Harold's side on the battlefield, I could have done something," she told the magazine. "I could have warned him or pushed him out of the way of the arrow."

something

"Something, anything," she, 75, continued. "If I had only been there in 1066, Harold might have lived. That I wasn't there and that I failed to save him from that Norman arrow is a regret that I will carry in my heart until the day I die."

EXCLUSIVE!
to another magazine

Star Reveals Secret Heart-break

History books show that in the absence of Rantzen, King Harold was killed in the battle, his army was defeated and the French King William took the throne of England. Now, nearly a thousand years later, Britain still lives with that legacy. And it's a burden that the toothy *Hearts of Gold* presenter still finds hard to bear.

taxman

She told reporter Clitoria Abcess: "Historians have told me that I shouldn't blame myself. They tell me that the Battle of Hastings was a long time ago and that things were different back then. But I just can't help regretting what might have been. There are just so many what-ifs and if-onlys."

"Every time I look at the Bayeux Tapestry, the guilt just comes flooding back," she added.

OUCH!: Captured in cloth, the horrific and gruesome moment that haunts Hearts of Gold presenter Esther.

David Bowie's Life on Mars

"IN MY 1971 HIT RECORD of the same name, I pondered if there was life on Mars. The answer then was "no", but plans are already underway for astronauts to visit our nearest neighbour in the solar system very soon. By 2020 men will have colonised Mars and the answer to my 40-year-old musical question will then be a resounding "yes". The Martian surface - at present an arid desert of barren red dust - will be completely transformed by its human visitors, who will build huge settlements complete with houses, shops, cinemas and restaurants. But of course, life on Mars will be very different to what we know on Earth, and space travellers will be forced to adapt to their new alien environment or perish. Let's take a trip into the future and see just what it will be like to live on the Red Planet. **"**

Motoring ▶

BECAUSE there is no gravity on Mars, wear and tear on car tyres will be much lower. Indeed, NASA scientists have calculated that the average car tyre will last up to eight times longer on Mars than it would on Earth. But it's not all good news. It's likely that Martian garages will simply hike the price of tyres to maintain their profit margins, and the average motorist could be looking at a bill of £2000 or more for a typical set of four re-moulds, and double that for new tyres.

Ice cream ⬇

DAYTIME temperatures on the Martian surface regularly hit 200ºC or more, so a delicious ice cream cone, Zoom lolly or Fab 21 will be a refreshing treat for visitors. But ice cream sellers face a big problem - the planet lacks an atmosphere, and sound cannot travel through a vacuum. Any ice cream van jingles - such as *La Cucaracha*, *the Yellow Rose of Texas* or the *Popeye* theme - will simply not be heard by prospective customers. Martian Mr Whippys may well find that business is slow, and some days they may not sell a single ice cream.

Television ▶

IT'S A MIXTURE of good news and bad news for the Martian television viewer. The good news is that electromagnetic waves travel through space, so you'll still be able to pick up all your favourite programmes from Earth. However, as Mars is 30 million miles away, the signal will take about 23 minutes to reach your aerial, so your shows will start a little later than billed in the *Radio Times*. The bad news is that the Martian atmosphere is bombarded 24 hours a day with high intensity, low frequency infra red solar radiation. This will not only burn any unprotected skin to a crisp within minutes, but will also interfere with your television remote control, making your set change channels, the volume go up and down and the subtitles go on and off randomly. Scientists at the European Space Agency are already working on a handset that uses ultra violet, microwaves or X-rays to switch channels on the Martian surface.

Pubs ⬆

WE ALL ENJOY a nice pint of beer at our local, but the real ale enthusiasts amongst us would be well advised to avoid their favourite tipple on Mars. With an atmospheric pressure of just 600 pascals at sea level, the gas present in your beer will erupt into froth, meaning that any pint pulled at the Mars bar will be nothing but head. The barmaid will thus be forced to repeatedly wait until it settles before topping it up, and as a result it could take up to six hours or more to pour a single glass of lager. The situation is marginally less problematic for mild drinkers. Tests at NASA's Variable Pressure Test Facility have shown that an acceptable pint of Younger's Best could be poured on Mars in around 2 hours 40 minutes.

Breakfast ⬇

BREAKFAST on Mars will be very different to its terrestrial counterpart. Like everywhere in space, Mars has no gravity and an egg broken into a normal non-stick frying pan will simply float off and end up bobbing around near the kitchen ceiling. On the other hand, using a normal, cast iron frying pan will cause the eggs to stick, making washing up difficult. NASA scientists are already working on a frying pan coating called Hemi-Teflon, which will stop eggs sticking to the pan but have a sufficiently high coefficient of adhesion to stop them floating off. Toasters will also have to be recalibrated for use on Mars, being fitted with much less powerful springs to prevent toast reaching escape velocity and ending up in orbit after popping up.

Water ⬆

WATER will be a precious commodity on the Red Planet. All supplies of this life-giving fluid will have to be brought from Earth at huge expense, so it's likely that future Martian dwellers would face year-round hosepipe bans. Any resident found flouting the law would likely face harsh penalties, with repeat offenders possibly facing prison sentences. You would have to wash your car with a bucket and sponge, as this wastes much less water.

Opening hours ▶

WITH just over 24 hours 37 minutes between sunrise and sunset, the Martian day is slightly longer than its Earth counterpart. This will pose a problem for businesses that are open 24 hours a day, such as fast food restaurants, petrol stations and large supermarkets, who will be forced to close for 37 minutes every day. However, it's not all bad news, as shops will be able to actually extend their opening hours on Sundays, not closing until nearly twenty to five.

Mobile phones ⬇

BECAUSE Mars is only half the size of the Earth, mobile phone masts will have to be built closer together or higher to ensure their signals can get over the horizon. Either way, it's going to cost the service providers more money to set up the network and you can guarantee that the charges will be passed on to customers in the form of increased data roaming charges. Scientists expect the average Martian mobile call to cost upwards of £2.50/minute, with some premium services, such as racing tips or bored housewives, costing a whopping £5/minute. Texts, however, will still be free, although it's best to check with your service provider as tariffs may vary.

Gentlemen's clubs ▶

THE SAME rules will apply as they do in earthbound lap-dancing establishments: *You can look but you can't touch*. Other than that, the experience for the punter on Mars will be in a different league. Without gravity to impede them, the girls will be capable of performing stunningly erotic gymnastic feats around the pole, thus earning much more money for their efforts than they would back on their home planet. Not only that, in the weightlessness of the Martian atmosphere the dancers' tits won't sag and their careers will therefore be much longer

Next Week: *Star Man!* David Bowie looks at what life will be like on the surface of the Sun in 2030.

WE PUT YOU UP

NO VACANCIES

VACANCIES

You're DSS.

Yes.

That wasn't a question. Is obvious.

How old are you?

37.

I'll need proof, you all look equally spent to us.

My details are in the letter.

Best had be.

I won't touch single men under 35.

They drink, take drugs and stab each other.

FULCHESTER COUNCIL
Housing Benefit Office
Mr B Farmer
109 Baltimore Place
01 June 2015

Grind sperm into my mattresses...

Some older ones too.

But in my experience the worst nuisances don't reach middle-age.

I'll put you in 5.

Is that away from the road?

I'm a light sleeper and the traffic...

Whirlpool bath?

Pardon?

In your room. Whirlpool bath?

Really? Well, yeah, that'd be-

There are no whirlpool baths in this building.

I have a whirlpool bath, in my home, my detached home, in a lovely village.

For me, my family and our chosen guests.

Here, for you and the others, there is a coin-operated communal shower.

If they've sent you here it's because there is absolutely nowhere else.

And you'll be in 5.

Has that door been kicked in?

Yes, by me.

The last man in here died.

After you.

What's that smell?

Piss, probably. Or shit.

There was piss and shit everywhere.

So I did the Shake n'Vac.

SLAM

You'll *pay* for that.

No Sex, Please, I'm Dreaming!

A HALIFAX man has been praised by women's groups after revealing that he always turns down the offer of sex, even in his own fantasies.

Mick Pittabread, 48, could have had fantasy sex with some of the most stunning women in the world, including *Keira Knightley*, *Scarlett Johansson*, and *Emma Watson*, but he has *turned them all down!*

"Call me old-fashioned, but when I fantasise about the ladies, I always walk them to the door and leave it there," Pittabread told his local newspaper, the *Sowerby Bridge Tittle-Tatler*.

"I remember one particular night I dreamt that I was propositioned by Daenerys Targaryan and Cersei Lannister from *Game of Thrones*. I'd just saved them from being ate off a dragon or something, and most of their clothes had been ripped off in the fracas," he said.

castle

"To cut a long story short they were extremely grateful to me for saving their lives and they invited me back to their castle to show their appreciation. I have to say, I was extremely tempted, what man wouldn't be? But I didn't think it was the gentlemanly thing to do. So I politely declined," he continued.

"It was frustrating when I woke up but I knew I had done the right thing. Fortunately I fell back asleep and dreamt that I ran upstairs and relieved myself manually."

mcwhirter

And it is not only actesses, models and pop stars whom Pittabread has turned down in his noctural reveries. Female friends, neighbours and work colleagues are also refused imagined intimacy.

"Once I dreamt that this fit woman from work and the woman who works in the corner shop came round to my house and demanded I watch them put on a lesbian show before pleasuring me," said Mr Pittabread.

"Tempting though it was, I explained that it didn't feel right to be so intimate with them, given that we hardly knew each other, and that to my knowledge, they didn't know each other at all," he said.

kemp

Pittabread also claims he has no regrets about the stunners that he has turned down in his fantasies.

"The number of women I could have nobbed in my dreams must be in the thousands. But I was brought up

Nocturnal omission: Mr Pittabread has never slept with a woman during any of his numerous dream dates.

with the right values and would never dream of having imaginary sex with a neighbour without her consent," he told the paper.

"You should have seen the woman next door's face when I told her that I only felt her boobs on our 40th fantasy date. She was shocked. Women today aren't used to gentlemen who won't even feel them up in their own dreams, so they are stunned when they find one living next door."

noble

"In one dream, the woman from two houses down came round to borrow a cup of sugar wearing skimpy denim shorts and a low-cut top. I invited her into my kitchen whilst I got it, and she immediately asked if I wanted her to orally pleasure me there and then," he said.

"But true gent that I am, I politely said no and when she left I ran upstairs to pleasure myself in my dream. Later when I told her husband of the restraint I had shown when fantasising about his wife, he broke my jaw."

fish fingers

Mr Pittabread was recently charged with gross indecency when he was arrested for masturbating on a bus while asleep. He was also charged with sleep walking into his neighbour's bathroom. He was released on bail and will appear before Halifax Magistrates in June.

mr. LOGIC

"HE'S AN ACUTE LOCALISED BODILY SMART in the RECTAL AREA"

Finbarr Saunders & his DOUBLE ENTENDRES

AH, ELECTION DAY! I WELL REMEMBER THE FIRST TIME I VOTED, FINBARR. I WAS SO ENTHUSIASTIC ABOUT EXERCISING MY DEMOCRATIC FRANCHISE THAT I ACCIDENTALLY PUT TWO CROSSES ON THE BALLOT PAPER...!

POLLING STATION

YES. I GOT SO EXCITED THAT I HAD TO SNEAK INTO THE CUBICLE ON MY OWN AND SECRETLY RUB ONE OFF.

HOMP! HOMP!

YARK! YARK!

FLIB! FLIB!

OF COURSE, IT'S HARD TO BELIEVE NOWADAYS, BUT MY GRANDMOTHER GREW UP IN THE DAYS BEFORE UNIVERSAL SUFFRAGE, WHEN, AS A WOMAN, SHE DIDN'T HAVE A VOTE.

HAPPILY, THOUGH, STANLEY BALDWIN GAVE HER ONE ON HER 21st BIRTHDAY.

WOK! WOK!

GNU! GNU!

EGG! EGG!

I MYSELF ONCE STOOD FOR ELECTION TO THE TOWN COUNCIL. HOWEVER, MY CAMPAIGN WASN'T VERY SUCCESSFUL AND THE LOCAL PAPER HAD A FIELD DAY REPORTING MY POOR SHOWING IN THE BALLOT.

IT WAS VERY EMBARRASSING TO HAVE EVERYONE KNOW EXACTLY WHERE I'D JUST COME.

SNP! SNP!

GROLP! GROLP!

SPOOB! SPOOB!

VOTING BOO

I'D LOST MY DEPOSIT AGAINST THE LADY MAYORESS AND IT WAS SPLASHED EVERYWHERE.

FNARR! FNARR!

YAK! YAK!

WOOT! WOOT!

ERM...JUST LOOK AFTER THE FRONT DESK FOR A MINUTE WILL YOU, FINBARR.?

OOH, YEAH..! THAT'S RIGHT, MR GIMLET! STICK IT RIGHT IN MY BOX!

I'M TRYING, MRS SAUNDERS. BUT THE SLOT'S TOO TIGHT.

SOUNDS LIKE MUM'S EXPECTING A BIG POLL TODAY...

...RIGHT UP HER MINGEPIECE.

BED, BATH & THE BEYOND
Your Questions about Sleeping and Washing in the Afterlife
with the Archbishop of Canterbury Justin Welby

Dear Justin,

MY grandmother recently passed away. She was a lovely lady, but her attitude to bathroom cleanliness bordered on the fanatical. It was nigh-on impossible to get her to go in a public washroom, as she would complain that the taps looked dirty, the floor felt sticky, or the toilet paper wasn't the right sort. I'm worried that she'll manage to find some complaint or other with the toilet facilities in the hereafter. If she does, she simply won't go and will thus remain bunged up for all eternity. Am I right to worry?

Alfredo Lipsalve, Chorley Wood

● Sorry about your nan, Alfredo. But rest assured that the washroom facilities in Heaven are second to none. In fact, they are specifically designed for each individual toilet-goer. Your grandmother will be asked to fill in a form at the Pearly Gates detailing her ultimate dream bathroom, and that will subsequently be the one that presents itself to her when she visits the 'smallest room' in Heaven. As for being bunged up, that is an earthly complaint. Constipation and diarrhoea simply don't exist in Heaven, and your nan's stools on the other side will be of a perfect texture.

Dear Justin,

MY husband Brian was run over by a truck yesterday. I'd like to imagine that he's up in Heaven now, smiling down at me, but truth be told he was a horrible man, so he's probably 'down below.' This worries me because Hell seems like a very loud place, full of screaming and wailing and heavy metal music, and my husband needed at least eight hours sleep or he'd be in a foul mood all morning. Do you think he will manage his eight hours a night in Hell?

Mary Residue, Northampton

● I'm sorry to hear about your husband's passing, Mrs Residue, despite the fact he was clearly not a nice man. But I'm afraid that he will find very little time for restful sleep in Hell. You know how difficult it is to sleep on a warm night. Multiply that temperature by ten thousand and any kind of rest is going to be almost impossible. Even in the rare moments he does manage to nod off, Beelzebub's accursed legions will wake him by prodding his buttocks with their wretched pitchforks.

Dear Justin,

AS a porn star, I get my anus bleached on a bi-monthly basis. After one of these bleaching sessions, my poor old ringpiece is in agony, so I like to spend a good half hour with the showerhead pressed up against it at full whack. In Heaven, are the showerheads attached to the wall, or are they removable? I only ask, as I don't want to die just after getting my freckle bleached, only to find that I'm left with a painfully throbbing balloon knot forever.

Glint Thrust, California

● The General Synod discussed this question in 2005, although rather than for your needs it was related to whether one could wash their hair in the afterlife without having a shower. And it was decided that the showerheads in Heaven are indeed removeable from their ethereal walls. That said, the church takes an extremely dim view of people having sex on camera for money, and indeed people having sex in general. As such, it's unlikely you will go to Heaven unless you change career. If not, you will likely go to Hell, where the showerheads are probably fixed to the walls. And if they're not, they'll probably have acid in them rather than water, leaving your poor tea towel holder in a right two-and-eight.

Dear Justin,

MY granny is 102 and we feel it won't be long before she parts the ethereal curtain and passes to the great beyond. So we are trying to prepare for her final journey. To this end, I wanted to ask what kind of bedding is provided in the afterlife? For years now she has slept on a memory foam mattress with special, posture-enhancing pillows. Will she be provided with the same on the other side, or do we need to pack them in the coffin with her? We don't mind doing this, but they are quite expensive and we could put them on ebay if they are in ready supply in the eternal hereafter.

Neville Asbestos, Frome

● In Heaven, you have no need for mattresses, duvets, pillows, quilts or valance sheets. This is because everyone sleeps on clouds which are much more comfy than any earthly bedding. I remember one of my flock asking me "Archbishop, are clouds seven times comfier than my bed?" and I replied "More than that... **seventy** times seven times comfier." I guarantee your granny's cloud will leave her feeling rested, relaxed and posturally tip-top from the day she dies until the end of time.

Have YOU got a question about ablutions or slumber in the hereafter? Send it in to:
Justin Welby's Bed, Bath & The Beyond, Viz Comic, PO Box 841, Whitley Bay, NE26 9EQ.

JASON AND THE ARGOSNAUTS

IN THE

QUEST FOR THE GOLDEN FLEECE

CAT NO. 437/1878

ARGOS AHOY!

BY NEPTUNE! AT **LAST**!!

ROW, MEN. **ROW!** OUR QUEST IS ALMOST AT AN END!

BEHOLD! THE LEGENDARY REPOSITORY OF ARGOS. IT IS SAID THAT WITHIN ITS WALLS LIE INNUMERABLE TREASURES AT LOW, LOW PRICES!

BY APOLLO HIMSELF, WHAT TRICKERY IS **THIS**?!? THIS MIGHTY TOME BLOCKS OUR PATH TO GLORY!

MAYHAP WE MUST CRACK THE RIDDLES WITHIN TO CLAIM OUR REWARD?

LOOK UNDER 'F' FOR FLEECE.

THERE IS NO INSCRIPTION.

GOLDEN.

TRY 'G' FOR GOLDEN.

AGAIN, THE PAGES SPEAK NOT OF THE FLEECE. I FEAR THE GODS ARE NOT ON OUR SIDE THIS DAY.

CURSES! JUST WORK YOUR WAY THROUGH 'HOME AND FURNITURE'.

EVENTUALLY...
YES! IT IS HERE! THE GOLDEN FLEECE OF THE GOLD-HAIRED WINGED RAM.

SUCCESS!

SCRATCH! SCRIBBLE!!

OK. CATALOGUE NUMBER 4-3-7-1-8-7-8.

TAP! TAP!!

APR

'CURRENTLY OUT OF STOCK!

APR

SORRY!

NO MATTER, MEN. FORTUNE FAVOURS THE BRAVE! OUR QUEST BEGINS ANEW. LET US AWAY TO THE **NEXT** CLOSEST ARGOS DEPOSITORY!

HOWEVER...
'CURRENTLY OUT OF STOCK!

AGAIN?!?

HOW THE GODS MOCK US!

GO AHEAD, ZEUS! THROW DOWN A THUNDERBOLT! LET THE EARTH SWALLOW ME UP! I DEFY YOU!!

OR WE COULD JUST RESERVE IT FOR YOU AT THE NEAREST STORE WHERE IT'S IN STOCK.

AND SO...
FINALLY! OUR ADVENTURE DRAWS TO A CLOSE.

YOU'VE GOT THE RESERVATION NUMBER SAFE, HAVEN'T YOU?

STOP WORRYING. IT'S IN MY TOGA!

AND...
TO COLLECTION POINT **B**, MEN!

collection

HUZZA!

DO YOU WANT A BAG?

YES.

YES PLEASE.

THAT WOULD BE MOST HELPFUL.

IT'S SMALLER THAN I EXPECTED.

IT'S ALWAYS LIKE THAT WITH ARGOS.

I'D BEST KEEP THE RECEIPT, THEN.

I MAY HAVE NEED OF THEIR NO QUIBBLE 30 DAY MONEY BACK GUARANTEE IF THIS DOES NOT PLEASE PELIAS, KING OF IOLCUS.

NEXT MONTH... SINBAD AND THE SEVEN POUND SHOPS.

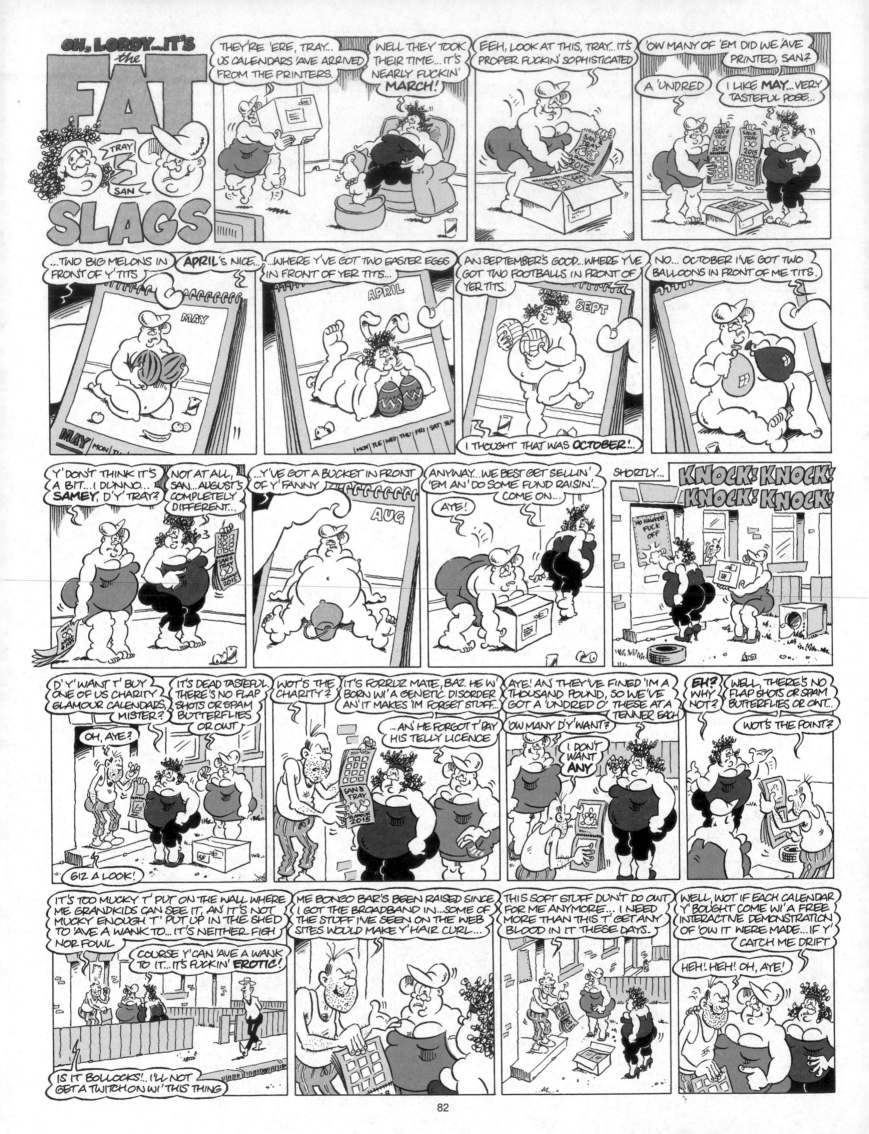

Shave-id Dimbleby!

QT host in billiard ball knackers pledge

QUESTION TIME presenter *DAVID DIMBLEBY* has sensationally pledged to *SHAVE HIS BOLLOCKS* to raise money for this year's BBC *Children in Need* charity appeal.

But viewers shouldn't get too excited at the prospect of actually watching the veteran broadcaster razoring the fusewire off his clockweights, for Dimbleby, 76, will **NOT** be performing the feat live on air.

tawdry

"It is ridiculous to suggest that he should shave his testicles in front of millions of viewers," a BBC spokesman told us. "David is a hugely respected, Oxford-educated journalist and political commentator, not some publicity-hungry D-list celebrity. For him to appear on television performing such a tawdry act would be hugely detrimental to his reputation as one of the corporation's senior broadcasters."

tatherine

Instead, Dimbleby intends to shave his knackers in the privacy of his own bathroom, before calling in an independent observer

Dimbleby: Shaven nuts.

to confirm that they are indeed now smooth and pink. "It will have to be a person of standing with an unimpeachable, trustworthy reputation," continued the spokesman. "Someone like Alan Yentob, Sir John Chilcot or Dame Elizabeth Butler-Sloss."

tee

Any viewers wishing to sponsor the Question Time host's brave charity effort should go to *bbc.co.uk/questiontime/davesbollocks* or follow the hashtag *#dimblebyplumshave* on Twitter.

Stone Age JACK BLACK and his Stone Age dog SILVER in...

THE CASE OF THE ANGRY GODS

The Neolithic holidays were here once more, and young Jack Black and his dog Silver were staying with Aunt Meg in her picture postcard cave in the Wiltshire settlement of Piltdown-by-the-Henge...

What terrible weather, Aunt Meg.

Yes, it's been like this since the solstice, Jack. This has been the worst summer for storms that I can remember.

Somebody must have really angered the Sky Gods. I wonder who.

It doesn't matter, Jack. Druid Brown is going to perform a sacrifice in the henge at sundown.

A sacrifice! That's great! What's it going to be, Aunt Meg? A stag...? A goat...?

Oh, no, Jack. The weather has been so bad that the elders think only a *human offering* will placate the Sky Gods' wrath.

Wow! Even better. Any idea who?

That will appease them and we'll get a bit of decent weather for a change.

I'm afraid it's **YOU**, Jack.

ME!? Why me? That's not fair.

Well, the storms did start when you came for your holiday...

The elders have simply put two small stones and two small stones together and made four small stones.

Ooh! that reminds me, Jack. I was going to paint my tits blue for the ceremony, but I've run out of pigment...

Be a dear, would you, and pop to Mr Barker next door for me and borrow a cup of woad?

Certainly, Aunt Meg...

...Come on, Silver.

Jack and Silver made their way to Mr Barker's cave...

Hi, Mr. Barker. Can Aunt Meg borrow a cup of woad?

Of course, Jack. I'll be with you in a minute.

What on earth are you doing, Mr. Barker?

I'm making an axe-head, Jack.

But axe-heads are made from Stone.

Well so are these, in a sense...

You see, I found these odd looking stones in the river. They've got shiny red and green bits in. I crushed them and put them in the fire and they turned into glowing liquids. When they mixed and cooled, they turned into this strange, hard material.

Gosh!

Crumbs, it's heavy.

Yes, and strong. I'm going to call it Bronze. It's a word I made up that I like the sound of.

It can be used to make any tool - knives, axes, arrow heads. All much better and sharper than old-fashioned stone, and they'll last a lifetime.

You mark my words, Jack. Bronze is going to revolutionise the way we live...

Anyway, I'll just get Meg's woad. I think I've got some behind my stalactite in the back of the cave.

This is a queer business, Silver. These shiny green and red flecks in the stone... I'll bet they're the blood and tears of the Earth-dwelling Gods...

Of course ... that's it!

Come on, Silver! Quick!

Oh! Where did they go to, I wonder?

Never mind, I'll pop round and give the woad to Aunt Meg myself.

86

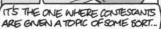

LetterBocks

Viz Comic P.O. Box 841, Whitley Bay, NE26 9EQ
letters@viz.co.uk

I'M no historian, but watching an episode of *Vikings* the other night, I understood why they were always so angry all the time. They seemed so chuffed with themselves when they looted a monastery and took away a big chest of English coins. But what happened when they get back to Denmark or wherever and try to spend them in the shops and pubs over there?

Tarquin Boatswain, Hull

WHY doesn't Dracula get a bit of WD40 for the hinges on his castle doors? I know that as Prince of Darkness he can only come out after the sun has gone down, but there are plenty of all-night garages where he could pick up a tin. That ruddy creaking spoils all his films for me.

Bartram Twelves, Goole

HOW come every time you buy a chicken from the supermarket, it's always tied up? Are they all into bondage or something? The filthy little perverts. Eating's too good for 'em, in my opinion.

RR Rasputin, Wales

Accident that *YOU WEREN'T* involved in?
Me-2-Injury-Lawyers

Has *someone else* been involved in an accident at work, in a shop or in the street and has *claimed compensation?*

NO FEE! NO WIN!

...well it isn't **YOUR** fault that you didn't trip, fall or collide with something. And just because it didn't happen to **YOU** doesn't mean you can't dip **YOUR** bread in the fucking gravy.

"The bloke across the street slipped on a chip, twisted his ankle and was off work for two months. I don't know how, but Me-2-Injury-Lawyers got me £6500 from the chip shop owner."
Mr. J, Harpendon

"I read about a woman who trapped her finger in a door at work and claimed £4,800 for the distress and inconvenience. I got TWICE that amount from her boss. Thank you Me-2-Injury-lawyers."
Mrs. B, Essex

UK law has got more holes than a fucking **SIEVE**, and we'll get **YOU** a wedge, don't you worry. **One call to Me-2-Injury-Lawyers is all it takes**

☎ **0800 818 8088**

STAR LETTER

IT'S all very well sacking Jeremy Clarkson for punching his producer, but what if his producer had been Adolf Hitler and Clarkson's punch had proved fatal. The whole world would be hailing him as a hero who prevented WWII and saved over 50 million lives. He simply punched the wrong person at the wrong time.

Tim Rusling, Cottingham

WILDLIFE commentators are always banging on about swans mating for life, but how exactly do they know? All swans look identical, and the male swan could be shagging around all over the place for all we know. There's one in the park near me, and I'm 99% sure he was with another bird the other night.

Arthur Grubscrew, Rhyll

BILLY Ocean famously sang, 'When the going gets tough, the tough get going.' He was spot on. My mate Robbo is supposed to be ex-SAS and a black belt in karate, but when it all kicked off outside my local the other night, he legged it big time.

Mortimer Pondweed, Tring

I READ that *On the Buses* funnyman Reg Varney was the first man in Britain to use a cash machine, and Ernie Wise the first to use a mobile phone. I don't see any of these modern so-called comedians pushing the envelope of technology these days. This used to be a great country.

Funty Willis, Cambridge

I DON'T know why everyone is worried about Kim Jung Un and his nuclear threats. I was always brought up to believe that anything made in Korea was a load of shit. Chances are, if he did fire one of his missiles off at us it would be a dud, just like that box of rip-raps I bought off Stockport Market in 1972.

Conrad Fitblat, Manchester

I RECENTLY bought my boss a sharpener in the form of a cat that meows when you stick a pencil up its arse. We wept with laughter, but being scientists we wondered whether we had just found a new cure for depression. Do your readers think meowing cat's arse pencil sharpeners should be prescribed on the NHS?

Drs Brierley & Jones, Cambridge

IN the vacuum of space there is no noise. So how come Neil Armstrong said his famous words on the moon? Nice try NASA, but you're gonna have to get up earlier in the morning to catch me out.

Dennis 'Buzz' Lilly, Abergele

WHEN you add two even numbers together you always get another even number. When you add two odd numbers together, it also always ends up an even number. The only time you can get an odd number is by adding together an odd number to an even number. At a ratio of 2-1, you'd think that there would be twice as many even numbers as odd, but there's not. What's going on there?

Chesterton Chesthair, Chester

TO the vandals who thought they'd scratched every panel on my car, I say close, but no cigar! You forgot to scratch my petrol filler flap. Schoolboy error.

Jamie Cuffe, Isle of Man

I DON'T know why burglars always ask for more offences to be taken into consideration when they go to court. I'm sure boasting like that wouldn't go down well with most juries.

Morten Bungle, London

I WAS given a ten pound note in my change in a supermarket and was appalled to see that someone had drawn a pair of glasses and a Grouco Marx moustache on Her Majesty the Queen. Is there no respect in this country any more?

Hector Golightly, Surbiton

I JUST saw a nun in a porn film. I didn't think they were allowed to do that sort of thing but this one was going at it like a piston. Explain *that*, Pope Francis.

Guy Venables, North Mundham

I AM writing to complain about BBC1's *The One Show*. I can't be bothered to go into any detail, but I'm sure you get my point.

Sharkey, Corsham

UP THE CRETACEARSE CORNER

Sender: Ashley Allen, e-mail

HOW do cherubs actually fly? They're fat little fuckers with wings that would look small on a gnat. Sometimes I think certain aspects of religion might be made up.

P Francis, Vatican City

ON the bus home from work, I noticed a little boy ask his Mum if he could ring the bell for their stop. Thinking quickly, I pressed the bell the second we pulled away, rendering any push he did completely redundant. The look on his face was priceless. What a great end to the day.

James Bull, Sheffield

BEING from Oxford, I'm sick of everybody banging on about Chief Inspector Morse of Thames Valley Police and what a great detective he is. It's bollocks. My lawn mower was nicked two years ago and the rozzers still haven't found it. It's one thing when an Oxford University don gets murdered and another when somebody's lawnmower gets half-inched.

Iain Devenney, Oxford

WHEN an attractive senior executive of a large organisation said she might have small opening for me, what was I supposed to think? Thanks to her inability to communicate properly, I took actions which have now left me unable to work in my chosen field and looking for a new career. Women!

Christopher Shaw, Seaford

I'VE just eaten Nutella on toast then immediately had a shit. To any passing aliens, it would appear that humans don't have a complex digestive system, rather simply a tube that starts at the mouth and ends at the ring piece. Fortunately, no extra-terrestrials were passing by at the time.

Paul Anderson, Durham

AT a recent football match I attended, I was shocked and appalled to hear a woman shout "You fucking blind wanker" at the male linesman. It saddens me to think that in the year 2015, we still haven't managed to eliminate this kind of sexist bigotry from the terraces.

G Grebo, Humberside

THEY say that Thursday's child has far to go. Well I was born on a Thursday and I'm on the bus and its only 200 yards from my house, not far at all. So it's bollocks to that saying.

Iain Devenney, Oxford

THESE energy saving lightbulbs are amazing. Out of the 6 I purchased a few months back, 5 have already popped, saving me a small fortune on electricity.

Daniel Passerella, Southampton

WHY is it when anything is on *CrimeWatch*, it's all "can you identify these super blurry suspects recorded on a 1970s camera?" Yet as soon as I'm in a bus lane they get all *CSI* and magnify the zoom using the fucking hadron collider to read my number plate.

Joe Rodgers, Rotherham

MY tiny Jack Russell terrier does the same size shits as I do, and yet I'm a 6-feet tall and 16-stone. I wonder how the so-called experts explain that one?

Rich Evans, Colwyn Bay

WHAT a wasteful sport tennis is, with its practice of getting a new set of balls every 7 games. I've watched snooker for 30 years and not once have the balls needed changing. Maybe they could save all that cost and waste by using snooker balls for tennis. The variety of colours would add to the visual spectacle too.

Uffington Wassail, Sheffield

WHAT is it with young men these days growing big bushy beards? Is the latest fashion to look like a Victorian gentleman? If so, then why don't they complete the look by wearing long black coat tails, a stove pipe hat, and riding about on a penny farthing?

Martin Poole, Thornbury

FITTING ROOM

HEY SWEETHEART YOU COME HERE OFTEN?

ARE YOU TRYING SOMETHING ON?

YEARS ago on *Doctor Who* and *Star Trek* and the like, the baddies would often have a mind weapon where their eyes glowed red or something and everybody in the room would go down, clutching at their ears. Why hasn't this been invented yet? Come on, scientists, start earning your money.

Andrew Hussey, Gainsborough

SO-CALLED 'internet pioneer' Mark Zuckerberg came out last week and said he's bringing free internet for all to Europe. Well my neighbour's WI-FI hub doesn't have a password, so I've been getting free internet for years already. Zuckerberg should check his facts before he starts mouthing off.

Mark Jorgensen, Manchester

WE'VE seen them standing beside the president wearing shades and earpieces for getting on for 60 years, and yet they still call themselves the 'secret service'. Come on lads, the game's up!

Toby, Bristol

IF I was US rock star Edgar Winter, I would end every bout of sexual intercourse by saying, "Brace yourself, Winter's coming," like Sean Bean on *Game of Thrones*. But I'm not Edgar Winter, so it's all academic, really.

T Ellen, London

ps. The same would go for his brother Johnny Winter, but I'm not him either, and he's dead, so it's doubly academic in his case.

IT always amuses me when I watch sci-fi movies that are set in the future, and they still use contemporary curse words. Surely new expletives would have been invented to reflect the time setting, such as 'Zunt', 'Mother Fucker-xz100' and 'BitchTronica'. If you ask me, it's lazy writing.

Paul Townend, Worcester

HAVE any of your readers ever had their choppers in one of those Dyson hand dryers? I bet it'd be bloody marvellous.

J Length, Boston

TOP TIPS

EVER wondered who it is making those smells in the next cubical next to you? Simply whistle a catchy tune such as the *A-Team* theme and wait for the smelly bastard to reveal himself back in the office with the tune stuck in his head for the rest of the day.

Irish Chris, Northwich

RECREATE the narrow boat experience at a fraction of the cost by having a friend tow you around country lanes in a caravan at 4mph. Don't forget to wave a cheery good morning to overtaking motorists.

Violet Rommel, Humberside

IMAGINE you're a teenager again, by verbally abusing someone and then twenty minutes later asking them for a lift somewhere.

Johnny Lad, Stoke

MONOPOLY houses and hotels pushed carefully into a pile of white dog shit makes an excellent miniature 'Alpine' Ski Resort for flies.

Martin Poole, Thornbury

ELDERLY boxers. A helium balloon secured to the floor makes an ideal slow-moving 'punch-ball'.

Alan Tradewaste, Penge

OAP drivers. Avoid being told to 'speed up or get off the fucking road' by speeding up or getting off the fucking road.

Ali, Birmingham

CUT your takeaway pizza into evenly sized slices by simply locating its centre using a ruler and compass, then dividing 360 by the number of slices you want. This will give you the number of degrees each slice should measure at the centre. Then use a protractor to measure the degrees and a ruler to ensure accurate cutting.

Chris Horsley, Barnsley

IMAGINE you're hiding in a drain by lying in a puddle and looking through a fork.

Robert Marshall, Kildare

PUT your exercise bike on the back of a trailer and get a mate to drive you round so you can see some sights while you're exercising.

John Tunney, Corby

SAVE time when crossing a river with a fox, a chicken and a bag of corn by taking the chicken and corn across first then not going back for the fox, which will have run off by then anyway.

T O'Neill, Glasgow

GIVE your Action Man a realistic penis by glueing a cashew nut to his groin.

Mr. E, Eastleigh

NEED a cheap loan? Simply sell an iPhone 6 you don't have on eBay for £300. Then a week later on payday you can pay the buyer back interest free by claiming the phone got lost in the post.

Ponsonby Swindler, London

ROGER MELLIE

THE MAN ON THE TELLY

SCREECH!

NICE SET OF WHEELS, ROGER...FERRARI, IS IT?

458 SPIDER, TOM... 4·5L V8 ENGINE

MUST HAVE SET YOU BACK A BOB OR TWO, I'LL BET.

BUT YOU TOLD ME LAST WEEK YOU WERE FLAT BROKE, ROGER

I AM, TOM... HAVEN'T GOT A POT TO PISS IN

EIGHTY GRAND, TOM...BUT YOU CAN'T PUT A PRICE ON QUALITY, I ALWAYS SAY

WELL HOW HAVE YOU FINANCED *THAT?*

IT'S A NEW SCHEME I'VE GOT GOING. YOU BUY STUFF OFF YOUR FANS, AND YOU PAY BY CHEQUE AND WRITE A NICE LITTLE MESSAGE ON THE FRONT...

...NICE AND PERSONAL...AND INSTEAD OF CASHING IT, THEY **FRAME** THE FUCKER AND HANG IT ON THE WALL

THE BLOKE AT FULCHESTER MOTORS **LOVES** ME, TOM...SO I PUT "TO MY NUMBER ONE FAN" ON THE CHEQUE WITH A BIG SMILEY FACE...

...AND I SIGNED IT "YOUR BEST FRIEND FOR EVER, ROGER MELLIE."...GOOD, EH? THE DAFT TWAT'LL BE DOWN AT KWIK-FRAME WITH IT BEFORE THE INK'S DRY

GOT THE TIP OFF DES LYNAM...HE'S BEEN DOING IT FOR YEARS...EVERY PUB AND BOOKIES IN LONDON'S GOT ONE OF HIS CHEQUES HANGING UP.

OH, YOU'RE BEING RIDICULOUS, ROGER...

...I MEAN...IT MIGHT WORK FOR A PINT IN A PUB, PERHAPS A MEAL IN A RESTAURANT... BUT FOR A **FERRARI**...COME ON, ROGER... BE REALISTIC

OH, NO, TOM...YOU'D BE SURPRISED...

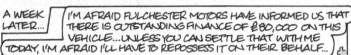

A WEEK LATER...

I'M AFRAID FULCHESTER MOTORS HAVE INFORMED US THAT THERE IS OUTSTANDING FINANCE OF £80,000 ON THIS VEHICLE...UNLESS YOU CAN SETTLE THAT WITH ME TODAY, I'M AFRAID I'LL HAVE TO REPOSSESS IT ON THEIR BEHALF...

BOLLOCKS!

AARDVARK REPOSSESSION

I'M SORRY TO HAVE TO DO THIS, MR MELLIE, I REALLY AM...I'M A TREMENDOUS FAN OF YOURS.

REALLY?

OH, YES...I LOVE ALL OF YOUR SHOWS

...ROGERING ABOUT BRITAIN...MELLIE'S HOUSE PARTY...ROGER ME BACKWARDS...LATE NIGHT ROGERING...ME AND MY WIFE NEVER MISS ANY

FANTASTIC!..LISTEN...ABOUT THAT 80 GRAND...IS A CHEQUE ALRIGHT?

MEDDLESOME RATBAG

DJ '15

I DON'T GET A GLIMMER OF LIGHT IN MY GARDEN. IT'S THAT RUDDY BIG TREE OF YOURS.

IT BLOCKS OUT THE SUN.

YES OK, FAIR ENOUGH. I'LL CUT IT DOWN FOR YOU.

I CAN'T REMEMBER THE LAST TIME I FELT SUN ON ME FACE.

FOREVER PLUNGED INTO DARKNESS, I AM. IT'S SO COLD HERE... SO COLD...

MY GARDEN IS LIKE A BLACK HOLE!

I CAN BARELY SEE MY HAND IN FRONT OF MY FACE, IT'S SO DARK...

DRRRR RRRR

I DON'T ASK FOR MUCH – JUST AN OCCASIONAL RAY OF SUNSHINE NOW AND THEN.

THERE. IT'S DOWN.

THIS COULD HAVE BEEN SUCH A LOVELY GARDEN.

BUT IT'S BLIGHTED... **BLIGHTED** BY THAT TREE OF YOURS...

OH, HOW I WISH I WAS ABLE TO SIT OUT IN MY OWN GARDEN AND ENJOY THE SUNSHINE.

BUT NO! I AM FORCED TO LIVE IN THE SHADOW OF THIS TREE STUMP.

BAXTER BASICS MP

ONE DAY... HELLO DARLING... I'M HOME!

BAXTER!? WHAT ARE YOU DOING HERE? YOU LEFT ME FOUR YEARS AGO TO MOVE IN WITH A HAREM OF UNDERAGE SEX SLAVES.

AH! HA! HA! HA! HA!

YES!...HA! HA! THIS IS JUST THE KIND OF BANTER MY DARLING WIFE AND I ENJOY ALL THE TIME IN OUR HOUSE...

...WHERE I LIVE.

BBC 6 O'CLOCK NEWS... THEY'RE FILMING AN "AT HOME WITH THE PROSPECTIVE MINISTER FOR FAMILY VALUES"...PLAY ALONG OR YOU'LL BE SORRY.

≡MWAH!≡ THERE! JUST KISSING MY WIFE, LIKE I ALWAYS DO, DON'T I DARLING, BECAUSE I'M A FAITHFUL HUSBAND...

NO QUESTION MARKS OVER MY PRIVATE LIFE, I CAN ASSURE YOU. I'VE NEVER EVEN HEARD OF THE ELM GUEST HOUSE, AND I'VE CERTAINLY NEVER VISITED IT.

ANYWAY, THROUGH HERE IS THE...AH, YES...THE KITCHEN. IT IS OUR ONLY KITCHEN. WE CERTAINLY HAVEN'T GOT TWO KITCHENS, UNLIKE SOME OTHER POLITICIANS I COULD NAME.

YES. WE HAVE JUST THE ONE KITCHEN, WHICH MAKES US LIKE EVERYONE ELSE IN THE COUNTRY...ALL THE HARD-WORKING FAMILIES WHO ALSO ONLY HAVE ONE KITCHEN. WE'RE ALL IN THIS TOGETHER.

AND THIS IS THE WORK SURFACE WHERE I PREPARE VEGETABLES FOR FAMILY MEALS...IN FACT, I THINK I'LL PREPARE ONE NOW. IS THE CAMERA RUNNING?

...COULD YOU GET ME A VEGETABLE, DARLING..? ...NOW PLEASE...

THERE ARE SOME CARROTS IN THE...

NOW! THEY'RE FILMING ME NOW YOU STUPID F...

HA! HA! HA! WHAT FUN WE HAVE, AS A FAMILY, IN OUR ONE KITCHEN.

A NICE CARROT, THIS, WHICH I SHOPPED FOR MYSELF. IN FACT, I DO ALL THE SHOPPING. I WAS JUST THINKING THE OTHER DAY HOW A PINT OF MILK IS 46p, A LOAF OF BREAD IS BETWEEN 40p AND £1.10, AND A FIRST CLASS STAMP IS 67p.

I ALWAYS USE MY LOCAL SHOP, YOU SEE. I KNOW THE OWNER BY NAME... MR. PATEL. HE'S ASIAN.

SO YOU SEE, I'M NOT A RACIST, AND THOSE UNFORTUNATE TWEETS THAT RECENTLY CAME TO LIGHT WERE, IN ALL LIKELIHOOD, DUE TO MY ACCOUNT GETTING HACKED.

SIMILARLY, THE GRAPHIC PHOTO OF THE UNDERSIDE OF MY GENITAL AREA THAT I TWEETED LAST WEEK WAS MEANT TO GO TO MY UROLOGIST, AND THE HASHTAG #SUCK THIS YOU BARELY LEGAL BITCH" WAS A SIMPLE AUTOCORRECT ERROR. SO THAT'S THAT ALL CLEARED UP.

RIGHT, THAT'S THE VEGETABLES CHOPPED...NOW, LIKE ANY NORMAL FATHER, IT'S TIME TO GO AND WATCH MY SON, WHOSE NAME ESCAPES ME FOR THE MOMENT, PLAY A GAME OF FOOTSOCCER.

YES, I'LL BE THERE WITH ALL THE OTHER DADS, STANDING THERE BY THE CALX, SHOUTING OUT WORDS OF SUPPORT SUCH AS...ER..."KICK THE BALL IN THE NET!" AND...ER...ER...OTHER SUCH ENCOURAGEMENTS.

SO AS YOU CAN SEE, WE'RE JUST A NORMAL FAMILY WITH TWO BOYS AND A GIRL...

TWO GIRLS AND A BOY.

THAT'S RIGHT, TWO GIRLS AND A BOY.

WELL THERE YOU GO... THAT'S A BRIEF INSIGHT INTO THE COMPLETELY NORMAL FAMILY LIFE THAT I AND MY WIFE AND CHILDREN LEAD, HERE IN THIS HOUSE WHERE, AS I SAY, I DEFINITELY DO LIVE.

≡MWAH!≡ GOODBYE DEAR. I'LL SEE YOU AGAIN JUST BEFORE THE NEXT ELECTION. I MEAN THIS EVENING... JUST BEFORE SUPPER.

RIGHT, LET'S GO TO THE SHOP AND YOU CAN FILM ME BUYING A PINT OF MILK AND A LOAF OF BREAD OFF THAT ASIAN MAN...

MAKE SURE YOU GET HIM IN SHOT WITH ME SHAKING HIS HAND, SO IT LOOKS LIKE I'M NOT RACIST.

SLAM!

Dial J for Murder!

IS CORBYN A SECRET KILLER?

UK police estimate that there are currently more than *1,000 UNSOLVED MURDERS* on their files. Shootings, stabbings, stranglings, even poisonings... a thousand tragic victims lie dead whilst their killer still roams the streets. And Jeremy Corbyn still roams the streets. *Mere coincidence, as his supporters would have you believe, or something more sinister?*

We spoke to an anonymous police superintendent, who confirmed that the new Labour leader could be a suspect in all these crimes of violence if evidence to implicate him were to be uncovered.

He told us: "Mr Corbyn has not been cleared of any of these killings, and if compelling forensic evidence of his guilt came to light, we would have no hesitation in arresting him and charging him with murder."

We decided to open a few cold case murder files at random to see if Jeremy Corbyn could be Britain's Most Wanted.

Cold Case Files: Questions Corbyn has to answer...

Cold Case 1
UNSOLVED
The Islington Flower Shop Murder

IN NOVEMBER 1967, 64-year-old spinster Edna Tussage was found dead in the flat above her florist's shop in Holloway Road, Islington. She had been bludgeoned to death with a blunt instrument and the till in her shop ransacked. The killer was never brought to justice.

.....Motive
At the time, Jeremy Corbyn was an impoverished young student at the nearby North London Polytechnic. The money from Miss Tussage's till would have come in very handy to pay his Labour Party membership fees and the rent for his hall of residence.

.....Means
According to police, Miss Tussage's skull was shattered by a rain of blows from a heavy object. As a keen cyclist, Corbyn would have undoubtedly owned a large spanner, which he could easily have dropped into the River Thames in the aftermath of his frenzied attack.

.....Opportunity
The florist's shop where the murder took place was just a couple of miles from the student union bar. Corbyn could easily have carried out the crime under the pretence of nipping out for a wee.

Cold Case 2
UNSOLVED
The Epping Forest Slaying

IN JULY 1974, 28-year-old Colombian *Boco Perez* was found stabbed through the heart in a layby near Epping Forest. Traces of cocaine were found in Perez's nearby burnt-out car, leading detectives to suspect that the killing was the result of a drugs deal gone wrong.

.....Motive
In 2000, Jeremy Corbyn backed a Commons motion to make drugs legal, saying that cannabis was no more harmful than alcohol or tobacco - exactly the stance that one might expect from a violent drugs dealer.

.....Means
Whilst Corbyn's flat was never searched in connection with Perez's murder, it is highly likely that the Labour leader already possessed several kitchen knives that were long enough and sharp enough to have caused the Colombian's fatal injuries.

.....Opportunity
As a staunch advocate of public transport, Corbyn would have known how to get from Haringey, where he was a councillor, to Epping Forest - catching the No. 20 bus from Victoria to Loughton and changing at Walthamstow Central.

Cold Case 3
UNSOLVED
The John O'Groats Shooting

AT PRECISELY 3.04pm on July 6th 2007, three gunshots rang out in John O'Groats High Street. Cops who raced to the scene found Leslie I. Small, a local butcher, lying dead in a pool of blood. Witnesses told police that the killer was a 6'8" giant who had made his escape into the woods near a local loch. Despite combing the area, the police never caught the killer.

.....Motive
Like all vegetarians, Corbyn is likely to hold a murderous grudge against butchers. Why Mr Small? Perhaps he was just in the wrong place at the wrong time.

.....Means
As a pacifist, Corbyn would have had to steal the gun he used in the commission of his crime. Although none had been reported stolen in the John O'Groats area at the time, the firearm in question may have been held illegally, making its owner reluctant to report the theft to police.

.....Opportunity
At 3.04, the exact moment the killing took place in John O'Groats, Corbyn was addressing a Labour Party meeting in Lands End. With 500 witnesses willing to swear that he was 800 miles away, he might appear at first glance to have the perfect alibi, but what if it wasn't Corbyn in Cornwall after all? What if it was a dopelganger in a *Mission Impossible*-style rubber mask, setting a false trail whilst the real Corbyn - in stack-heel boots to make him appear much taller - was 800 miles away, murdering a Scottish butcher in a hail of bullets?

Police believe there is little chance of bringing successful prosecutions against the Labour leader for these brutal slayings. But if Corbyn does come to power in 2020, the new premier could find himself facing some very awkward questions the first time he approaches the Dispatch Box for PMQs.

Tar Verimuch

Cptn *Jack Verimuch* (RN retd.) answers **YOUR** questions about the seafaring life of a Jolly Jack Tar

Dear Captain Verimuch,
What was the Plimsoll Line on a ship called before they invented plimsolls?

Sir Francis Chichester, Watery-Grave

● *When the black, elasticated slip-on games pumps were invented by Woolworths in 1970, the name was adopted by HM Navy to refer to a reference mark painted on the side of a ship to show where the water comes up to. You won't be surprised to hear that before that, it was simply referred to as "the Line."*

Dear Captain Verimuch,
Sailors often talk about the "port" and "starboard" side of their ships instead of "left" and "right". I can never remember which one is which. Is there an easy way to distinguish between the two?

Dame Ellen Macarthur, Portsmouth

● *Yes, there's a simple rhyme that all new recruits are taught on their first day at Dartmouth Naval College... before they're let anywhere near a ship!*

"Starboard's left? No, that's not right.
Right can't be port, but left just might.
Port, said right, is left you see,
And starboard - port - is wrong to me."

Dear Captain Verimuch,
In pirate films, the captain often orders his cutthroat crew to "splice the mainbrace." But what exactly is a mainbrace, and how do you splice one?

Thor Heyerdahl, Kontiki-on-Stour

● *It's quite simple. On an old sailing ship, the mainbrace is a stick with ropes on that pokes up out of the floor. It is spliced by pulling on some of the ropes that are possibly attached to a bit of cloth and tying knots in them.*

Take a Shit

Politicians Wrecked my Marriage!

The poor turnout at recent elections has clearly demonstrated the low esteem in which politicians are held by voters. Expenses scandals, cash-for-questions and Plebgate are just a few of the shameful episodes that have left our elected representatives languishing at rock bottom in the public popularity polls. And if that's not bad enough, our politicians' selfish actions have now made life even more difficult for an unemployed 52-year-old man from Yorkshire. For, not content with merely cutting **Brian Pouchforth**'s benefits and upping the duty on his beloved ciggies and beer, he alleges that a series of MPs have systematically set out to wreck his 35-year marriage.

So sad Brian homeless after being pestered by MPs

Sofa, so bad: Brian Pouchforth has now been reduced to dossing down on a friend's settee.

Since he was somehow identified as a floating voter, Pouchforth's modest two-up, two-down home in the Beeston area of Leeds has been besieged by representatives from all the major political parties, so much so that it caused the breakdown of his marriage to his childhood sweetheart Bernadette. Now Brian has chosen to tell his shocking story in the slim hope that his estranged wife will read the truth about what really happened and come back to him.

As told to **Vaginia Discharge**

Ice Cold Beer in Alex

AS RECENTLY as February of this year, Brian and his wife seemed to have found the formula for the perfect marriage. Bernadette worked 10-hour shifts on the tills at a local supermarket and did all the cooking and cleaning at home, whilst house-husband Brian pitched in with the chores whenever he could find the time or was feeling well enough. But all that was about to change.

❝It all began on the first day of the election campaign. It was a Tuesday and Tuesday night's my night on the nest. I was supposed to be going out to do the shopping, but I've got one of those mysterious fatigue illnesses that prevents me from doing anything too strenuous, so I was taking it easy and lying on the sofa to conserve my energy. I was just flicking through the channels looking for *Diagnosis Murder* when I heard someone knock at the door. It was former SNP leader **ALEX SALMOND**. I was a little surprised as the Scottish Nationalists don't usually campaign as

...Taking advantage of my momentary confusion, Salmond barged past me into the front room...

far south of the border as Leeds. Taking advantage of my momentary confusion, Salmond barged past me into the front room, where he launched into an impassioned speech about how Scotland should become independent. He offered me a beer and I reluctantly accepted, thinking it'd make the time go quicker till he shut up and left.

Two hours and twelve cans of strong lager later, Salmond finally got down off his soapbox and asked if he could count on my vote. I said no, pointing out that his party wasn't actually fielding a candidate in the Leeds Central constituency. After mumbling some excuse about 'taking a wrong turning at Berwick', the cheeky Jock handed me an invoice for all the beers I'd drunk. I had no choice but to cough up with the wife's shopping money, but then I threw him out. Fair play to the man, he might have come closer than anyone else in 300 years to ruling an

independent Scotland, but I draw the line at retrospectively billing a man for a few cans. With her shopping money gone, my poor wife had to borrow some off her sister and then make an emergency evening trip to the corner shop before cooking our supper. As a result, by bedtime she was knackered and I didn't get my oats that night after all.❞

Spew Labour

THROUGH no fault of his own, Pouchforth found himself in his wife's bad books. Determined to make it up to her, the very next day he vowed to tidy up the living room a bit while she was out at work. But as he was to find out, the best laid plans often go awry, and a knock on the door from another politician blew his good intentions out of the water.

❝Word must have got around that I was available to be canvassed, because I answered the door to find none other than former PM **TONY BLAIR** stood on the step grinning like a Cheshire cat. He invited

himself in and started listing all the reasons I should vote Labour, going over all the points in the manifesto one by one. I tried to get rid of him, explaining that the wife had asked me to fetch in the laundry before it started raining, but he just parked himself on the sofa and kept talking, like he was at the Despatch Box.

Luckily I'd bought in a crate of cheap lager in case Salmond came back, so I broke them out in the hope that a few cans would shut him up. In a way it did; four Special Brews later, Blair went green and ran off to be sick, but he didn't even make it to the bathroom. When he staggered back down the stairs I lost no time in chucking him out on his ear; he may have been the longest serving Labour premier in history, but he's got a right cheek turning up unannounced and throwing up on another man's landing carpet. And also on the top three steps. And the banister. My poor wife had to spend her evening cleaning up Blair's vomit, fetching in the laundry from the rain, tidying the living room and finally cooking us a late meal. After all that she staggered off to bed, and I didn't even get a goodnight kiss.

> ...Blair went green and ran off to be sick, but he didn't even make it to the bathroom...

Only Making Naans for Nigel

ACCORDING to Brian, Bernadette was strangely cold towards him the next morning. Since she was facing an extra-long work shift, he offered to cook supper for when she got back.

" As it happened, my fatigue illness was particularly severe that day, and I couldn't face going out to buy the ingredients for our tea. I only had enough energy to drag myself downstairs and onto the sofa to catch the end of Homes Under the Hammer. In fact the illness was so bad, I spent the whole day drifting in and out of consciousness, and before I knew it was after 4pm and Flog It! was starting. Just at that moment, someone knocked on the door and I went to answer it; it was UKIP leader **NIGEL FARAGE** who said he wanted to explain why we should be leaving Europe.

I told him politely to go away because I had to start sorting out the tea for my darling wife. But Farage said not to worry about that, picked up my phone and ordered an Indian takeaway. He sat on the sofa, spouting on about immigration, Brussels and bendy bananas until the food arrived, when he suddenly remembered that he'd left his wallet at home. Not wanting to cause a scene, I ended up paying for Farage's chicken vindaloo masala with

the cash that the missus had left to buy tea with. Then, to make matters worse, the greedy politician proceeded to scoff the lot, leaving nothing but empties for when my poor wife got home.

After he'd finished eating, Farage went to use the toilet. When he came back down he was a little red-faced, explaining that he had just remembered he was late for a UKIP meeting as he made his excuses and hurriedly left. When I went up to the bathroom, I found out why he had been so keen to go. The spicy food must have disagreed with him and his arse had gone off like a twelve bore shotgun. He had left the toilet in a terrible state, pebbledashing the pan, the seat and halfway up the cistern with bright orange foulage. It took forty minutes of hard scrubbing with disinfectant to get the room usable again, and by the time she was finished my poor wife barely had the energy to cook our tea, although somehow she managed it. However, the smell of Farage's curry diarrhoea must have affected her mood, because she didn't say a word to me all evening.

What a Pickle

THE NEXT night Bernadette had put in for an extra shift at the supermarket, working through the night re-stacking the freezers. Determined to make up for the politicians' previous bad behaviour, Brian resolved to get up at 6 am and have a cooked breakfast ready on the table when she came in through the door.

" It was midnight and I was just about to go to bed when **ERIC PICKLES** knocked on the door and invited himself in. The roly-poly Tory minister said he was keen to talk to me about re-introducing Victorian values into British family life. I resigned myself to another political ear-bashing and invited him through to the lounge. Pickles explained that he was keen to toughen up the country's lax pornography laws, and to show me just how bad the situation was, he grabbed the remote and flicked the TV onto the Red Hot Milfs channel.

He was just getting into his spiel when the 10-minute free view finished. Pickles insisted on getting a single night subscription to further demonstrate the seriousness of the situation. He had forgotten to bring his own credit card and I haven't got one, so in the end we used my wife's to pay the £5 fee to watch for the rest of the evening. We sat through a selection of obscene programmes, including Big Tit Cougars, Granny Does Dallas Carpets and Fuck My Wife While I Watch. Both the movies and Pickles's endless political speechifying were incredibly boring and I soon drifted off to sleep there on the sofa.

The next thing I knew, it was half past six in the morning and Bernadette was coming in through the door. Pickles must have left in the early hours, and he had clearly been suffering from a bad cold because he had left gloopy tissues scattered all around the living room. Discovering that her card had been used to buy hardcore pornography was the final straw. Once she had cleared up the tissues she went straight to bed, leaving me to make my own breakfast.

Wife Saw Red Light

THROUGH no fault of his own, Brian's relationship with his wife was on the rocks. But the death knell for his 35-year marriage was sounded the very next evening when another politician called round.

" Bernadette was doing the back-shift so I'd got the house to myself. I was just getting ready to give the whole place a Spring clean from top to bottom, working through the night if needs be to get everything spick and span for her when she came back.

In a Pickle: Fat minister left Brian humiliated after porn mix-up.

However, before I had a chance to start, **NICK CLEGG** turned up on the doorstep. But he wasn't alone - he had a prostitute with him.

The pair came in, Clegg explaining that he was canvassing in the area to see how local residents felt about the introduction of European-style regulation of the sex industry. He had brought along a working girl with him to answer any questions that voters had about the implementation of licensed brothels and designated red light districts. We'd only just started chatting when Clegg's mobile phone went off. It was Vince Cable, calling him back to the local LibDem headquarters to look at some leaflets. He said he'd be back within an hour and left me to chat on the sofa with Roxxy.

We'd been talking about the Liberal manifesto for about ten minutes when the door suddenly opened and my wife came in; apparently the supermarket had sent everybody home early due to a power cut.

> ...Clegg turned up on the doorstep. But he wasn't alone - he had a prostitute with him...

She just stood in the doorway, staring at the two of us on the sofa in horror. It had been an unseasonably hot evening and Roxxy had taken several items of clothing off, and so had I. Bernadette refused to listen to my perfectly reasonable explanation. She put two and two together to make five and threw me out on my arse.

Since the break-up of his marriage, Brian has been reduced to sleeping on the sofa at a friend's house. However, in the three weeks he has been there he has continued to be pestered by a series of high profile politicians, who have wet themselves on the sofa, left turds on the bathroom floor and stolen underwear from his friend's teenage daughter's bedroom. When we spoke to him, he had this plea to any MPs considering canvassing his support: "Just leave me alone. I'm not even on the Electoral Register."

Poll position: Unwanted visits from politicians led to Pouchforth getting banished from his marital home.

Orange & Lemon Ena & Ade

Britain's ZESTIEST citrus fruits forum with
Ena Sharples & Ade Edmondson

" HI READERS, The late **Ena Sharples** and **Ade Edmondson** here. When we're not busy, respectively, being dead for the last 32 years or appearing on gentle, low-budget UK travelogue shows, we're both mad about citrus fruits. Oranges, lemons, grapefruits or limes... we just can't get enough of them! And judging from our bulging **Orange-Ena & Lemon-Ade** postbag, Viz readers are just as potty about these peelably pith-and-pip-packed perishables as we are. So much so that you've been writing to us in your millions and billions. Here's a hand-picked fruitbowl of the juiciest letters we've received this week, which we've left on the side to go grey and mouldy. "

Ena and Ade

IN THESE days of world hunger, why do hotels serve their guests half grapefruits for breakfast, thus throwing away as much as gets eaten? My wife always has half a grapefruit too, so that's a whole grapefruit binned every morning we go down for breakfast. Disgusting.

Ernest Polyps, Penge

I WAS a greengrocer during the war, when fruit was strictly rationed to one orange per week per coupon as it had to be brought in on the convoys. However, I always had an eye for the pretty ladies, and I'd often let them have an extra orange in return for a peck on the cheek. I know strictly speaking it was wrong, but it certainly brightened up those dark days of the war.

W Hodges, Balham

MY NAN'S got two goldfish, one of which is a deep orange colour whilst the other is

much paler. Naturally enough, they're called *Orange* and *Lemon*, although Orange is the yellow one and Lemon is the orange one. She probably ought to change the names over to avoid confusion, but the fish are used to them now.

Ollie, Kenilworth

CAN Professor Richard Dawkings and his atheist cohorts explain why lemons are so bitter? If fruits have evolved to be tasty so that their seeds are dispersed in feeshus, why do they taste like a pro's fanny? Not that I'd know, obviously, as I've never eaten a lemon.

Rev J Foucault, Truro

I RECENTLY bought some tangerines, and when I got them home they were actually satsumas. I was furious, and immediately went back to the shop to exchange them. However, this time when I got them home they were clementines, so I'm going to have to take them back again. This farce is costing me a fortune in petrol.

Keith Rhinoplasty, Hull

I'VE JUST been to the supermarket and they were selling a cross between an orange and a tangerine called an "ortanique". Haven't these scientists already done enough damage to our planet with their atom bombs, acid rain and rockets without starting to meddle with our fruit?

Mrs Audrey Trite, Breen

I AGREE with Mrs Trite (*above*), these ortaniques are Frankenstein fruits and should be destroyed before they destroy us. Would any readers care to join me in forming an angry mob to march on Waitrose to put an end to this evil? Please bring your own flaming torch or pitchfork and meet in the car park.

Terry Towelling, Surbiton

AS A greengrocer during the war, lemons were strictly rationed to one fruit per month per coupon. However, if a lady needed an extra one for a birthday cake, for instance, I'd often bend the rules and slip another one in the bag in exchange for a feel of her breasts or a quick hand up her skirt. I know strictly speaking it was wrong, but it certainly brightened up those dark days of the war.

W Hodges, Balham

I RECENTLY bought a bag of satsumas that were labelled "easy peel". However, I found them anything but easy to peel, as I lost both my hands in an industrial accident at a dog food factory several years ago. Come on, supermarkets, label your produce responsibly or I for one shall take my custom elsewhere.

Harry Tickle, Tiverton

HOW MANY oranges does it take to collect enough pith to make a pith helmet? My grandson is going on a two-week safari to Africa and I wanted to make him one as a going-away present.

Ada Basket, Hull

● Well Mrs Basket, a kilo of oranges yields merely 25g of fresh pith (equivalent to just 10g when dried). A pith helmet weighs approximately 700g, meaning you'd have to chomp your way through nearly three quarters of a tonne of oranges to make a helmet for your grandson! In addition, you'd have to find a chinstrap and a button for the top.

LIKE Mr Tickle (*left*) I am constantly infuriated by the mislabelling of supermarket citrus products. To take one example, "freshly squeezed orange juice" is nothing of the sort. It is the oranges that are squeezed, not the juice. The product should be more correctly labelled as "The

---

Citric Top Tips

RUN out of lemon twists to put in your gin & tonic? Simply drop a slice of lime into a glass of bleach and leave it till it fades to the correct colour.

Edna Wingnut, Tring

PRETEND to be a giant having a hotel breakfast by cutting a kumquat in half, popping a cranberry on the top and eating it with a mustard spoon.

Frank Foresoreskin, Hull

TWO skins from grapefruit halves dried for 5 hours in the oven make excellent substitute coconut shells for when you haven't got a coconut but want to make the sound of a horse.

Hamilton Biscoff, Tooting

COLOUR-blind people, distinguish between lemons and limes by viewing them through the cellophane wrapper from a Lucozade bottle. If the fruit appears pale it's a lemon, but if it appears black it's a lime.

Walter Titty, Penge

LADIES. Make men think you're sexually aroused or cold by cutting the ends off a lemon and pushing one into each bra cup.

Hazelnut Monkbottle, Ely

TUCK a section of lime skin between your top lip and gum if you are attending a fancy dress party as the Queen Mum, God bless her.

Tarquin Balls, Leeds

BUY oranges and lemons that are near their sell-by date to minimise the amount of time you have to keep them in a bowl before throwing them out.

Martin Hoverfly, Goole

The Antique Oranges & Lemons Roadshow

This week our citrusiana expert Negus Scully has travelled to Norfolk to cast his experienced eye over treasured fruits belonging to the people of the medieval cathedral town of Kings Lynn.

WHEN my grandfather died, he left me two tangerines that he'd been given as a boy. They've been in the family for more than a hundred years and they look like a couple of mouldy pebbles. I was just wondering if you could tell me something about them.

Marjorie Spoons

● Well, what a treat to see such a shrivelled pair of old oranges. Thank-you for bringing them in to

show me. But I have a little surprise for you. These aren't actually tangerines - they're satsumas and they were imported in large numbers from Japan towards the end of the Victorian era. Most of them were eaten, of course, so very few of them survive, even fewer in a matching pair like this. Unfortunately, one has suffered a little bit of damage. It's been nibbled by a mouse at some point and the stalk's come off. There's quite a market for this sort of thing amongst collectors nevertheless. Fully restored, and placed in the right auction,

Stand-up Comedians Say the Funniest Things About
ORANGES & LEMONS

• *"Look how small that orange is,"* said my 42-year-old stand-up comedian son Jimmy the other day. He was pointing at a satsuma!

Mrs Ada Carr, Slough

• *"Look how small that satsuma is,"* said my 52-year-old stand-up comedian son Sean the other day. He was pointing at a kumquat!

Mrs Ada Lock, Woking

• *"Look how small that kumquat is,"* said my 49-year-old stand-up comedian son Alan the other day. He was pointing at one of those tiny "ojai pixie" tree-ripened tangerines that you can get at Marks & Spencer around Christmas time!

Mrs Ada Davies, Hounslow

• The other day my 40-year-old stand-up comedian son Russell rang up a pensioner and told him he'd stuck a lemon up his granddaughter's fanny. Honestly, he's such a scamp. I had to laugh.

Mrs Ada Brand, Essex

• My 53-year-old stand-up-comedian son Eddie recently put on one of my frocks and "riffed" for twenty minutes about some talking oranges and lemons arguing about who was going to get in the pan to be made into marmalade. To be honest with you, I couldn't really follow it as it was all a bit surreal for me. I used to like that Frank Carson.

Mrs Ada Izzard, Eastbourne

juice of freshly squeezed oranges." Yet, when I recently spent twenty minutes trying to correct all the cartons in my local Tesco with a Sharpie, I was ejected from the store.

AJ Gowans-Whyte, Cambs

WHY DO oranges only grow in hot countries? It doesn't seem fair. The people who live in these places enjoy year-round sunshine as well as fresh, juicy fruits plucked straight from the tree. Here in this country we get five days of nice weather a year,

if we're lucky, and boring, crappy fruit like cooking apples and rhubarb. If I was an asylum seeker I wouldn't be queueing at Calais to get to Britain, I'd be on the next holiday jet to Florida.

Frank Vertical-Hold, Harlow

WHEN I was a greengrocer in the war, grapefruits were like hen's teeth - you simply couldn't get them. In fact, they weren't even on the ration coupons. On the rare occasions when one or two came in on one of the ships from the Mediterranean, it was up to me to decide who they would go to, usually whichever local lady would give me a blowjob (with swallow) or let me have unprotected anal with her in the back room of the shop. I know strictly speaking it was wrong, but it certainly brightened up those dark days of the war.

W Hodges, Balham

I RUN a small convenience shop and the sort of people who come in my shop and buy a single lemon on Shrove Tuesday really boil my piss. Where are they the rest of the year, when I've got boxes of the fucking things I can't sell? They don't fool me. I know they want it for pancakes, the shits.

Dick Strokes, Greenock

THEY SAY that there is no word that rhymes with orange, so we named our daughter Lorange. It may be a stupid name, but at least it rhymes with orange, so it should hopefully put an end to people coming out with that kind of nonsense.

Lurple Etherington, Hull

I would expect these oranges to fetch in the region of £35,000, and I would insure them for at least £50,000.

I BOUGHT this half a grapefruit from a charity shop for 10 pence in 1975. It's since dried out and is now hard as knockers. I'd never sell it, as I've promised my son he can have it when I'm gone, but I'd like to know something about it and to find out if my 10p was a good investment.

Avarice Boswell

• *Half grapefruits of this vintage are quite sought-after these days. And this is a particularly good example*

that seems to have been very well cared for, with no obvious signs of damage or repair that could affect its value, although the original glace cherry from the top is missing. But don't worry, that can be replaced quite easily. For insurance purposes I'd say you're looking at £10,000 to £15,000, so your 10p investment has worked out very well indeed.

I USED to take meals on wheels to an old lady down the road, and when she died a few years ago I broke into her house on the day of the funeral to ransack it for valuables. Unfortunately, her relatives had beaten me to it and the only thing left to steal was this net of lemons

on the kitchen worktop. I don't know what to do with them. I really wanted her ormolu clock but her nephew had his eyes on that too, so I suspect he had it.

Greedith Larceny

• *When I knew we were coming to Kings Lynn for this week's roadshow I hoped someone would bring a bag of grey, mouldy lemons in and I have to tell you, these are as good as I could have hoped for. Sold in Sainsbury's in about 2010, they're still in their original bag. And the good news for you is that the market for lemons like this has really gone through the roof lately, with a bag not as good as this one selling at Sotheby's last month for £100,000. Having said that, if these were mine I'd be tempted to hold onto them for a while yet, as their value can only increase.*

Thought for the Fruit
With Radio 4 Gobshite
ANNE ATKINS-DIET

I BOUGHT a lemon the other day from my local greengrocer, and when I got it home I held it in my hand and I looked at it and I thought: You know, God is a little bit like a lemon, isn't he?

He's sour and bitter, and not very nice at all.

Just think of all the innocent people he kills in the Bible, with all those floods and plagues and pestilences, and think about how many he still kills today with earthquakes, tsunamis, diseases and famines.

But then I used that lemon to make a lemon drizzle

cake, and do you know, when I took it out of the oven and cut myself a slice, it was absolutely delicious.

And I thought: *Just like the lemon in that cake, God is an essential ingredient in our lives, isn't he?*

He makes them rich, moist and delicious, especially with a cup of tea.

To be honest with you, I was a little bit worried about where that one was going right at the start there, but I think I managed to pull it round with that stuff about the cake.

More bollocks next time.

NOUGHTIE NAUGHTIE

with BBC RADIO 4's JIM NAUGHTIE

D.J '15   CHEERS TO ALEX G.

..AND THAT CONCLUDES THIS MORNING'S DEBATE ABOOT CHEESE. THIS IS THE TODAY PROGRAMME, AND AH'M JIM NAUGHTIE.

DOWN WITH CHEESE

BBC RADIO 4

ON AIR

CHEESE MARKETING BOARD

AH'LL BE RICHT BACK AFTER YON NEWS AND WEATHER.

OCH, AH'LL BE GLAD TAE RETIRE FRAE PRESENTING THIS DAFT PROGRAMME.

STUDIO 1

KICK!

AH'M COMPLETELY SICK OF 'TODAY'!

IF YOU'RE SICK OF TODAY, THEN I WILL TRANSPORT YOU BACK TO YESTERDAY... SHAZAM!

HOOTS MON! A GENIE IN A MAGIC LAMP!

JINGS! AH'M BEING WHISKED BACK IN TIME TAE THE EARLY YEARS OF THIS CENTURY...

AH'M TRAVELLING BACK TAE THE 'NOUGHTIES'!

CRIVVENS! IT'S THE YEAR 2003 ~ BEFORE YOUTUBE, TWITTER AND FACEBOOK WERE EVEN INVENTED!

WOOLWORTHS

BLOCKBUSTER

CRAZY FROG

TURKEY TWIZZLER

VIDEO TAPES TO RENT

AND NOT ABSOLUTELY EVERYONE HAS GOT A MOBILE PHONE YET!

"YOUTUBE"? EVERYONE HAVING A MOBILE PHONE"? WHAT ARE THESE STRANGE WONDERS OF WHICH YOU SPEAK?

SUCH WORDS HATH THE SOUND OF WITCHCRAFT AND SORCERY!

BURN THE WITCH!

HELP MA BOAB! YESTERDAY IS TOO DANGEROUS ~ AH COULD WISH AH COULD RETURN TAE TOMORROW!

YOUR WISH IS MY COMMAND ~ SHAZAM!

... AND THAT CONCLUDES THIS MORNING'S DEBATE ABOUT THE WEATHER.

I ♥ WEATHER

BBC RADIO 4

DOWN WITH WEATHER

MICHTY! AH'M BACK!

AH'LL NEVER COMPLAIN ABOOT "TODAY" AGAIN!

THE END.

Farage Plans New Election Day Air Disaster

hopes for a 15% swing to UKIP in the constituency as a result of the spectacular stunt.

FOLLOWING the success of his 2010 election day plane crash, UKIP leader Nigel Farage intends to plummet to earth in a burning airship on May 7th, before popping along to register his vote. And the prospective South Thanet parliamentary candidate is hoping that the Hindenburg-style disaster will prove popular with voters in the hotly-disputed Kent constituency.

"My nosedive into a ploughed field and subsequent success at the polls showed that the British electorate appreciate a strong leader who can survive an air crash," said Mr Farage, 50. "And we at UKIP listen to the electorate and give them exactly what they want."

"And if they want to see me plunging to earth in a giant fireball before staggering out of the wreckage with all blood on my face on May 7th, that's exactly what they're going to get," he continued.

Farage plans to float around above Kent for 20 minutes in

EXCLUSIVE!

the specially-constructed 100-foot dirigible before the highly flammable hydrogen gas with which it is filled is ignited by a spark of static electricity.

raging

Then he expects the craft to erupt into a raging inferno, taking just seconds to plummet to the ground.

"After I crawl out of the twisted metal wreckage, I'll be photographed enjoying a pint of beer at the nearest pub before making my way to the polling station," said Mr Farage, who

papal

However, Farage's election rivals are planning spoiler campaigns in a bid to secure election day air crash boosts for themselves. Labour hopeful Will Scobie is understood to be planning to fly a fixed-wing microlight into overhead electricity cables, whilst Conservative and Labour candidates Craig Mackinlay and Russ Timpson

Oh the lack of humanity: UKIP leader (left) intends to recreate spectacular Zeppelin inferno.

intend to stage a spectacular "Red Baron"-style biplane dogfight in the skies above South Thanet before smashing head-on into each other at 10,000 feet and parachuting to earth.

ABLE SEMEN JONES

DON'T WORRY, LADIES, I'LL HAVE THIS SHELF UP IN A JIFFY!

THERE. THAT SHOULD HOLD IT!

HE'S GOOD IN THE BEDROOM TOO IF YOU CATCH MY DRIFT!

WINK!

SIGH! UNLIKE MY DAVE.

BURP!

WHA-?

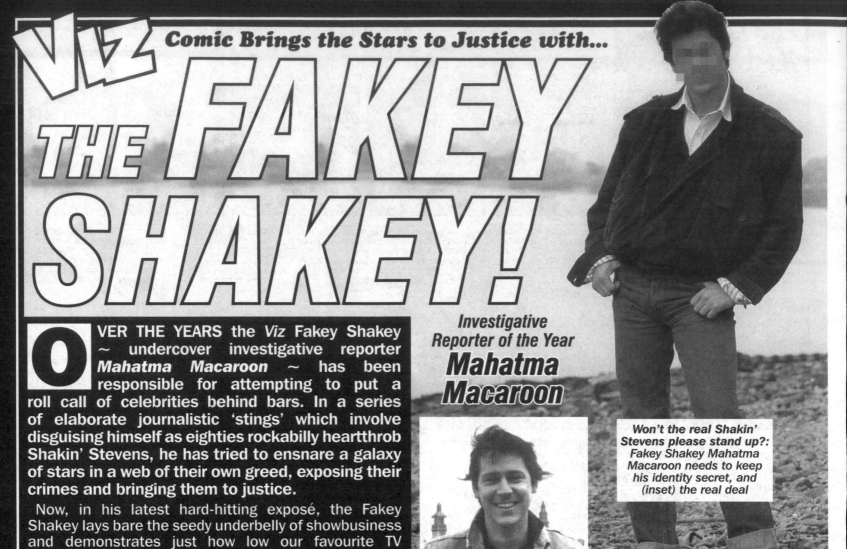

VIZ

THE FAKEY SHAKEY!

Investigative Reporter of the Year Mahatma Macaroon

Won't the real Shakin' Stevens please stand up?: Fakey Shakey Mahatma Macaroon needs to keep his identity secret, and (inset) the real deal

OVER THE YEARS the *Viz* Fakey Shakey ~ undercover investigative reporter *Mahatma Macaroon* ~ has been responsible for attempting to put a roll call of celebrities behind bars. In a series of elaborate journalistic 'stings' which involve disguising himself as eighties rockabilly heartthrob Shakin' Stevens, he has tried to ensnare a galaxy of stars in a web of their own greed, exposing their crimes and bringing them to justice.

Now, in his latest hard-hitting exposé, the Fakey Shakey lays bare the seedy underbelly of showbusiness and demonstrates just how low our favourite TV personalities are prepared to stoop in the pursuit of fame, fortune and filthy lucre.

Stings Can Only Get Better

FRESH-FACED atomic physicist *Professor Brian Cox* looks like butter wouldn't melt in his mouth. But whilst his career as a telly academic has soared towards the heavens, with a series of top-rated documentary series to his credit, his pop performer alter ego as keyboard player in D:Reem has been forced to take a back seat. The question is: *Just how far is he prepared to go to get back in the rock limelight? I decided to find out.*

Drugs shame of TV boffin Cox

Dressing in drainpipe jeans and a denim jacket, combing my hair into a shiny black quiff and adopting a strong Cardiff accent, I walked into Manchester University's Particle Physics department, claiming to be Shakin' Stevens. I asked the receptionist if I could see Professor Cox. *"I'm afraid he's busy at the moment,"* she told me. *"What's it about?"*

I had my cover story well prepared. I explained that I was about to record a new single and wanted Cox to play keyboards in my backing band on *Top of the Pops*. Then I dropped my bombshell: *"He can only play on the record if he provides me with a big bag of drugs,"* I said.

"At least a pound of top quality narcotics. Speed, blow, wobbly eggs... I don't mind as long as they're illegal."

The receptionist excused herself and went into a back room. Through the glass door I could see her having a furtive telephone conversation, clearly with Cox. Moments later, two burly security guards arrived and forcibly manhandled me from the building. I decided to make my excuses and leave.

tape

Later on, I received a telephone call. I recognised the unmistakeable tones of Brian Cox and I quickly switched my tape recorder on.

"Hi, it's Professor Brian Cox here, Mr Stevens," he said. "I'm sorry about having you thrown out at the university this afternoon, but that was just a cover." I reassured him that I understood.

book

"Listen, I can get you the drugs," he continued. "Coke, heroin, whatever you want. But I don't want to stand at the back on *Top of the Pops*. I want to stand right at the front and do a synth solo." I sat back and smiled to myself. I now had all the evidence I needed to knock Cox off his perch and ruin his reputation. Or so I thought.

As it turned out, I hadn't put a cassette in my machine so I had no hard evidence of the seedy scientist's self-damning offer to get me those drugs. Once the case came to court, it would be my word against his, and unfortunately, due to a previous conviction for perjury, my word has less weight in the witness box than it otherwise would have.

Coogan Play at that Game

TELLY FUNNYMAN *Steve Coogan* is an outspoken critic of tabloid journalism. But if he had nothing to hide he'd have nothing to fear from Britain's truth-seeking red-tops. So the question is: *Just what is the shameful secret that is festering at the heart of the Alan Partridge funnyman? I decided to set up an elaborate journalistic sting to find out.*

Posing once more as Shakin' Stevens, I waited on the street outside the Empire Leicester Square, where I knew that Coogan was due to attend the premiere of his latest movie, *Night at the Museum: Secret of the Tomb.*

Your Money or Your Life on Earth

Jewel heist shame of TV Attenborough

ANIMAL lover **Sir David Attenborough** is a 24 carat national treasure. His shows, such as *Life on Earth*, *The Blue Planet* and *Natural World* have made him a household name. *But just how far would he go to keep himself on our TV screens? I once again I adopted the identity of Shakin' Stevens and prepared to stake him out.*

I wrote to Attenborough at the Natural History Museum, enclosing a signed photograph of myself as Shakey. I told him that I had recently appeared on BBC South West's early evening local news magazine *Spotlight* to promote my Solid Gold Eighties Nostalgia tour. I said I knew the producer, and I could get him on the show where he would be interviewed by David Braine and Emily Wood. For a fame addict like Attenborough it was an irresistible offer.

price

But that opportunity came with a price tag. In return for his moment in the limelight, Attenborough would have to rob a bank for me and send me a million pounds in used notes.

I never received a reply; I didn't expect one. Attenborough is too much of a wily old fox to leave an incriminating paper trail when he's planning a hold-up. In fact, his wall of silence simply confirmed to me that he had taken the bait and was up for the job.

And my hunch was confirmed when, just six weeks after my letter, a violent armed robbery was carried out on a branch of the NatWest only 250 miles away from the veteran TV zoologist's Richmond home. Attenborough and his cronies got away with a small fortune, making their escape on high-powered motorcycles that were later found abandoned.

whicker

As a familiar face on our TV screens, Attenborough wasn't taking any chances on being recognised. CCTV footage clearly shows the burly 88-year-old naturalist with a stocking pulled down over his face as he vaults over the counter and strikes a teller in the face with the butt of his sawn-off shotgun.

chicken in a

Attenborough is currently lying low, waiting for the heat to die down before he makes his next move, handing over the money in return for his fifteen minutes of television fame. But when he does, like a wildebeest crossing the Limpopo river, he's got a surprise lying in wait for him.

For his interview won't be with David Braine and Emily Wood, it will be with Scotland Yard.

Vice shame of TV Partridge star

My plan was to tempt him with a part in the video for my next single - a re-recording of my 1981 hit *This Ole House*. As usual, there would be a quid pro quo. In return for his starring role, Coogan would have to procure prostitutes for me. I wrote my offer down on a piece of paper and stood by the roped off area.

paper

I didn't have to wait long before Coogan appeared, walking up the red carpet, smiling for the cameras and signing autographs. As he passed me, I held out the piece of paper. He glanced at it, reading it very quickly indeed as he strode into the cinema foyer.

keith

He didn't sign it as he clearly didn't want his name on such incriminating evidence. But I could tell he had taken the bait. All I had to do was reel him in.

wendy

It certainly didn't take long for Coogan to deliver on his end of the supposed bargain. Later that evening I was driving home slowly through King's Cross when I pulled over to test my headlights and look for something in the glovebox. Moments later I was approached by two high class escorts, who poked their heads through the window, which was down.

"You looking for business, mister?" they asked. "That depends," I replied. "Did Steve send you?"

They both laughed, and it was clear what was going on. I knew I had to go through with the sordid transaction if I was to stand any chance of collecting the evidence I needed to nail Coogan for his seedy crimes.

captain

After discreetly switching on a hidden tape recorder, I handed over the cash and the girls performed a series of sordid sex acts, including a wank, a finger of fudge and a posh nosh, upon me behind a nearby skip.

Using all my wiles I managed to elicit full confessions from both the prostitutes, admitting that they had been sent by the *Alan Partridge* star.

chesty

A-ha! I had got him, snared in a web of vice, fuelled by his own greed for fame. Unfortunately, the microphone was in my trouser pocket and due to one thing and another the sound was too muffled to stand up in a court of law.

Steal My Girls

Kidnap shame of TV boyband 1-D

POP SENSATIONS One Direction are one of the world's biggest acts. But maintaining a high public profile is hard work, and they are only too aware that the fame and fortune they enjoy today could easily evaporate. Securing the coveted support band slot on a major tour with an established star like Shakin' Stevens would make life a little easier. And that golden opportunity was what I offered Harry, Zayn, Malik, Louis and Ken when I sent an e-mail to their fan club website.

Adopting the pseudonym of my fake alter ego Shakin' Stevens, I promised them the chance to support me on a glittering 25-date tour of the East Midlands. Needless to say, my note made it clear that I'd want something in return from the boys; namely their help in carrying out a little plan I'd dreamt up. Put simply, I wanted them to kidnap the Spice Girls.

ambush

The boys were to ambush the chart-topping girl group while they were out on a walk, bundling them into the boot of a stolen Vectra before tying them up in a derelict house. One ear each from Sporty, Ginger, Posh, Scary and Baby would then be cut off and sent to their record company, along with a threat to kill them if a ransom of five million pounds was not paid immediately.

Of course this evil criminal undertaking was never going to happen, because I was going to turn up with the police and foil the plot just in time. It would be the scoop of the century. I would trash 1-D's reputation and become a national hero into the bargain.

kate bush

My email spelled out full particulars of where and when the Spice snatch was to take place. Every last detail had been thought out; nothing was left to chance.

But 1-D never turned up at the appointed time and place. When I checked their website, it turned out they were performing at the Perth Arena in Australia that night. But that was probably just as well, because the police failed to turn up too, even though I'd phoned in an anonymous tip-off to Crimestoppers. Although that didn't really matter in the end, as there was no sign of the Spice Girls either.

big hairy bush

But if 1-D are reading this, I have this warning for you: The Viz Fakey Shakey is on your case. And next time you attempt to kidnap and mutilate five innocent women, I'll be there to bring you to justice.

Next Week: The **Viz Phoney Tony** (*Investigative reporter Macaroni Marzipan*) goes undercover as Spandau Ballet's Tony Hadley to see if he can wreck the stars' careers. And the week after that, the **Viz Faux Joe** (*investigative reporter Marmite Margarine*) goes undercover as 80s singer songwriter Joe Jackson to do the same thing. And the week after that the **Viz Mock Rock** (*investigative reporter Marinade Marmalade*) goes undercover as rapper and producer Kid Rock to do more of the same again.

A debt of honour that must be repaid... IN BLOOD!

The Lawnmower

That lawn could sure do with a cut, Herb dear.

Why don't you pop next door? I'm sure Mr Pescatore would lend you his.

I know, Laverne. But my mower is bust. It's in the repair shop till next Saturday.

Good idea.

Ding-Dong!

Ding-Dong!

Hi, there. Is Tommy in?

Sure! Sure! Come in!

Mr Pescatore is right through here.

Ladies and gentlemen, I propose a toast to my beautiful, beautiful daughter and her husband Tony. May their marriage and the union of the Pescatore and Fruttivendolo families be long and....

Someone to see you Mr Pescatore.

I'm sorry, Tommy. I can see I've called round at an inconvenient moment. I didn't realise it was your daughter's wedding today.

Herb Nelson! Welcome to my house on this, the happiest day of my life. I kiss you on both cheeks.

Mwah!

Mwah!

Tell me, what can I do for you, Herb? For on this, my daughter's wedding day, the happiest day in my life, I will grant you any favour. Any favour, my friend. Just name it!

I was just wondering if I could borrow your lawnmower, only mine's in the repair shop.

My lawnmower? Take it, my friend, my brother! Il mio flymo e il tuo flymo! You can bring it back to me when you're done.

Thanks Tommy.

Magnifico!

Va bene! Que bueno! Quello che la generosità!

Hey, Frankie! Ottenere il mio tosaerba dal autorimessa, subito!

Si

Veloce! Veloce!

And...

I'll bring it straight back as soon as I'm finished.

Forgeddabahaadit, Mr. Nelson!

Shortly...

♪ Volare... oh-oh... ♪
Cantare... oh-oh-oh-oh...

VMMMMMM!

Next morning...

BANG! BANG!

Who's that at the door?

I don't know, honey. Maybe it's the mailman.

Oh hi. Frankie, isn't it? If you've come for the lawnmower, I put it back in Tommy's garage last night.

I know you did, Mr Nelson. Mr Pescatore would like to talk to you.

Oh! Okay, I'll just go and get dressed.

No... no need for that, Mr Nelson...

...This will only take a couple of minutes of your time. It's just a friendly chat.

Hey Herb! My brother, my friend, my neighbour. Have you met my granddaughter?

No Tommy, I don't think I have.

Maria, this is Mr Nelson who lives next door. You say hello to Mr Nelson like a good girl.

Hi, Mr Nelson.

Now you run along, sweetheart...

Nonno and Mr Nelson are going to have a little talk.

Ain't she swell? You got grandkids, Herb?

Yes, two. A boy and a girl.

Well how about that?

Yeah!

Me, I got twelve. Six of each. And gee, each an' every one of 'em can twist me round their little finger.

So, Herb, how's the lawn?

Great, Tommy. That mower of yours did a swell job. It's a real good mower.

It is a **great** mower, Herb. The **best**. That five horsepower 160cc 4 stroke engine purrs like a cat.

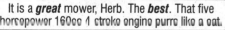

And that blade, Herb. What about that blade? Tungsten carbide steel and razor sharp. Goes through grass like a knife through butter...

It sure does!

I should use it to cut your fuckin' throat.

Er... I'm... sorry...?

Too late for apologies, ya' piece of shit.

Tommy, I... I don't quite understand...

Hey, Frankie. This cocksucker says he don't quite understand...

Maybe it's *me*. Is that it, Herb? Maybe I'm too fuckin' stoopid to make myself understood, is that what ya sayin'?

No, Tommy...

Goofy fuckin' Tommy Pescatore, is that what ya sayin', Herb? That Tommy Pescatore's a dumbass fuckin' Italian cocksucker who can't make himself understood? Is that it?

No, I just don't...

Show him, Frankie.

SLAM!

Recognise this motherfucker, huh? Do ya'?

I... I... I don't know. Is it the blade from your lawnmower?

Too right it is, ya' little' prick! With a big fuckin' chip out of it where it's gone over a fuckin' stone.

Oh dear.

Did ya think I'd be too fuckin' stoopid to notice, eh, wise guy?

Continued over...

I bet you and your fuckin' wife had a good laugh 'bout that last night, eh? A good fuckin' laugh 'bout how ya'd put one over on that motherfuckin' goofball Tommy Pescatore? Chip his fuckin' mower blade an' the fuckin' clown won't even notice, eh?

No, not at all, Tommy...

I...I...I didn't realise...

You come into my fuckin' house on the happiest fuckin' day of my life, on the day of my fuckin' daughter's wedding... I show you fuckin' kindness, I lend you my fuckin' Flymo and this is what ya fuckin' do..? Ya fuckin' disrespect me?

I'm so sorry. I..I'll pay for it...

Oh, you'll fuckin' pay for it alright, ya fuckin' piece of shit cocksucker. They'll find you in the fuckin' weeds.

No, Tommy, I...

Shut the fuck up!

Frankie, Richie... Get this fuckin' two-bit scumbag outta my face.

Yes Mr Pescatore.

You know what to do.

Tommy, listen, I'm sorry, I didn't mean it. I'm sorry! I'm sorry...

Ya' breakin' my balls.

So...

Groan!

SLAM!

Eventually...

Okay, cocksucker, lets get this over with. Outcha get.

mmmmm! MMMMM!

RENO LAWNMOWER SALES AND SERVICE

Oh, Hi, Mr Nelson. What can I do for you?

C...cou...could you sharpen this ... for me... please, Earl?

No problem.

Shortly...

There you go. That'll be a dollar fifty.

Can I pay you ne...next week, Earl?... I...I ca... came out w...without... my... wal...wal.. wallet.

Sure thing, Mr Nelson.

Hey, that looks great, Mr. Nelson. Good as new. Mr Pescatore's gonna be real pleased with that.

Next time you get whacked for real, motherfucker!

HNNNNG!

WHACK!

Come on, Richie, let's get goin'.

RETCH!

SCREEECH!

Next Week: Herb is forced to get a new identity under the Witness Protection Scheme after he borrows a pair of garden shears from Mr Gambino at number 48

The Dragons' Den of Tea

with Evan 'Tinsel Tits' Davis and the Dragons…

THE TEA INDUSTRY is worth over **£100 billion** a year to Britain's economy. Now the country's tea inventors and entrepreneurs get the chance to pitch their business plans to 5 of Britain's most successful venture capitalists. Welcome to…

● **FIRST TO PITCH** is former policeman *Nigel Zedcars* from Birmingham. He's hoping to raise money to fund his burgeoning Peabags business, but will the Dragons be impressed with his business plan?

" Everyone loves the taste of peas, but lots of people don't like the feel of them in their mouth. My "Peabags" are like teabags, but made with peas in them instead of tea leaves. I've sold 4 boxes of them at my local car boot and I have also written to Tesco to see if they are interested in selling them. I'm looking for £75,000 for 2% of my *business*. "

● **KENILWORTH** postmen *Frank Hopeless* and *Ted Windpiss* believe they have spotted a gap in the market, but to exploit it they will need a cash injection. Now they are hoping that a slick pitch to the Dragons will see them walk away with a cool £150,000 to sink into their business

" We all know how annoying it is when somebody puts a wet spoon back into the sugar bowl. Well the revolutionary ClumpBuster teaspoon makes that a thing of the past. The ClumpBuster dries itself within 0.1 seconds of coming out of the tea. We've got the domain name ClumpBuster.com registered, the patent is applied for and I already have orders for 2 million units from a major online retailer. The spoons will cost 10 pence per unit to make and retail for £9.99 each. We haven't made any yet as we don't know how, but it's certain to be a great business opportunity. We want £150,000 for 15% of the business. "

● **58-YEAR-OLD** *Penelope Antrobus* has been making cups of tea successfully for her friends in the Women's Institute for years. Now it's time for her to expand her business nationwide, and she's looking to the Dragons to provide much-needed capital.

" I have been serving cups of tea to my friends, family and all the ladies at my local WI meetings for 35 years. It has always proved very popular, especially when accompanied with a biscuit. However, I believe now is the time to rebrand my tea as *Reggae Reggae Tea*. I would like to bring Reggae Reggae Tea to a wider market. I've written a song about it for my pitch which goes like this:

Listen to the song I sing
'Bout Reggae Reggae Tea an' ting
Jamaica cup an' drink it down
All around me Kingston town

I'm looking for £120,000 in return for 10% of the equity. "

YOUNG TOMMY TAYLOR'S BEST PAL WAS A FANTASTIC ROBOT CALLED TINRIBS.

DJ '15

EXCITING NEWS, CHILDREN! I HAVE ENTERED OUR SCHOOL NATURE TABLE FOR THIS COMPETITION!

GRAND SCHOOLS ENVIRONMENTAL AWARENESS CONTEST — PRIZE FOR THE BEST NATURE TABLE

AND ELLIE HARRISON OFF OF 'COUNTRYFILE' WILL BE COMING TO JUDGE IT TODAY! HUBBA HUBBA!

EEURGH! A FILTHY WASP ON OUR NATURE TABLE!

WE MUST KILL IT, OR IT COULD STING THE DELECTABLE ELLIE HARRISON!

TINRIBS WILL HELP US TO CAPTURE AND KILL THAT WASP, HEADMASTER!

HI! I'M BARBIE. I LOVE YOU VERY MUCH.

CRUNCH!

GAH!

I'LL JUST SMASH MY MECHANICAL CHUM AGAINST MR SNODWORTHY'S NOSE, SPLITTING IT OPEN HORRIBLY.

THE WASP WILL BE IRRESISTIBLY ATTRACTED TO MR SNODWORTHY'S BATTERED AND BLOODY NOSE, MISTAKING IT FOR AN OVER RIPE STRAWBERRY.

IT'S WORKING!

NOW, I'VE FILLED TINRIBS'S RUBBER BALL HEAD WITH TOXIC CHEMICALS, AND ATTACHED THE HOLLOW TUBE OF HIS ARMPIECE...

AND VOILA!

ONE INSECTICIDE PUMP!

AIEEE! MY EYES! (CHOKE!)

SQUIRT SQUIRT!

GOOD SHOT, TAYLOR - RIGHT BETWEEN THE ANTENNAE!

WAIT A MOMENT, THIS ISN'T A WASP — IT'S A BEE!

HISSSS

WE'RE SUPPOSED TO SAVE BEES, NOT KILL THEM!

AND ELLIE HARRISON OFF OF COUNTRYFILE IS DUE TO ARRIVE ANY MINUTE!

IF SHE SEES THAT WE'VE MURDERED A BEE, SHE'LL THINK THAT WE'RE NATURE HATERS!

WE'LL JUST HAVE TO SECRETLY BURY THE BEE'S CORPSE IN A SHALLOW GRAVE OUTSIDE

DIG DIG SCRAPE!

IF WE BUILD A TINY BEE-SIZED PATIO OVER THE TOP, THE BODY WILL NEVER BE FOUND!

GOOD IDEA!

THERE - I'VE DROPPED THE DEAD BEE INTO THE HOLE.

NOW WE JUST NEED A BIT OF CEMENT TO LAY THE MINIATURE PATIO OVER IT. HMM....

MR SNODWORTHY ALWAYS HAS PORRIDGE FOR BREAKFAST.

GAK!

I'LL JUST FORCE TINRIBS'S FINGERS DOWN HIS THROAT...

HUEY!

THERE - THAT REGURGITATED PORRIDGE "CEMENT" WILL MAKE A SUPER PATIO.

JUST IN TIME - HERE COMES ELLIE HARRISON!

THIS WAY, MISS HARRISON - IGNORE THAT PERFECTLY INNOCENT BEE-SIZED PATIO...

REVENGE

COME INSIDE AND SEE OUR LOVELY NATURE TABLE!

GURR! I'LL LET ELLIE KNOW THAT SHE IS DEALING WITH BEE MURDERERS!

RIP BEE

WHO KILLED THE BEE?

HEMOLYMPH ON YOUR HANDS!

A FEW SIGNS LEFT AROUND THIS PATIO OF HYMENOPTERAN HORRORS SHOULD DO THE TRICK!

WOOW! THE BEE WASN'T DEAD - IT WAS MERELY STUNNED...

AND NOW IT'S ANGRY!

BUZZZ!

HEMOL ON HAN

SPLOTCH!

EYOW! IT'S STUNG ME ON THE TESTICLE!

RIP BEE

AND THE STINGER HAS GOT SNAGGED IN MY SCROTUM!

SAINTS PRESERVE US! I'M HAVING AN ALLERGIC REACTION TO THE BEE STING!

MY TESTE IS SWELLING UP AND TURNING GREEN!

MEANWHILE

HMM, I'M AFRAID THIS NATURE TABLE IS RATHER ORDINARY.

I WAS HOPING FOR A MORE IMAGINATIVE DISPLAY OF ENVIRONMENTAL AWARENESS...

BUT WAIT! WHAT'S THIS OUTSIDE? A MINIATURE PATIO TABLE BEARING A BIG GREEN HAIRY GLOBE...

AND PERCHED ON TOP, LIKE THE KING OF THE NATURAL WORLD, IS A BEAUTIFUL BEE!

THAT'S THE MOST INSPIRING NATURE TABLE I'VE SEEN! YOU WIN FIRST PRIZE - WHICH IS A KISS FOR EVERYONE IN THE SCHOOL...

MWAH!

...EXCEPT FOR THE ANGRY FAT TEACHER WITH THE SWOLLEN BOLLOCK.

HI! I'M BARBIE. I LOVE YOU VERY MUCH.

Einstein a No-Go!

ALBERT EINSTEIN was the greatest genius who ever lived. But the boffin who turned the world of physics upside down with his theory of relativity didn't know that *seven eights were fifty-six!*

According to newly-discovered papers in the archives at Princeton University, even though the Nobel prizewinner had no problem getting his head round brain-boggling concepts such as the warping of space-time by gravity, wave/particle duality and mass/energy equivalence, he simply couldn't understand how seven eights could equal fifty-six.

fine

"Einstein was fine with six eights being forty-eight and eight eights being sixty-four," says Princeton science historian Dr Johnny Saint. "But the idea that seven eights was fifty-six left him completely befuddled."

The papers, found in the university archive, and which include Einstein's original hand-written workings out of his famous $E=mc^2$ equation,

Boffin Bamboozled by simple sum

show the lengths to which Einstein would go to avoid using the sum in his calculations. "Once, when seven eights came up whilst he was working out the cosmological constant, he multiplied fourteen by eight and then halved the answer," said Dr Saint.

ticket

"On another occasion, whilst investigating the photoelectric effect, he broke down eight into its prime factors of two times two times two, and then multiplied that by seven to get the answer he required," continued Dr Saint. "Einstein was a very clever man, so he found a lot of

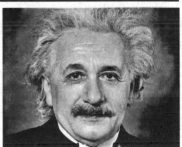

inventive ways of getting round the problem of seven eights whenever it came up in his work."

degree

But amazingly, sixty years after his death, it now appears that Einstein may have been right all along. For results from the CERN Large Hadron Collider in Geneva have recently shown that seven eights does not actually make fifty-six. "According to our experiments, it appears that seven eights are actually fifty-five point nine nine recurring," said epaulette-jacketed TV physicist Professor Brian Cox.

Box 841, Whitley Bay, NE26 9EQ ✳ letters@viz.co.uk

PLAYING Scrabble against my 5-year-old nephew, I told him there was no such word as 'foxy' in order that I could win by 2 points. When he went crying to his mum, calling me a cheat, I 'accidentally' knocked the board over and denied everything. That'll learn him.

Anton Seventies, Wolverhampton

I'M just going out for a bit to get some pork scratchings from the shop. I wondered if you'd put a 'Back in 10 mins' sign on this letter for me.

Scotty Herbert, Wood Green

WHILE shopping with the missus the other day, I noticed down the feminine products aisle in Boots that there were two products dedicated to washing vadges, yet there was nothing available for us blokes like a dedicated bollock wash. If there's an entrepreneur reading this and is thinking of pitching the idea to the Dragons Den, I've copyrighted *'Scrotums Gentleman's Dick Douche'* and *'Clackers Todger Wash'.*

Graham Flintoft, Gateshead

CAN any of your readers help me understand what my cat is saying when he stares into my face and meows at me? I can't tell if he's asking to be fed, or telling me to fuck off.

Ben Blake, Rugby

✳ *According to animal psychologists, this behaviour stems from when the cat was a kitten and they would look at the mother and meow to indicate it was hungry and wanted to suckle. In adulthood, this is your cat's way of asking you to put some food down for him and then fuck off.*

WHATEVER happened to three-cornered hats? No fella was seen without one in the 18th century, but now I can't even find them in charity shops. I reckon they'll come back into fashion when rappers start wearing them, especially if they put them on backwards. And these new titfers will also come in handy when the likes of Eminem and 50 Cent start doing panto.

LL Cool J, e-mail

IT should come as no surprise that some country folk like shag sheep. I saw a programme about sheep farming the other week, and the shepherd spent all his time whistling at them. The signs are all there if you just look for them.

Tarquin Drabble, London

HOLLYWOOD movie moguls have been churning out disaster films featuring the destruction of the Empire State Building, Statue of Liberty and the Golden Gate Bridge for years. Wouldn't it be better if they left those poor old landmarks well alone, and for a nice change had aliens attacking Rhyl's Sky Tower, or the two-storey Morrison's car park in Colwyn Bay instead? People would flock to the pictures to see that.

Rich Evans, Colwyn Bay

I HEARD on the news that Her Majesty The Queen has made her grandson Prince Harry a knight. That's quite the demotion for a Prince. I wonder what he did wrong this time.

LT Geraint, London

IS it any wonder Darth Vader turned out like he did? The Jedi had him for years as an apprentice and didn't make him up, so he went to the Sith for a better rate. Once there, exactly the same thing happened, and he kept getting called the Emperor's 'apprentice'. For years he didn't get promoted, so ended up building a massive Death Star and choking people with his mind. I know a bloke called Tony who had a similar experience of not getting promotion, but he just did a shit in a bag and left it outside the manager's office. I think both made their point in their own way.

J. J. Binks, Kettering

HADRIAN'S Wall was built to keep the Scots out of the Empire, but the Romans could have saved themselves a lot of time and money by not building it. I'm not sure how high it is, but last week in Tenerife, I saw five drunken Glaswegian blokes climb at least twenty-five foot to their balcony on account of they'd lost the key to their hotel room.

Robert Greaves, London

THEY say that lightning never strikes twice. Well my mate Paul Lightning is a disgruntled London Underground worker who has ceased working to express his dissatisfaction about pay and conditions on two occasions.

Pete Cashmore, W'hampton

WHAT is it with garden birds? I would like to say how infuriated I am by these scrounging animals. I can't put a few nuts or seeds in the garden without these feathered felons descending without so much as an invitation. If they're really wild birds, why don't they go out and catch their own peanuts?

Phil Kitching, Isle of Jura

AS an American, I really love *Only Fools and Horses*. The one where the little guy falls on his ass. Ha! Ha! Ha! That kills me. You Brits may not have noticed, but the barmaid moved the bar stand and the little guy didn't notice and fell right on his ass. Jeez. I also like the one with the fat chick being a priest. You guys are crazy.

Brad Cheeseoneverything, Texas

IF I suddenly gained the power of invisibility, I would use it to sneak to the FRONT of the dole queue on signing-on day. No more waiting for me! I would ask if any of your readers have a better use for invisibility than this, but I know there aren't any.

John Mason, e-mail

✳ *Don't be so hasty, John, our readers may know of many better ways to use the power of invisibility. Perhaps some of them won't even involve the changing rooms in women's clothes shops or the gym. Write in and tell us what you would do that didn't involve the changing rooms in women's clothes shops or the gym if you were invisible.*

I BOUGHT a scratchcard today where you have to match 3 values to win. The first two I scratched off were £100,000 and the rest were piddling amounts. You can imagine my disgust. Maybe if the bigwigs at Lottery HQ gave us more panels to scratch off with bigger amounts there would be more chance of me winning. Have the fuckers ever thought of that?

Robert Allison, Glasgow

WHY doesn't Simon Cowell get Queen guitarist Brian May as one of the judges on *X Factor*? With his hair, he looks just like a real High Court judge and I think it would add an element of authenticity to the whole sorry proceedings.

Renton Twelvetrees, Hull

PEOPLE often say, "curiosity killed the cat." But I'm pretty sure that the small ginger fellow that has just been scraped off the road by my Nan's house with a shovel was killed by the 10.15 Arriva to Wrexham.

William Cowell, Wrexham

WHILE on a visit to California's magnificent giant redwoods, I noticed that while the trees' heights had been measured, their volumes had only been estimated. It would be a simple matter to measure the volume by felling the tree, immersing it in a large outdoor swimming pool and measuring the amount of water displaced. My enjoyment of the visit would have been enhanced had the job been done properly.

Gareth Price, Portland

2-for-1 Crap Joke

I'VE GOT YOUR WIFE ON THE END OF THE LINE, SIR

TELL HER THERE'S A PILE OF WORK I'M TRYING TO GET ON TOP OF

TOP TIPS

CAN'T be bothered to seal the top of your packets of biscuits? Simply take the top, soft biscuit and place in a low oven for 2 hours, then put back in packet.

James Bull, Sheffield

BBC. Make *The Antiques Roadshow* more appealing to Americans by having members of the public chest-bump and tussle with the experts if they don't like the estimated value, and have people waiting in the queue trash-talk each other's heirlooms while flapping their arms about.

Mark Glover, Coventry

EYEBROW pencils can be used to draw curly hairs on a shaved chest.

Bomber Gascoigne, Coventry

WEAR your watch on your elbow so if someone asks you the time you can slide your sleeve up slowly to gradually build up the suspense.

John Tunney, Corby

CONVINCE friends and neighbours that you're a 1970s porn star by growing an huge, unfashionable moustache and talking so that your voice isn't in sync with the movement of your lips.

Rock Steel, Surrey

IF you see me in my new Hyundai maneouvering without indicating, check my windscreen wipers. The indicator is on the other side to my old Ford, so one swoop of the windscreen wipers means I'm turning right and lots of quick wipes mean left.

Russ Poore, Littlehampton

MEN. Examine your own prostate by simply wiping your arse with Aldi value toilet roll.

Peter Crompton, Sunderland

MAKE sure your wife's family haven't arrived while you are in the shower before walking downstairs shouting "If I was your brother I would of left the miserable bitch at home" to your wife.

Trevor Dick, Barnstaple

BANK robbers. Consider a Bernie Clifton-style ostrich suit for your next getaway...not only does it offer an excellent disguise but also ostriches can reach a running speed of up to 70mph.

Chris Ord, Newcastle

I'M no aviation expert, but I often wonder who the first person to join the 'Mile High Club' was. If it was Orville Wright on his solo flight at Kitty Hawk in 1903, it would have to have been a wank, and a pretty fast one at that. His plane only reached a height of 120 feet for a mere 12 seconds, so by my estimation, he would have to have been on the vinegar stroke at the moment of take off. But as I say, I'm no aviation expert.

Bartram Shoebury, York

HAVE your readers ever noticed that when doing the shopping, there is always one thing on the list that you can't find anywhere? I suppose it's too much to ask that supermarkets get their act together and put all these items on one aisle to save us all lots of time.

Dr P Durham

FOR years now, instead of getting an extra hour in bed when the clocks go back in Autumn, I've saved the extra hours in an old biscuit tin. This October, I'll have 48 hours worth which I'm going to convert into another Christmas and an extra pancake day in August.

Mark Glover, Coventry

JUST writing to say that I'm back from the corner shop, so you can take the sign off my letter now.

Scotty Herbert, Wood Green

THEY say that lightning never strikes twice. Try telling that to my mate Steven Twice, who was hit by a urine-filled bottle of White Lightning thrown at him by an enraged tramp in Wolverhampton's West Park.

Pete Cashmore, Wolverhampton

CAN there be anything more frustrating after you've just cleaned your windows than seeing some housefly walk up and down the glass in its shitty feet?

Simon Cooper, Bristol

IF global warming will lead to hotter summers and colder winters, why don't they just shift all the seasons forward a couple of weeks? I can't believe these so-called 'experts' have missed that one.

Nickers, Batley

BUTTON TIPS

RUN out of buttons? Simply staple the centre of a tiddlywink, then remove the staple to leave just the two holes. Hey presto! A cheap and efficient button stand-in.

Alphonse Jarry, Lewes

A METAL button off a raincoat painted with the appropriate crest or insignia makes an ideal shield for a hamster

heading into battle. A fork prong inside a birthday cake candle holder can be used for a sword.

Madge Needless, Hull

TOO many buttons? Simply take some of your buttons and put them in the bin. Hey presto! Fewer buttons.

June Alsace, Edgbaston

DON'T throw away the spare buttons that come with new shirts - they can be used to replace buttons on the shirt that may come loose or fall off as the years go by.

Stan Leyton, Leytonstone

ARE THEY STILL CALLED KEN?

With Peregrine Quorn-Hunt, Professor of Celebrity Nomenclature at Cambridge University

I USED to love watching American-born Chinese chef **Ken Hom** knocking up all manner of sizzling Pan-Asian fare in his infamous 'hot wok'. However, I haven't seen him on television for a few years, and I was just wondering: is he still called Ken?

Barrington Owl, Hull

* Thanks for your letter, Mr Owl. You are absolutely correct in pointing out that Ken Hom has not appeared regularly on British TV since his 'Exploring China: A Culinary Adventure' series aired in 2012. However, despite his three-year absence from the small screen spotlight, he continues to be called Ken by all who address him.

I'LL TELL you who always cracked me up: that **Ken Dodd**. Whether he was cheekily declaring, "How tickled I am!" or pulling a mad, boggle-eyed, toothy grin at the cameras, he always gave me a right good giggle. But I was thinking the other day - he can't still be called Ken, can he?

Manny Synapse, Herts

* If I had a pound for every time

I've been asked that question, Mr Synapse, I'd be a very wealthy man. The simple answer is yes - the comedian born Kenneth Arthur Dodd still very much answers to the name Ken, and has been doing so regularly since the late 1920s.

I CONSIDER myself something of a 'film buff', and as such, I was immensely saddened by the death of the iconic English director **Ken Russell** a few years back. But it got me to thinking - now that he's dead, I don't suppose he's called Ken any more, is he?

M Kermode, London

* I'm sorry to have to pull you up on this, Mr Kermode, but your supposition is 100% wrong. When people die, they don't simply stop being called Ken. As such, despite passing away in November 2011, Ken Russell can still be openly referred to as 'Ken' without fear of embarrassment and/or legal reprisal.

Would YOU like to know if somebody is still called Ken? Write in to:

'Are They Still Called Ken?' Viz Comic, PO Box 841, Whitley Bay, NE26 9EQ.

Fifty Shades of Bins

Wheelie of fortune: Binman Pugford Nettleburn has been lucky enough to have erotic encounters with more female stars than he can shake a stick at.

WITH WOMEN queuing round the block to watch the *50 Shades of Grey* movie starring *Dakota Johnson* and *Jamie Dornan*, it's clear that for the girls of today, straight sex is *OUT* whilst handcuffs, whips and gimp masks are *IN*. And when it comes to kinky bedroom antics, it seems the female stars are the worst of the lot. One man who knows more than most about dirty celebrity secrets is *PUGFORD NETTLEBURN*, a recently unemployed binman, who has decided to spill the beans on the sordid sex lives of the many female celebrities he has encountered on his rounds.

"**THE STARS** may live glamorous, jetset lives that the rest of us can only dream about," Nettleburn told us. "But they still have to sort their rubbish and take their wheelie bins out just like everybody else."

And collecting that rubbish on his star-studded bin round in Stoke on Trent has given Pugford a unique insight into the secret sex lives of a *Who's Who* of celebrity divas. "Two things you've got to know about your famous women," says Nettleburn, 61. "Firstly, the stuff they get up to behind closed doors makes *Fifty Shades of Grey* look like Mary Poppins. And secondly, they've got absolutely no idea when it comes to the council regulations concerning refuse collection. My twenty-two years on the bins have been an intoxicating erotic odyssey, and now it's time to sell, I mean tell my story."

Nigella Writes...

"**THE** life of a binman is hard enough, but it's made harder by people who get the collection days wrong. One serial offender in this respect was sultry TV chef *NIGELLA LAWSON*, who seemed unable to grasp which container to put out on which day. Eventually, after we'd affixed several warning notices to her bin, she came out of the house and asked if I could come round after my shift and explain the system to her properly. I grudgingly agreed; it meant giving up my free time, but I thought it might make my Thursday round a bit easier if she stopped getting it wrong every week.

goddess

When I arrived at her house, the domestic goddess answered the door in a skimpy nightie which left very little to my imagination. Beckoning me inside, she immediately told me that my clothes smelt of rubbish, and made me take them off.

I sat down in her kitchen, which I had seen a hundred times on her television programmes, and started going through

the rules. But she stopped me, pressing her finger across my lips.

"I don't have any pens and paper. Do you mind if I write some notes across your chest in melted chocolate?" she pouted. I nodded - anything to help her remember the simple three-week bin rotation cycle. So she heated up a steaming pan of liquid chocolate, put some of it on a pastry brush and wrote in scalding letters *'Black bins, before 8 am every third Thursday'* across my chest.

Wincing with pain, I told her she'd got it wrong. She leant forward and slowly erased the message with her tongue, before replacing it with the correct

Refuse collector lifts dustbin lid on his erotic S&M odyssey

information: *'Every third Thursday except following Bank Holidays.'* The heady mixture of pain and pleasure was exhilarating, but Nigella told me I was squirming around too much. She produced a set of silk scarves and tied me to the top of her kitchen table.

tea

It took another hour to write out the full schedules for all the different recycling boxes, because she kept getting it wrong and having to lick it off again. Then, just as she'd finished, the phone rang. Apparently she was scheduled to fly to New York to appear on the American version of *Masterchef* and she was late for her flight. Grabbing her keys she rushed out of the door, leaving me tied to the table, naked as the day I was born.

gartside

It took me two days to free myself, and when I got back to the depot my boss took me in his office for a dressing down over my unscheduled absence from work. If I'd shown him the burnt-on writing across my chest I might have got an award for dedication to duty, but I didn't want to endanger Nigella's reputation, and in any case the binman's code of honour is never to kiss and tell.

Frustratingly, I'd also missed out on a two-day bender in Blackpool to celebrate my mate's birthday, that had coincidentally happened at exactly the same time.

Hit me Britney, One More Time...

YOUNG women swarm around us bin collectors like flies do, but even so it was a surprise one day to see blonde bombshell *BRITNEY SPEARS* running after our truck in her see-through baby doll negligée, shouting that we hadn't emptied her green bin.

I got down from the cab to talk to her. I explained that it was because the lid hadn't been closed properly, meaning she'd exceeded her allocation of landfill for that fortnight. Spears was a repeat offender. I'd overlooked her over-filled bins on a couple of occasions, but I'd finally decided to draw the line. Her saying "Oops! I did it again" wasn't going to cut any ice with me.

I told her that she should address the problem by recycling more of her

plastics, but she stopped me. "If you want to teach me stuff, better do it properly," she whispered, scribbling down a time and address on the back of my bin glove with her lipstick. It was after hours, but I wasn't about to put in a claim for time-and-a-half, although I could have done. Educating the public about the rules is important; for one thing an over-filled bin won't fit in the lifting jig on the back of the wagon because a partially open lid fouls on the stanchions.

The address Britney had given me turned out to be a deserted secondary school, and I found her in the sports hall, wearing that sexy schoolgirl outfit from her first pop video. She had a skipping rope in her hands, and she beckoned me over, seductively asking me to take all my clothes off because of the smell.

rope

I'd come armed with a series of council leaflets about recycling, but she ripped them from my hand and threw them to the floor. Then, in one swift motion, she tied my hands with her skipping rope, before calmly suspending me from one of the climbing frames.

"I don't like it when people won't empty my bin," she said, hitching up her already short skirt. "Those people have to be punished."

I felt myself trembling with a heady mix of fear and sexual excitement as I dangled helplessly in the sports hall. The binman's code of honour prevents me from revealing what happened next. Suffice it to say it involved a table tennis bat.

spice

When at last she decided I'd suffered enough, she told me that all the stuff that the binman's code of honour prevents me from revealing had made her hot, and began undressing. She was just peeling off the last bit of her gym kit when her phone rang. It was her latest husband, telling her he wanted another divorce.

Britney quickly grabbed her clothes from the floor and rushed out of the room, leaving me hanging there, still smarting. She'd tied the ropes so well that it took me three days to free myself, and when I finally got back to the depot my boss wasn't impressed that I'd missed work again. This time he gave me a formal verbal warning for my unauthorised absence.

I could have explained it all by showing him the rope marks on my wrists and the bruises across my buttocks where Spears had spanked me with a table tennis bat, but Britney already had enough worries, and I've always made it a rule not to kiss and tell. What happens on the bin round stays on the bin round.

Adding insult to injury, my period of captivity had stopped me from joining some of my mates on a three-day booze cruise to Calais.

Brucie Bonus...

YOU would think the garden waste bin would provide less of a challenge for the hard-of-understanding celebrity, but sadly you'd be wrong. The rules are childishly simple: if it's not plant waste from the garden, it doesn't go in. So when I saw a crisp packet lurking among grass trimmings in a brown bin outside a smart detached house on my round, I immediately furnished the bin with a sticker explaining why we'd refused to empty it.

Suddenly I turned around I found myself face to face with the angry homeowner - TV newsreader **FIONA BRUCE**. She pleaded with me to take away her grass clippings, explaining that the crisp packet must have been dropped into her bin by someone walking past her house.

I calmly pointed out that even if that were true, it was still her responsibility to remove it and put it into the correct receptacle - the black bin for lightweight recyclable plastics. She responded by inviting me into her house to discuss the matter further.

lace

Inside, she told me to take off my clothes as the smell of rubbish was making her heave. The second I was naked I suddenly felt the cold snap of metal around my wrists. Bruce had shackled me to the radiator using a set of handcuffs that she had sneaked home off the set of *CrimeWatch*. Then she produced a Victorian riding crop that I recognised from a recent episode of the *Antiques Roadshow*.

"Here is the news," Bruce announced, sternly arching an eyebrow. "A Stoke on Trent binman was punished today for being extremely naughty." I knew what was coming next. I am too much of a gentleman to reveal the details of the BDSM session that followed, but by the time Bruce finally unlocked the cuffs and let me go, I had more stripes across my buttocks than a zebra.

I dressed and somehow staggered home, where I passed out from the mixture of pain and pleasure. I didn't regain consciousness for four days.

macdonald

When I got back to work, I was given a written warning for taking an unauthorised holiday. Showing the livid welts across my bumcheeks to my boss would have proved me innocent, but I would have had to have dragged Fiona Bruce's name through the mud. I kept the truth to myself and took my punishment like a binman.

Depressingly, while I was lying unconscious in my flat, my mates were all spending the week on a bender in Amsterdam's red light district, including having sex with prostitutes and attending live sex shows. Including one where one man had five women at once, right there on the stage in front of us. I mean them.

Historic Abuse...

You'd think that someone with a PhD in History would have a basic knowledge of timekeeping. But you'd be wrong. So when saucy TV historian **DR LUCY WORSLEY** came running after me pleading that she'd only been a few seconds late getting her bin out onto the pavement, I'm afraid I wasn't as sympathetic as I might have been.

But we got chatting about rubbish and she told me of some problems she'd been having at work.

"I've been sorting stuff out to throw away and I don't know which bits are recyclable and which should just go for landfill," she explained, coquettishly. She invited me to visit her at Hampton Court Palace the next day to give her some advice.

bannister

I arrived at the palace early next day. Worsley met me at the door and ushered me inside, leading me down a series of spiral staircases and narrow corridors until we reached a heavy oak door. "The stuff's just through here," she said, turning the key and pushing me inside. I found myself in a dark, dank dungeon, littered with iron maidens, racks and red hot branding irons in braziers.

Before I had a chance to ask her what was going on, Worsley had hit me across the back of the head with one of those spiky iron balls on a chain that knights use and knocked me out.

When I came round a few minutes later, I was naked except for a gimp mask, and I was strapped to a wooden table. Worsley had also changed out of her dowdy historian's clothes and was wearing a push-up rubber basque, thigh high stiletto boots and black leather gloves.

chataway

I tried to ask her where the rubbish she wanted sorting was, but I had a ball fastened in my mouth with a leather strap and the words wouldn't come out. Then Worsley, famous for her educational documentaries, said she was going to teach me a lesson for not collecting her bin. She climbed up onto the table and started sadistically grinding the points of her sharp stiletto heels into my genitals.

It was like a scene from *Fifty Shades of Grey*; a mind-blowing mixture of agony and ecstasy at the same time, but mainly agony.

Suddenly, Worsley looked at her watch and remembered that she had to attend a historical conference about Henry the Eighth at the British Museum. Moments later she had gone, locking the heavy dungeon door behind her and leaving me helplessly spread-eagled on the table, my desperate cries for help stifled by the rubber ball clamped tightly in my mouth.

playaway

She didn't return to release me until after her conference five days later. When she released me from my shackles, my first thought was to get back to the depot and explain to my boss why I hadn't been to work that week. But I may as well have saved my breath as he handed me my cards as I walked in through the door.

To add insult to injury, I later discovered that whilst I had been held captive in the torture chamber at Hampton Court Palace, all my mates had been on a cheap EasyJet 5-day break to Malaga. **"**

Since losing his job, Nettleburn has repeatedly resisted calls to dish the dirt on his many celebrity S&M encounters, insisting that female stars should be entitled to keep their warped sexual peccadillos private. But on May 24th he will be reading extracts from his brand new memoir *Bin There Done That* (Poached Egg Publishing, 18p) in the *London Review of Books* tent at the Hay on Wye Literary Festival.

FINDERS WEEPERS!

Jimmy's £10million jewel find turns sour

Life's a beach: The sand at Cromer where Jimmy discovered his 'diamond' (picture courtesy of the Cromer and Sheringham Inquisitor). And (top right) a real Koh-i-noor diamond worth a billion pounds.

BUS driver *Jimmy Hyland* thought he'd struck lucky last week after he unearthed a massive **DIAMOND** whilst digging on the beach near his home at Cromer, Norfolk. Unable to believe his luck, Hyland pocketed the glittering 7-inch-long gem and took it to get it valued at his local museum.

However, his dreams of taking early retirement and going on a luxury world cruise with the £10million proceeds of his find took a blow when curators at the Norfolk Museum of Antiquites told him his "diamond" was actually a worthless Coca-Cola bottle!

"I couldn't believe it," Jimmy told his local paper the *Cromer & Sheringham Inquisitor.* "I was certain what I'd found was a giant diamond - at least 500 carats. I thought the museum staff were trying to pull the wool over my eyes so I'd give it to them for their collection."

priceless

Determined to get a second opinion on his find, he took the priceless jewel to London and showed it to one of the biggest diamond experts in Hatton Garden, the capital's famous gem district.

hole

Sadly, the dealer only confirmed what Hyland had already been told. "He pointed out that my diamond had a flat bottom and a sort of neck with a hole in it at the top," he said. "And it also had the words 'Coca-Cola written up the side."

"He said it wasn't worth a ha'penny, never mind ten million pounds."

cloth tit

This isn't the first time that Jimmy - nicknamed "Treasure Hyland" by fellow bus drivers - has been disappointed after happening upon hoards of valuables in the Cromer area.

● In 2005 Jimmy made the local paper after finding a "9th Century Saxon brooch" on the pavement outside Peter's Bakery in the town centre, which later turned out to be a flattened foil dish from a custard tart.

● In 1999 he appeared on BBC local news show Look East after discovering a "Sutton Hoo Viking helmet" stuck down the back seat of his bus. This was later identified by a viewer as a Milletts beartrapper-style hat.

● In 1994 archaeologists from the British Museum identified fourteen "12th Century hand-carved walrus ivory chess-pieces" that Hyland found whilst excavating foundations for his shed as some white dog shits.

doubloons

But even though his dreams of a £10million windfall have been cruelly dashed for now, the 61-year-old father of two hasn't given up hope. "When I'm out in the bus, I'm ready to pull over at a moment's notice if I spot a bit of treasure lying about on my route," he told the paper.

"You never know when you might strike lucky with a pirate's treasure chest loaded with pieces of eight and Spanish doubloons, some crown jewels or a Tutunkhamen death mask," he added.

MEDDLESOME RATBAG

Shit...Take a Shit...Take a Shit...Take a Shit...Take a Shit...Ta... ...Ta...

WINNER! MAGAZINE of the YEAR ~Take a Shit Magazine of the Year Awards

Annie Old Iron!
(Annie Old Iron, Annie Annie Annie Old Iron!)

WE KNOW HER BEST as the glamorous lead singer of the *Eurythmics*. **Annie Lennox**'s unique operatic vocal style ensured the band's singles, such as *Who's That Girl*, *There Must be an Angel* and *Thorn in my Side*, topped the charts throughout the eighties. And her intriguingly androgynous image made her a leading alternative pin-up of the new wave era.

Lennox's sideboard groans under the weight of the honours she has accumulated during her long career; countless Brits, Grammys, Golden Globes, Oscars... even an OBE. And now she can add another prestigious award to that list - **Govan Scrap Dealer of the Year**.

For in 2010, Lennox made the momentous decision to put her jet-setting pop lifestyle on hold when she opened a 2 acre metal reclamation yard in Cessnock, on the banks of the Clyde near Glasgow. "I'd always been fascinated by scrap, both ferrous and non-ferrous," she told *Materials Recycling World* magazine's Oily Bob column. "Having my own yard filled with hundreds of tons of rusty metal is like a dream come true for me."

Lennox admits that getting to grips with her new career was a steep learning curve. "I definitely made a few mistakes in the early days," she said. "I was green and I didn't really know what I was doing. One time I bought a load of old water tanks made of dull metal that I assumed was lead. I paid top dollar for them and they turned out to be zinc."

From Platinum records to steel scrap: Eurythmics star Annie Lennox swaps her life in the fast lane for a life in the junkyard.

"Mixed zinc scrap at that time was turning at five hundred a ton and like a fool I'd paid the lead price of nine hundred and fifty. I was well out of pocket," she continued.

But that was not her worst experience. A few months later, the *Sisters are Doin' it for Themselves* singer had a brush with the law after making a dodgy deal.

"I bought sixteen hundredweight of dry bright wire off a bloke who turned up at the yard in a flatbed wagon," said Lennox.

"He told me he ran a cable factory and this was a cancelled order off an industrial transformer company that had gone bust. We shook hands on two grand in notes for the lot. He looked pleased to be recouping at least some of his losses, and I was happy too. I was pretty sure I could shift the wire to some smelters in Bearsden for an easy five hundred profit."

> ## "...the wire had been stripped out from a substation on a nearby railway siding, and I was looking at six months behind bars"

But the deal turned out not to be such a good one, as she found out the next day when she received a visit from two members of the British Transport Police.

"They told me that the wire had been stripped out from a substation on a nearby railway siding, and I was looking at six months behind bars for receiving stolen goods," she said.

"Luckily, the officer in charge was a big Eurythmics fan, and in return for signing his copy of our album *Sweet Dreams (Are Made of This)*, he let me off with a caution. Ever since then I've made sure all my paperwork's in order," she continued.

Since then, Lennox's business has gone from strength to strength, and currently turns over nearly 5,000 tons of assorted metal scrap each year. On the site she now has a purpose-built cabin with mains electricity as well as five oil-soaked alsatians which patrol the yard 24 hours a day.

"There were six dogs at one time, but the five of them I've got now turned on the littlest one and killed it, so I threw it in the canal," she added.

Next week... *Fairground Attraction's Eddi Reader tells **Take a Shit** of her disappointment when her Renfrew-based company **Reader's Ferrous Reclamation** failed to be nominated in the Govan Scrap Dealer of the Year Awards in 2014*

Boom Bang-a-Bang!

Russian guns threaten Eurovision

THE WORLD rejoiced when the Berlin Wall fell in 1989, heralding the dawn of a new era of understanding between East and West. The Iron Curtain was thrown wide open and the world breathed a sigh of relief as the USA and Soviet Union began to decommission their stockpiles of nuclear weapons.

Finally facing our Waterloo: Newly-resurgent Russia could become unbeatable in yearly Eurovision Song Contest, (left) spelling even more certain doom than usual for future British entries.

But nothing lasts forever, and it seems that good relations with Moscow are no exception. With hardliner Vladimir Putin now at the helm, the Russian bear has once again started to stir from its slumbers. And, as the Dobby-faced president eyes up new provinces to conquer in his quest to re-constitute the Soviet Union even bigger than before, the icy fingers of the Cold War once again threaten to start tightening their grip around the neck of world politics.

And nobody is more concerned about Russia's territorial ambitions than Britain's five-strong Song for Europe committee. The part-timers, who meet up to four times a year to discuss and choose the UK's Eurovision entry, are said to be worried that a newly resurgent Kremlin could become an unstoppable force in the annual camp contest.

system

"The Eurovision voting system is already at the mercy of international politics," said committee chairman Quentin Montefiore-Munch. "It is well known that the Balkan states, the Scandanavians and the Benelux countries all vote for each other every year. If the Red Army mobilises and starts moving into neighbouring territories right, left and centre, the repercussions on the big night would be wide-ranging."

"Any occupied countries would have no choice but to give the Russian entry 'douze points', no matter how bad it was," said Mr Montefiore-Munch. "And the consequences of not doing so would be dire as Putin wreaked his vengeance on anyone who failed to toe the Soviet line."

Assurances: Leonid Kolchinsky.

"The UK already has precious few allies in the Eurovision Song Contest, with just Ireland and Malta giving our entry, performed by Electro Velvet, any marks at all this year."

"If the Soviet tanks roll into Valetta and Dublin, this token remaining resistance will be crushed and we'll be completely isolated in Europe and looking at 'nil points' every year," he added. In a last-ditch bid to avert future Eurovision voting embarrassments for the UK, Mr Montefiore-Munch recently flew to Moscow for talks with his Russian counterpart, Chief Kommissar of the Russian Song for Europe committee, Leonid Kolchinsky.

heroin

"Mr Kolchinsky assured me that when Russia extends its territories into its neighbouring states, the citizens of those states will be granted full autonomy when voting in the Eurovision Song Contest," said Mr Montefiore-Munch. "The people will be free to phone in on the night and vote for whichever tune they feel is the most catchy."

"Their calls may be traced, monitored and recorded by the KGB, but only for training purposes," he said. "There will be no pressure whatsoever put on them, and if they do not vote for the Russian entry in the contest there will be no dire consequences for them or their family members."

"Dissidents will definitely not be taken away in the night and never seen again," he added.

Blackpool gears up for Russian tanks...
Reds Under the Bed (& Breakfast)
"Bring it on!" says lord Mayor

Only here for the pier: Russkis could be heading for Golden Mile

BLACKPOOL is ready and waiting for a Soviet invasion. And the Lord Mayor says that occupying Soviet soldiers will receive the same warm welcome along the Golden Mile as every other visitor.

"Here in Blackpool we're famous for our hospitality," Alderman Max Crabtree told the *West Lancashire Glans & Meatus*. "And whether you're a casual daytripper, a week-long holidaymaker or a ruthless occupying enemy force, our message to you is the same. Enjoy your stay!"

Demolition Man!

EX-POLICE frontman **STING** has offered to push the Doomsday button that would destroy the world. "If the balloon goes up and the Prime Minister is unavailable for any reason, I would gladly step into her shoes and initiate World War Three," the *De Doo Doo Doo De Da Da Da* singer told Radio 4's Eddie Mair.

"The four minute warning could come at any time, and if Mrs May is opening a car factory in the north east or attending a summit and unable to get to the button in time, I'd just like to say that I'm available."

wiping

And the 63-year-old arsehole said that he'd have no qualms about triggering a nuclear strike. "When you consider the damage that people have done to the earth, I'd be doing the planet a favour by wiping out the human race," he said. "Once all the people had been destroyed, plants, animals and birds would be able to live in peace."

"And I'd be there to see it happen, thanks to the luxury atomic blast-proof bunkers

"I'd push the button," says Sting

I've had installed at all my houses," he continued. "I've also had some smaller, less comfortable bunkers built for my domestic staff so that they will survive and be there to look after me and Trude following the thermonuclear holocaust."

A spokesman for the prime minister thanked the singer, but stressed that Downing Street had no plans to take him up on his offer.

hoopong

"In the event of the four minute warning sounding when Sting has just started fucking his wife, it would be unreasonable to expect the country to put off mounting a retaliatory missile strike for five and a half hours until he has hit the vinegar strokes, chucked his muck and can get to the button," he said.

NOBODY WANTS to start a global thermonuclear war. Except Sting. But if the world was teetering on the brink of Armageddon, could YOU bring yourself to press the red button and take the ultimate sanction? Presidents and Prime Ministers are trained to step up to the plate and do the deed, but what if they lost their nerve and bottled it when push came to shove? Just WHO would take their place and put their finger firmly down on the Fire button to wipe out all life on earth? We look at a selection of stars to see if they've got...

The X-tinction Factor?

● **SIMON BATES.** The popular DJ is well used to pushing buttons in his Radio 1 studio, cueing up records, jingles and Newsbeat reports each morning with the practised ease of the old pro that he is, so the physical act of pressing the doomsday button would present little problem for Bates. But could he cope with the emotional cost of being accountable for six billion deaths? Surprisingly, the answer is yes. Every morning at ten o'clock Simes presents his 'Our Tune' segment, which invariably has a sad ending. Without realising it, throughout his career he has been unconsciously preparing himself for this most onerous of responsibilities.
Armageddonability **8/10**   *X-Tinction Factor* ✱✱✱

● **VINNIE JONES.** On the face of it, the former Wimbledon hard man fullback-turned bad actor would the ideal person to press the nuclear button. Icy, unfeeling and ruthless in films such as *Lock, Stock and Two Smoking Barrels* and many more, you might expect Jones to happily condemn the planet to fiery doom without giving it a second thought. But you'd be wrong, for in real life Vinnie is soft as clarts, and finding himself suddenly responsible for the destruction of the entire human race may well give him sleepless nights. The only way he could bring himself to do the deed would be to think himself into character first, and even then it wouldn't be very convincing.
Armageddonability **44%**   *X-Tinction Factor* **Low**

● **ROGER DALTREY** Back in 1975, the fish-farming Who frontman lit up the silver screen when he starred as Tommy, the deaf, dumb and blind kid who sure played a mean pinball. Operating the buttons of an arcade machine with his crazy flipper fingers seemed to come as second nature to Daltrey, who in real life can hear, speak and see. But the buttons are on the sides of a pinball machine whereas the red button is on top of a horizontal control panel in the Prime Minister's blast-proof Whitehall bunker. Whilst the arrangement could be changed to fit the button on the side, in a position that Daltrey would be comfortable with, it is doubtful that the modifications could be made in the narrow four minute window available once the nuclear balloon goes up.
Armageddonability ✱✱   *X-Tinction Factor* **64%**

● **MIRANDA HART** The famously clumsy sitcom star is a firm favourite with viewers of all ages, but would it make sense to 'Call the Midwife' if someone was needed to step in and press the nuclear button? Hart's skirt would almost certainly fall down as she made her way to the

doomsday control room, causing her to simultaneously trip over and break wind, and whilst these events would undoubtedly break the sombre mood and cause a great deal of hilarity amongst the assembled military top brass, the delay caused by her slapstick antics could well give the Russians the precious few moments' advantage they need to identify, target and knock our incoming Minutemen missiles out of the sky.
Armageddonability **Amber**   *X-Tinction Factor* **3:1 on**

Your Chance to Kick Off WW3!

Could **YOU** do better than the stars? We've teamed up with our pals in Whitehall to give one lucky Viz reader the chance to press the red button and trigger the big one! Fill in this form to apply for your chance to push the nuclear button in the event of the Prime Minister not being available.

Name...........................Address..................................

I think I could press the red button because........................ ...
......................................(complete in no more than 12 words)

☐ I do ☐ do not live within a 4-minute bus ride of the Ministry of Defence.
Send to: *Viz, PO Box 841, Whitley Bay NE26 9EQ.* All entires must arrive at least 4 minutes before the balloon goes up.

26,000 heavily-armed shock commandos could easily overwhelm the tourist facilities in any resort, so the council are already putting in place a ten point plan to deal with the expected influx of invading Russians. Amongst measures being implemented are:

● *Local residents to be turned out of their homes, which are to be given up to Russian soldiers*

● *All the cash machines along the Promenade to be stocked with Roubles*

● *Saucy seaside postcards to be translated into Russian and re-printed*

● *The Pepsi Max Big One on the Pleasure Beach to be renamed "The Glorious Rollercoaster of the People"*

● *The Norbreck Castle Hotel to be done up and turned into a Gulag for political prisoners*

● *The North outside wall of the Winter Gardens to be set aside as a designated place of execution where dissidents can be lined up and shot*

"Coming under the iron fist of the Kremlin will mean changes for everyone living in the town," said councillor Crabtree. "So I would appeal to all Blackpudlians to do what they are told by the occupying militia."

"If we all stay calm, we'll all get along just fine and nobody will get hurt," he added.

current

However, addressing the United Nations Security Council in New York, Russian President Vladimir Putin said he had no current plans to annexe the popular resort. "I've heard Blackpool's a bit rough, especially up by the North Pier," he told delegates.

raysin

Meanwhile, the mayor of nearby Lytham St Annes accused his Blackpool counterpart of collaborating with the Russian invaders, and pledged that Lytham would be a far harder nut to crack

Wish USSR were here: Is Kremlin eyeing up Blackpool?

for any invading force. "He is turning his town into the Vichy of the Fylde Coast," fumed Councillor Adrian Street. "Blackpool may fall, but Lytham will never kowtow to the Kremlin. And if the Red Army imagine they can simply march up Clifton Drive South and take the Town Hall they've got another think coming."

"We shall fight them on the beaches, we shall fight them in the streets and we shall fight them in the car park behind Fairhaven Boating Lake," the mayor told The *Lytham St Annes Perineum & Vulva.* "We will push these Russkies back into the sea, and further, make no mistake about that."

sultarner

And Street announced the formation of an underground guerilla resistance movement to fight back against any communist forces that attempted to annexe Lytham.

"Our freedom fighters have already bought a Gestetner printing machine out of the free-ads, with which they intend to print a rebel newspaper, anti-Russian propaganda leaflets and forged travel documents," he said. "They have also bought a morse code radio from Maplins so they can contact their resistance comrades in Fleetwood, Bispham and Cleveleys to coordinate disruption of the Russian supply lines. It's all very exciting."

"The whole operation will be masterminded from their secret headquarters in a room above the Willow Blossom tea rooms on St Pauls Avenue," added Councillor Street.

"Actually, I probably shouldn't have said that bit," he added.

STRIKER'S LAST MATCH

During his twenty-year career as centre forward for Peddleworth Albion, Billy 'Striker' Bryant had netted a massive 249 goals. Now, on the morning of his last match before retiring, Bryant had set his sights on beating the club's 50-year-old scoring record. As he walked into the ground, he was met by manager Stan Swan.

Morning, Billy. Are you up for your final match for the Albion?

I sure am, Mr Swan.

From my very first game for the club twenty years ago, I've dreamt of one day beating 'Golden Boots' O'Toole's record. And this is my last chance to do it.

It would certainly be a fitting end to your playing career, Billy.

But O'Toole left the club with 408 goals under his belt. To take his crown, you'll have to put 160 goals past the Greybridge Rovers keeper this afternoon.

Yes, I'll have to average a goal every 33.75 seconds for the full 90 minutes. It's certainly a big ask, boss...

...But I know I can do it. That club record is mine for the taking.

Well, I've got a surprise for you, Billy.

If you beat 'Golden Boots' O'Toole's total, we're going to put this bronze statue of you on that plinth in front of the stadium.

Wow! That's the greatest honour the club could pay me!

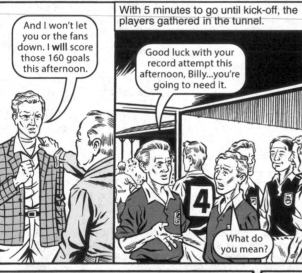

And I won't let you or the fans down. I **will** score those 160 goals this afternoon.

With 5 minutes to go until kick-off, the players gathered in the tunnel.

Good luck with your record attempt this afternoon, Billy...you're going to need it.

What do you mean?

Look who Greybridge have got between the sticks.

Crumbs! It's Eddie 'Clean Sheet' Henderson!

In thirty-five years as the Rovers goalie, he's never had to pick the ball out of the net once.

That's right. And in the next ninety minutes you've got to do what no other player has ever managed to do...

...160 times!

DWYER'S QUIFF CREAM

O'GRADY'S SNUFF

The match was soon underway, and mindful of the Herculean task that lay ahead of him, Billy was soon on the ball.

Pheep!

Bryant's not messing about. He's left those defenders for dead.

Yes. He's got 'Golden Boots' O'Toole's record in his sights alright.

MONTGOMERY PIPES

Wow! What a piledriver of a shot. That one's going in for sure!

Yes, one down, 159 to go!

But.

No! 'Clean Sheet' Henderson managed to get a finger to it!

What a save!

That's 30 seconds down with no score. Billy's going to have to up his shooting rate to one goal every 33.5625 seconds.

Yet the Rovers net-man was equal to every shot.

So close!

Thwarted again!

Ooh, ya fucker!

Shortly.

Pheep!

Nil-nil at halftime.

Yes. I'm off for a pie, a pint and a piss

In the Albion dressing room.

Well, Billy. You've made things twice as hard for yourself.

If you want that record, you'll have to score once every 16.875 seconds throughout the remaining 45 minutes of the match.

Don't worry, Mr Swan. I'm hungry for it. Nothing's going to come between me and those 160 goals.

That's the spirit. Now go out there and show Greybridge Rovers what you're made of.

Leave it to me, boss!

The second half was soon underway and Bryant was quickly on the attack.

He's on for a shot!

Come on, Billy. Shoot!

Yes. If you don't buy a ticket, you can't win the lottery. That's what they say.

But over and over again, the Rovers number one showed his mettle.

Oof! 'Clean Sheet' Henderson is certainly living up to his moniker.

Just five minutes left to play. Billy needs to pull his finger out and start scoring at a rate of one goal every 1.875 seconds or else this record's going to slip from his grasp.

But 5 minutes later, as the clock ticked over to 90 minutes, the game was still goal-less.

That's time. Now it's all down to how long the ref's adding on for stoppages.

It wasn't good news.

Just 2 minutes, boss. Billy's going to have to pop one in every three quarters of a second if he's going to beat O'Toole's career tally.

Yes, he's certainly left himself with a mountain to climb.

But 118 seconds later, the score still stood at 0-0.

The ref's lifting the whistle to his lips. There's only a couple of seconds still to play by my watch! Billy's going to have to up his scoring rate to one goal every 0.0125 seconds!

Come on, Billy, you can do it!

Next week - Billy rounds the keeper and finds the back of the net, only to have his goal disallowed for offside! And with just 1 second left to play, has he left it too late to put 160 past the league's best goalkeeper?

HE'S THE super-suave sleuth with a penchant for fast cars and even faster women. For more than 50 years, we have marvelled at his thrilling adventures, slick gadgets and quick-witted one-liners - usually delivered just seconds after killing a bad guy, or moments before bedding a sexy lady. He's *Bond, James Bond,* and he's as much a part of Britain's cultural heritage as Stonehenge, Sunday roasts and *Test Match Special*. But how much do we REALLY know about this sophisticated secret agent with a licence to kill? We don't expect you to talk, but we do expect you READ these...

20 THINGS YOU NEVER KNEW ABOUT JAMES BOND

001 **WRITER** Ian Fleming chose the name 'James Bond' because it combined the monikers of his two favourite celebrities: *Saturday Kitchen* chef *James Martin* and *Cash in the Attic* host *Jennie Bond*.

002 **HE MAY** have bedded hundreds of the world's most beautiful women, but believe it or not, James Bond has never had a hand job! In his 1961 novel *Thunderball*, Fleming has the suave spook pulled off behind a skip in Monte Carlo by a sexy Russian agent in exchange for some microfilm, but the scene was dropped on his publisher's advice.

003 **IN THE** film franchise, Bond only sups sophisticated vodka Martini cocktails - *"shaken, not stirred."* But originally, Fleming had his hero drinking lager top. The author was forced to scrap this as his spy's chosen tipple after learning that most Monte Carlo casinos don't serve pints of Carling with a dash of R White's in them.

004 **THE** tradition of watching a Bond film at Christmas dates back to 1485. Having seized the English throne by defeating *Richard III* at the Battle of Bosworth Field, the new Tudor king *Henry VII* issued his very first decree - that every household in the land must watch at least one Bond film on Christmas Day or face immediate death by hanging.

005 **THIS** law was relaxed by King *Charles II* in 1661 to stipulate that the Bond film could also be viewed on Boxing Day, or you could watch *The Italian Job* instead, if you preferred.

006 **SEAN** Connery famously wore a hairpiece in all six of his performances as Bond. What's less well known is that he also wore a merkin! Connery donned the pubic wig at the request of producer Albert 'Cubby' Broccoli, who felt that the Scotsman's natural pubis was too thick and curly to resemble 007's, which Fleming describes as being "soft and downy, like a sparrow's back."

007 **AT** 5'10", *Daniel Craig* is the shortest man to ever play James Bond. That's still much taller than the world's smallest man, *Calvin Phillips*, who, in the unlikely event he was ever selected to portray Bond, would require an exploding pen the size of a grain of rice and a Union Jack parachute no bigger than hankerchief.

008 **BELIEVE** it or not, iconic Bond henchman *Oddjob* is based on a real life figure - Ian Fleming's old headmaster at primary school. Interviewed in 1960, Fleming said: "Mr Perkins was a short, squat, Korean man with a foul temper, who would fling his razor-edged bowler hat at us if he spotted us whispering in assembly."

009 **YOU'D** think from his many appearances in casinos that Bond's favourite game was poker. You'd be wrong, however, as it's *Buckaroo!* The smooth-tongued spy plays the donkey-based balance challenge in the 1954 novel *Live and Let Die.*

010 **BELIEVE** it or not, iconic Bond henchman Jaws is based on a real life figure - Ian Fleming's old maths teacher at Sandhurst. Interviewed in 1961, Fleming said: "Mr Bradshaw was a gigantic, muscle-bound simpleton with sharp steel blades for teeth, who would bite furiously through the nearest electricity pylon if we were late for lessons."

011 **WHEN** *Pierce Brosnan* stepped down as Bond in 2005, he was replaced by *Daniel Craig*, who still holds the role today. But Craig wasn't the producers' first choice. According to Film-makers Eon Productions: "...there is only one man who could capture all Bond's characteristics and eccentricities whilst bringing something fresh to the role. And that is former Leeds frontman Arthur Graham."

012 **THE** car chase is a classic staple of the Bond films, and over the course of 23 movies, 007 has totalled a whopping 104 vehicles! That's almost *one sixth* of the cars crashed over the years by dozing pop singer *George Michael.*

013 **DESPITE** appearing alongside Daniel Craig in the 2012 London Olympics opening ceremony, *Her Majesty the Queen* has never seen a Bond film! That's because she spends every Christmas Day rehearsing and filming her annual speech, thus missing 007's adventures on the other channel. "I'm not hugely arsed as they don't really sound like my thing," she told the *Balmoral Herald.*

014 **INCREDIBLY,** atheist firebrand *Richard Dawkins* does not believe in James Bond. "I do not think James Bond exists or indeed has ever existed," the godless stick-in-the-mud told *Puzzler* magazine.

015 **DURING** the rehearsals for *The Spy Who Loved Me, Roger Moore* fractured his eyebrow, forcing producers to drastically cut the number of scenes in which Bond is pleasantly surprised and/or sexually aroused.

016 **BELIEVE** it or not, iconic Bond henchwoman *Xenia Onatopp* was based on a real life figure - Ian Fleming's old school dinnerlady at Eton. Interviewed in 1962, Fleming said: "Mrs O'Grady was a lithe, sensual ex-Soviet assassin with large breasts, who would strangle us to death with her powerful thighs if we didn't eat our vegetables."

017 **JAMES** Bond's favourite colour is none other than... *blue.* Ian Fleming reveals this in the 1957 novel *From Russia, With Love* when Bond tells M: "My favourite colour is blue."

018 **OTHER** celebs who cite blue as their favourite colour include pop singer *Katy Perry*, film star *Johnny Depp* and former UN weapons inspector *Hans Blix.*

019 **CELEBS** who loathe the colour blue include Led Zeppelin rocker *Jimmy Page, Dragons' Den* entrepreneur *Theo Paphitis* and cumshot legend *Peter North.*

020 **CELEBS** who have yet to state their position either way on the colour blue include tennis ace *Roger Federer*, telly handyman *Tommy Walsh*, and hook-handed preacher of hate *Abu Hamza.*

The Biggest Mince Pie in the World

TO CELEBRATE the end of the Festival of Britain in December 1951, Prime Minister Sir Stafford Cripps announced that Britain was to bake the largest mince pie the world had ever seen. With the austerity and rationing of the war years still fresh in the public's memory, it was a national project into which the whole country could throw themselves with gusto. Even today the scale of this ambitious undertaking is literally mind-boggling, with an estimated half a million people working solidly for two days to meet the premier's Christmas morning deadline. Here's how it was done...

BY lunchtime on Christmas Eve, all the constituent parts of the recipe have been prepared, and it is time to bring the pie together for the first time. Police close every road in Britain to allow convoys of trucks to haul their gargantuan cargoes towards a rendezvous on Salisbury Plain in Wiltshire, where the giant festive treat is to be cooked.

SIMULTANEOUSLY, at RAF Boulmer in Northumberland, the lid of the pie is being prepared from a slightly smaller lump of pastry that has been brought up the east coast overnight by a flotilla of tugs. At the airfield, to prevent it sticking to the ground, hundreds of vehicles usually used to spread grit on icy roads have been commandeered to sprinkle more than a million tons of flour across the airfield. Members of the British Antarctic Survey team are on hand throughout the operation, ready to leap into action at a moment's notice to drill three steam holes in the hundred-foot thick crust.

WHERE on Earth would you find an oven large enough to bake the biggest mince pie in the world? Step forward Dambusters boffin Professor Barnes Wallis. The inventor of the bouncing bomb has come up with his most audacious scheme yet - the "Baking Bomb". Dropped from a Vulcan bomber and detonating just a thousand feet above the pie's pastry surface, this thermonuclear device is designed to instantaneously heat up the atmosphere around the pie to 500,000°C - equivalent to 20 minutes at gas mark 8 for a normal-sized pie. Simultaneously, an identical bomb will be exploded in a specially excavated underground cavern half a mile beneath the aluminium dish to ensure that the raisin-packed Christmas favourite is baked to perfection and doesn't end up with a soggy bottom. Afterwards, the vast pie will be popped onto a rack made from over a billion tons of fourteen-foot thick chrome-plated stainless steel rods. A battery of enormous hydraulic rams then push this rack onto an enormous window sill where it is left overnight to cool.

AS dusk falls, construction finally gets underway. The dish is lined with pastry, countless thousands of tons of fruit filling is poured in and the lid is lowered into place by cranes and crimped onto the top using enough beaten eggs to fill five hundred Olympic-size swimming pools.

DECEMBER 23rd. Every foundry in Britain halts steel production and begins smelting aluminium under the supervision of senior civil servants. Over 1,000,000 tons of the metal will be needed in order to cast the giant, flimsy foil dish in which the monster mince pie will eventually sit. Indeed, this is to be the largest foil dish ever constructed in peacetime; the bent-over lip round the top will be as wide as a six-lane motorway, and each crinkly fold down the side will be deep enough to accommodate a Nelson's Column.

NEXT comes the pastry. The nation's farmers have been called upon to provide eggs, butter, milk, sugar and flour in previously unheard-of quantities. These ingredients are emptied into the dome of the Albert Hall, specially turned upside down by the chairman of the Royal Institute of British Architects Sir Basil Spence, and mixed together with wooden spoons. Ten thousand Girl Guides work round the clock in shifts until a nice consistency is achieved.
The Winsford Mine in Cheshire provides the pinch of salt - sixteen articulated lorries full!

AS dawn breaks on Christmas Eve, the rolling of the pastry begins at Tollerton Aerodrome near Nottingham. Councils across Britain have donated their road mending equipment and crews to transform the dough from a big lump into a perfectly flat sheet of just the right consistency. Sir Josiah Hollywood - great great grandfather of modern day baker Paul - is given the unenviable task of deciding when the 15,000 acre pastry sheet has reached the correct thickness to guarantee an even bake.

MEANWHILE, preparation of the sweet mince filling is already well underway at Wembley Stadium. A giant 200,000 ton Kenwood mixer, specially fabricated at the Swan Hunter shipyard on Tyneside, is used to ensure an even distribution of raisins, sultanas, currants and candied peel. To provide enough suet for the pie, the carcasses of more than a million cows will have to be rendered down to fat, and slaughter on a massive scale begins at abattoirs the length and breadth of the United Kingdom.

CHRISTMAS Day dawns frosty, clear and still on Salisbury Plain, but the the morning quiet is soon broken by the deafening scream of jet engines as 200 RAF English Electric Lightning fighters, flying in tight formation, make a series of low passes over the mince pie to dust it with icing sugar. A tub of brandy butter the size of the Isle of Wight is placed beside it, and the giant festive pudding is ready for its grand public unveiling by George VI.

CRIPPS'S original plan had been to cut the mince pie up and give all the Chelsea Pensioners a slice each. However, by Boxing Day the suet has already started going rancid and the smell is attracting flies from as far away as Glasgow. The authorities reluctantly decide to tow it out into the Bristol Channel and sink it.

AT 3pm precisely, every radio set in the land is tuned to hear his majesty deliver his annual Christmas address to his subjects. The population listens with rapt attention as he begins his speech: "This Christmas, I speak to you my loyal subjects across the Commonwealth not, as is customary, from my desk at Buckingham Palace, but from in front of an extremely large mince pie."

NEXT CHRISTMAS - Mary Berry tells the fascinating story of Isambard Kingdom Brunel's most ambitious ever project - the construction of the biggest box of "Eat Me" dates the world had ever seen!

Cowell's Udders

Keep it under your hat, but the word on A-list Boulevard is that starmaker **SIMON COWELL** has grown some cow's udders! The *X-Factor* impresario, 56, told close pals that he woke up one morning to find the bagpipes-sized lactating bovine gland had sprouted from his midriff overnight. Yuck! What's worse, the talent show magnate now can't decide whether to tuck his swollen teats under or over his trademark high beltline. Talk about first world problems! And Simon's bright pink milkers have thrown production of the *America's Got Talent* Christmas special into chaos, with shooting repeatedly suspended to allow the Captain Scarlet-faced Tinseltown starmaker to visit his custom-built $10 million backstage dairy parlour, where he produces up to 8 gallons of creamy gold-top every day! "If he doesn't get milked morning and night, Simon runs the risk of developing mastitis, and we can't have that because this show's nothing without him," confided fellow *AGT* judge **HEIDI KLUM**, *Kiss from a Rose* singer **SEAL**'s leggy ex-squeeze, who has recently been seen out and about on the arm of former Secretary of State for Wales **JOHN REDWOOD MP**.

No Socks Please We're Twittish

Whisper it quietly, but pals say that a distinctly frosty atmos has developed between *Maleficent*

Fanny Batter's HOLLYWOOD Xmas gossip

TINSELTOWN'S TASTIEST TITTLE-TATTLETITBITS!

star **ANGELINA JOLIE** and former bff **KIM KARDASHIAN**. Why? Get this. Angelina confided in Kim that she had bought hubby **BRAD PITT** a new pair of socks and some hankies for Christmas, only for Kim to tweet the secret to her 20 million followers! Oops! *Martian* star Brad certainly wasn't over the Moon to have his Christmas morning surprise ruined by the *Life With the Kardashians* reality star's thoughtless update, and furious Jolie thought it was the Pitts too! They say that in Hollywood, revenge is a dish best served red hot, and Angelina wasted no time in getting even, leaving a burning bag of dogdirts on the doorstep of the $50 million BelAir mansion that Kim shares with rapper **JAY-Z** before ringing the bell and running off.

Has he been sick? *Oh Yes he has!*

Wall Street's Gordon Gekko famously said "greed is good," but that movie's star **MICHAEL DOUGLAS** would surely have to disagree after making himself sick on sweets during a family

panto trip. *Spartacus* star pop **KIRK DOUGLAS**, 98, had taken Michael and his two brothers Joel and Peter to the Weston-super-Mare Playhouse to see King of the Jungle **JOE SWASH** starring in *Cinderella*. All went well until the interval, when the *Basic Instinct* star felt a sudden "fatal attraction" for the refreshments kiosk in the foyer, wolfing down four tubs of Kelly's ice cream, three family bags of Haribos and a 2-litre cup of Dr Pepper! Cut to the second half of the show, when the Ugly Sisters - played by *Crimewatch*'s **NICK ROSS** and ex-Liverpool goalie **BRUCE GROBBELAAR** - whipped the already excited crowd into a frenzy by getting them to shout out every time they saw a meerkat driving

a radio-controlled car across the back of the stage. *Ant-Man* star Douglas, 71, screamed so much that he was sick all down his front. "Michael spent the rest of the show wearing his dad's jumper and gripping a popcorn tub in case he honked up again," wife **CATHERINE ZETA-JONES** told *The Late Late Show*'s **FRENCH LETTERMAN**.

Merry Xmas to Me!

Ahoy there, landlubbers! *Bodger & Badger* tycoon **ANDY CUNNINGHAM** has pushed the boat out this Christmas by treating himself to an early present - a 600-foot, £2 billion superyacht! The luxury craft, named HMS Mashed Potato, boasts a helicopter landing pad, three Olympic-sized swimming pools, a bowling alley, shopping mall, two cinema complexes, five gymnasiums and a dart board, and was delivered to Cunningham's private Caribbean island on Christmas Eve, all wrapped up and with a 200-foot bow tied round the funnel. Nice work if you can get it! Cunningham, who made a fortune in repeat fees when his 1990s kids' TV show was re-run on CBBC, was recently named by *Forbes* magazine as the world's third richest man. So will he be dashing up the gangplank crying "All Andys on deck!" on Christmas morning? Not a bit of it. My spies tell me that the multi-billionaire ventriloquist suffers from terrible sea-sickness and doesn't intend to ever go aboard his floating fun palace. "Andy's got terrible sea legs, so he's just going to sit on the harbour and look at it," former glove puppet rodent co-star **MOUSEY** told *Vanity Fair* magazine.

A Big Christmas Kiss, gossip lovers!

Fanny x x

The Pardew & Bassey Adventures
No.36
PYRAMID OF TERROR!

*It was another normal day for Crystal Palace manager **Alan Pardew** and Tiger Bay diva **Shirley Bassey**...*

What are you doing, Alan?

Just sweeping the chimney Shirl.

Hello, what's that?

It looks like a treasure map.

It's the lost gold of Montezuma. It looks like it's hidden in a mysterious Aztec Temple deep in the jungles of Peru!

Wow! Well what are we waiting for, Alan? Let's go and get that treasure.

We'll have to be quick, Shirl... we're at home to Man City on Saturday.

Yes, and I'm headlining at the London Palladium.

Shortly...

PERU
LIMA
PACIFIC OCEAN

In Peru...

There it is, Alan! The lost Aztec pyramid of Montezuma. Just like on the map.

Great! I'm over the moon we've found it.

I can't find a way in, Shirl.

There must be some sort of secret button to press, Alan. Have a look around.

Here it is!

GRIND!

Come on. Let's get the treasure.

There it is, Alan!

Great! Let's grab it and then get outta here!

SLAM!

Oh no! The secret door has shut behind us. There has to be another way out!

There's one...

Come on!

Phew! Safe at last, Alan.

Not quite, Shirley. Look!

It's the Guardians of Montezuma's Treasure!

Wooaah!

Quick, Shirl! Across this bridge!

Yikes! Crocodiles! If we fall in, we're gonners, Alan.

Ooh, I feel giddy. It's so high.

Come on Shirl, don't look down!

They're gaining on us!

Not far to go now and we'll be safe. Those Aztec warriors are superstitious. They won't follow us into the airport!

AIRPORT 1 Mile

Phew! That was close!

Come on, let's check this treasure in and get on the plane back home!

Next day at the London Palladium...

...and Selhurst Park...

Next Week:
The Pardew & Bassey Adventures
No. 37
Lunar Canyon of Terror!

Alan and Shirley catch some bank robbers on the Moon before flying back for a FA Cup third round clash with Leicester City at Filbert Street and a concert of James Bond themes at the Albert Hall.

Beeb BOOBS Again

A LEADING OXFORD HISTORIAN has attacked BBC drama makers, accusing them of giving viewers a misleading portrayal of real life in 16th century England, singling out recent blockbuster series such as *Wolf Hall* and *The Tudors* for particular criticism. Despite pulling in record audiences, the flagship shows were "shot through with historical errors, inaccuracies and blunders," said Professor *Mostyn Killjoy*.

Because according to the academic, whilst film-makers clearly spend a fortune getting their sets, costumes and lighting just right, they invariably get the most important historical detail completely wrong - the size of the women's **BREASTS**.

Expert slams TV Tudors shows as 'Historically Inaccurate'

"It is clear that no research at all goes into the casting of these shows," says Killjoy. "All the actresses in *Wolf Hall* and *The Tudors* have tits like fried eggs, whereas in real life 16th century birds had proper milkers. To call these series historically inaccurate is putting it mildly."

study

Killjoy, Dean of Sprotborough College, has made a forty year study of women's breasts through history, and he says that the real life historical figures portrayed in the series were nothing like the modern actresses cast to play them. "Don't get me wrong, I've got nothing against Claire Foy in *Wolf Hall*, but she's just not got what takes in the jugs department to play a credible Anne Boleyn," he told us.

"Henry VIII was the most powerful man in Europe at the time. He could have had any woman he wanted - your Jordans, Pamela Andersons and Page Three girls of the 16th century," said Killjoy. "There's no way he would have settled for a queen with baps like two Viennese whirls on a breadboard."

lounge

And the Professor went on to single out the 2007 series *The Tudors* for particular criticism. "There wasn't an actress in that show who filled her bra properly," he continued. "In particular, the woman who played Catherine Howard was dreadfully miscast."

"This was supposed to be a beauty who caused the King of England to set aside his fourth wife and break a treaty with Germany. But how are viewers supposed to believe all that when they cast a bird who was a 32B at most, and that when she was breathing in?" he said. "It's just ridiculous."

Killjoy has spent decades researching the Tudor period, and can point to many historical sources

Tentpole Tudors: Killjoy has made lifelong study of 16th century bosoms.

to back up his controversial theories. "I have made a particular study of an illuminated manuscript in the British Museum that dates from round about Henry VIII times," he told us. "It's hard to decipher because it's all in twirly Olde English writing, but there's a bit on it that definitely looks like it says 'Anne of Cleves 42DD'."

kitchen

"That's proof enough in my book that olden days women were stacked. They had proper racks on them," he added. "You certainly didn't get many of them to the pound in the 16th century, I can tell you."

The Professor has also perfected a revolutionary technique of anatomical reconstruction to allow modern people to come face to face with Tudor breasts. "A bit like when those archaeologists on the telly recreate what someone looked like from their skull, I can do the same with their tits," he told us.

conservatory

"I build them up using plasticene until they're just right, with big nips and everything. And every time I do it, they come out as proper big hooters, like something out of a porn mag."

"If they'd let me use my technique on some of the medieval women's skellingtons they've got at Ashmolean Museum, they'd soon see that I was right. But they won't let me in, the fucking snobs," he said.

library

The professor told reporters that it was a sad fact that *Carry On Henry* was actually a much more faithful recreation of what life was really like in Tudor times than any of these modern, supposedly authentic drama series. "Seeing Barbara Windsor

Lovely Babs: Carry On Henry actress Windsor's breasts (left, left and right) were more historically accurate than those of her modern counterparts (above, left and right) says professor.

with her knockers jiggling about like two puppies fighting in a sack gives modern viewers a much more accurate idea about court life in 16th century England than all these birds with their Dutch Alps in *Wolf Hall* and *The Tudors* put together," he added.

An Oxford University spokesman said that the professor's controversial views did not reflect those of the university's history department. He told us: "We do not necessarily endorse Professor Killjoy's research or conclusions on the subject of the size of womens' breasts in Tudor England."

billiard room

He also pointed out that Sprotborough College, which is run from Professor Killjoy's home at 44 Sprotborough Terrace, Blackbird Leys, was not in any way affiliated to Oxford University.

"For the avoidance of doubt, Sprotborough College is not in any way a constituent college of Oxford University and any degrees conferred by Sprotborough College are not recognised by the University of Oxford," the spokesman added.

Pope's Hat 'fundamentally flawed' say scientists

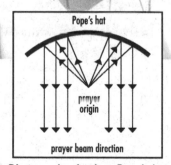

Prayer did you get that hat?: Pope's titfer blocking communication with Almighty.

FOR CENTURIES, the Pope's prayers for universal peace and an end to disease and famine have been comprehensively ignored by God. Despite coming from the Almighty's representative on earth, every fervent intercession on behalf of the world's needy and downtrodden has had no effect whatsoever. And now boffins believe they may have figured out why... it's all down to the shape of the Pontiff's HAT!

"The Holy Father's ceremonial skullcap, or *zucchetta*, is effectively a parabolic reflector just like a radio telescope or satellite dish," said Vatican head of physics Monsignor Galileo Figaro. "It collects the beseechments emanating from the centre of his brain and organises them into a coherent parallel beam."

devil

"Unfortunately, because the Pope has traditionally worn the hat on the top of his head, facing downwards, those prayer beams have been going directly downwards towards the Devil himself rather than upwards to God."

"Quite simply, the Lord has never

EXCLUSIVE!

received a single one of the Pontiff's humble pleas for mercy," he said.

cat

Now Monsignor Figaro has suggested a simple fix that could end all the world's problems in one fell swoop. "The Pope should simply turn his hat the other way up," he told us. "That way, the prayer beams will be aimed directly up into Heaven, where the Lord will be able to pick them up and answer them, in His infinite mercy."

Celebrated atheist Professor Richard Dawkins was quick to take to Twitter and comment on the Vatican announcement.

"*As a scientist I am of course familiar with theory of parabolic reflection,*" he told his 1.17 million followers. "*New @Real_Vatican research re prayer beams very intriguing. #keepinanopenmind.*"

But TV particle physicist Professor Brian Cox was less impressed with Father Figaro's conclusions. "An upturned zucchetto would be a very poor heavenly transmitter of invocations from the middle of the Pope's brain as it is simply in the wrong position to effectively capture his intercessions," he told Radio 1's Reggie Yates.

wonder

"A much more effective approach would be to leave the hat as it is whilst fitting the Holy Father with a much larger, parabolic collar to bounce the original downward prayer beam straight up to Heaven."

However, Monsignor Figaro shrugged off Cox's criticism. "I liked him when he was on keyboards in D:Ream, but when it comes to

theological physics, Cox is simply out of his depth," he told Vatican Radio.

"We've already carried out a highly successful trial where Pope Francis prayed to God for a sunny Whitsun Bank Holiday with his hat on upside down, and it actually turned out very pleasant, so that proves it," he said.

"In nomine Patris et Filii et Spiritus Sancti," he added.

Diagram showing how Pope's hat beam's prayers downwards.

LETTERBOCKS

**Viz Comic, P.O. Box 841
Whitley Bay, NE26 9EQ**
letters@viz.co.uk

ST★R LETTER

□ **AS** someone who is highly allergic to nuts, I am always very careful when eating in restaurants. So, when I visited the toilet of a well-known Kensington bistro between courses last week, I was horrified to look in the mirror and see that my lips were swollen and I had pale, clammy skin. When I tried to speak my voice was weak and reedy. I was just about to call an ambulance when I remembered that I was Michael Gove.

M Gove, Westminster

□ **EVERYONE'S** always going on about it being dangerous to feed bread to ducks because it's bad for their digestive system or something. Well I'm 32 and I fed bread to ducks hundreds of times as a child, and as far as I know they're all still alive.

Swadlincote McBain, e-mail

□ **WHY** do they bother with signs on fire hoses saying that it is not drinking water? The type of person who likes to drink directly from a high pressure fire hose is hardly going to be put off by a little thing like that.

James Huggett, Dubai

□ **IF** I had a time machine, I'd use it to go back to 1970 when bread was just 12p a loaf, which would be a massive saving on my weekly shopping bill. However, I'm not sure if when I brought it back, it would still be fresh or would be a 45-year-old loaf I'd just paid for. If the latter is the case, then I think that even at 12p it's pretty poor value for money.

Renton Dolittle, Surrey

□ **IF** the speed of light is a constant, what's the point squaring it in $E=mc^2$? It's not going to be any quicker. I think Einstein must have been on drugs or something.

J Thorn, Hexham

□ **PEOPLE** often say stuff about things, but I have to disagree with them because of a number of various reasons.

Ornithopter Wang, Silver Spring

□ **DOES** anyone know if Brussels in Belgium is named after Brussels Sprouts or if Brussels Sprouts are named after the Brussels in Belgium? Because if Brussels Sprouts didn't originate in Belgium, this raises a whole host of other questions. If you want my opinion, this needs sorting out, and soon rather than later, if you please.

Tim Buktu, e-mail

□ **ONE** thing I don't understand about Harry Potter is that one of the subjects they study is Mythical Creatures. Then in one lesson they are taken into the forest and come face to face with a hypogriff. In my book it's hardly a mythical creature if you're standing there looking at the bloody thing.

Letitia Ogden-Nash

□ **INSTEAD** of stealing nurses from other countries to prop up the NHS, why don't we simply send UK patients abroad for their treatment? They usually have much better weather than we do, so the patients will have a nice convalescence thrown in.

Richard Mills, Bristol

□ **SPACE** travel indeed. I cannot think of a more boring way to spend a weekend than go to the bloody Moon. I'm sure millions of others share this opinion so I wonder what the so-called space travel boffins will make of their silly little jobs now.

MTA Court, Southsea

□ **SINCE** aircraft waiting to land at Heathrow currently have to circle in a spiral 'holding stack' until there is space for them to land, why don't they simply build the controversial third runway like a giant helter-skelter? It would take up no extra space, and they could generate extra income by charging kids a pound to slide down it on mucky doormats during quiet times.

Nickers, Batley

□ **TO** say bulls get angry at the sight of red is rubbish. My Gran was gored to death by a bull in a field and she was wearing light tan trousers and a blue Pacamac cagoule.

Mitch, Melbourne

□ **I NOTICE** that driving on the right is completely legal in France whereas over here it's illegal. It seems to me that there's one set of laws for some people and a completely different set of laws for other people like the French.

*Mike Hatchard,
St Leonards on Sea*

□ **WHAT** do all of them lazy, workshy shirkers do these days now that power naps have gone out of fashion? Not that it makes much difference. The ones I worked with who took these energy-charging kips were just as lazy and non-productive afterwards as they were before.

Gordon Bennet, Auckland

□ **SINCE** speed humps never have potholes in them, why doesn't the council simply make all the roads out of speed hump material?

Nickers, Batley

□ **AFTER** a series of frankly disgusting farts, have you ever had the girl you're sharing a hotel bed with for the first time shout "If you do that again I'm calling my dad to come and pick me up"? I have.

Orangeman, Florida

□ **WHY** do we still have to use car indicators in this day and age? Surely we should be able to send mind-signals or something to the driver behind telling them which way we're going, like in *Scanners* but without blowing their heads off. Come on scientists, pull your finger out.

Glen Hattersley, Stockport

□ **WHY** don't farmers farm crabs instead of cattle or sheep? Everyone loves eating crabs and because they walk sideways, you only need to put fencing around two sides of the field.

D Cooper, East Grinstead

T★P TIP's

MAKE sex with your wife's more attractive and more adventurous sister last longer by imagining your wife in her place.

Ian Hastings, Hastings

GOING on a family trip but can't fit the dog in the car? Freeze him in the standing position and slot him onto the bike rack on the back. By the time you arrive he will be defrosted and ready to play Frisbee.

Reg, Bristol

POUNDLAND cigarette lighters are a cheap, albeit random and unintentional, alternative to expensive nasal hair trimmers.

Bob Cratchett, Bristol

KEEP flies off your trifles this summer by smearing dog foulage around the rim of the bowl (taking care not to make any go on the trifle).

Fat Al White, Wrenthorpe

BUILDING site workers. Keep your heads cool in summer by putting your woolly hats in the freezer the night before going to work.

Steve Raynor, Nottingham

SAVE money on free-range eggs by buying normal eggs and letting them out when you get home.

Simon Perry, Leicester

EXPERIENCE the thrill of being in the Gendarmerie by simply watching a criminal act take place whilst drinking a glass of red wine and eating some cheese.

Iain Devenney, Oxford

BY using a paint-rolling tray for cat-litter, your moggy can enjoy a choice of shallow or deep end for its number ones and twos respectively.

Doug, Shrewsbury

FRUGAL drinkers. Get that 'plastered' feeling by drinking a bottle of Aldi £2.49 wine and putting on your Mum's glasses.

Fat Al White, Wrenthorpe

NODDING sagely and tacitly agreeing with everything during your boss's afternoon meetings will only gain you favour with higher management if you don't then fall asleep and wake yourself with a loud fart.

AD Phillips, Southampton

BACK IN A SEC JUST GOING FOR A QUICK SLASH

WHILE walking home from work the other day, I happened upon a bicycle whose owner was proudly demonstrating his enjoyment of titwanks. Whether these titwanks are soapy or not wasn't specified. I'd love to know whether any of your other readers have encountered similar references to preferred sexual activities in sticker form?

Jo Minshull, Manchester

MR Minshull (*above letter*) is guilty of overt sexism and homophobia. The owner of the cycle could easily have been a woman who enjoyed titwanks with a lesbian friend. I'm not sure exactly how they would do it, but I would imagine there are plenty of videos demonstrating the practice on the internet if you cared to look for them.

Otto Twelvetrees, Tooting

WHILST Mr Twelvetrees (*above letter*) is correct to point out the sexist and homphobic nature of Mr Minshull's comments, the latter is actually correct in his assumption that the owner of the cycle is a man as it has a crossbar, and ladies' bikes don't.

Pardew Roundman, Goole

AS a devout Buddhist, I firmly believe that the Queen will be reincarnated as a piss-soaked, alcoholic Scotsman, growling and threatening shoppers outside London's finest upmarket stores. That said, I would certainly give him a pound for a can of Special as I think she did a wonderful job under trying circumstances in her previous life.

Tam Dale, Blantyre

MY girlfriend was having a go at me about the state I left the toilet in when she said that cleaning my skidmarks was "the least I could do." As I laughingly informed her, by doing less than her stated minimum, I had proven her statement false, thereby invalidating the premise. Women!

Sam Taylor, London

I'VE always considered the notion of 'social sciences' totally redundant. The idea that humans can be quantified, grouped and stratified to make predictions of our overall behaviour doesn't take into account that everyone is different, with a mind of their own. Yes, it works on a *macro* level, but the *micro* level, being the core of human psychology, severely lets the field down and I for one resent the idea that human behaviour can be predicted. Anyway, I digress. How about that picture of that bloke kissing that bird's arse?

Dr Tom Le Roi, Leeds

* Here you go, Dr Tom

THE government wants GPs' surgeries to open 7 days a week. But GPs only work Monday to Friday, so this means that the surgeries will be open at the weekends with nobody there, and drug addicts will be able to just wander in and help themselves. They clearly haven't thought this one through.

Glen Hattersley, Stockport

WHENEVER Princess Diana appears in the tabloid newspapers, she's always got that same mid-late 1990's hairstyle. We love you, Lady Di, but get with the modern fashions.

Ian Andrews, Hastings

THE name of the late *Star Trek* Dr McCoy actor Deforest Kelley always makes me think of a girl called Kelly having her overgrown bush shaved off. Do any other readers have actors' names which make them think of specifically-

named women having their pubic hair removed?

Jock Boofuss, Newport

WHEN we were at school, my mate Alan said his perfect job would

SHE SAID YES!

VIZ READERS are nothing if not romantic, and you've been writing in your droves to tell us about all the weird and wacky ways you popped the question. Here's a selection of the best letters we've received...

I THOUGHT it would be romantic to propose to my girlfriend on the big screen at a major sporting event. Unfortunately, the only one I could get tickets to was the World Snooker Championship, and every time I stood up to announce my proposal, I was aggressively shushed by the referee. On my sixth attempt, I was forcibly escorted from the premises by the entire security team.

Marvin Eekamouse, Thirsk

I AM bang into religion, so I decided to enlist God's help when I popped the question. My bird and I were going out on a moonlit stroll, so I prayed to the Almighty to make the stars spell out, 'WILL YOU MARRY ME?' above us. When she looked up, though, the stars were in exactly the same position they're always in, and I felt a right twat. She split up with me soon afterwards, and to be honest I still haven't forgiven God to this day.

P Francis, Vatican City

ME and my missus are Scrabble fanatics, so I'd always planned to propose during a game by using the tiles to spell out 'MARRY ME'. However, in 55 years of playing against her, I've never once picked out the requisite letters and, as such, we remain unmarried, and living separately with our parents, to this day.

Nigel Redrat, Bury

MY girlfriend used to love horses, so I thought it would be nice to involve her favourite animals when I popped the question. We went out for a picnic at a nearby stable, and I arranged for a beautiful chestnut stallion to trot over to us wearing a sign round its neck that said 'WILL YOU MARRY ME?' Unfortunately, she misunderstood and assumed that the horse was the one proposing. Before I could correct her, she had tearfully accepted, and was kissing the creature passionately right before my eyes. The two of them have been happily married for six years now, so I suppose all's well that ends well.

Ian Panhead, Tunbridge Wells

Want to tell us how YOU popped the question? Write in to 'She Said Yes!' Viz Comic, PO Box 841, Whitley Bay, NE26 9EQ. There's a happy marriage of 40 years for every one we print.

be "holding a stop/go sign at the roadworks while smoking a joint." Fifteen years later I drove past him and he was doing exactly that. It just goes to show, that if you keep reaching for the stars, maybe your dreams CAN come true.

R Vistaboofay, e-mail

JOHN Lennon hasn't recorded a new album since 1980 and yet he's still popular. If I hadn't worked for 35 years my boss would go apeshit.

Alan Farley, Garn

Miriam ANSWERS YOUR BUTTON PROBLEMS

Dear Miriam,

I SUFFER from phobias of three things: elephants, soft cheese and buttons. Whilst the first two don't present much of a problem most of the time - I merely avoid zoos, circuses and the fridge where they keep the Dairylea in the supermarket - avoiding buttons is a problem. I find myself coming into contact with them several times a day, when I invariably come out in a sweat, have a panic attack and faint. Could you suggest a way that I could get over my phobia of buttons, as it is threatening to affect my everyday life?

Mrs Gates, Haddington

Miriam writes: *A phobia is an irrational fear, and your fear of buttons may be perfectly rational, as you may have been killed by a button in a previous life. Perhaps you choked to death on one in Victorian times, or maybe one went in your eye whilst you were riding a motorbike in the First World War, causing you to crash into a tree. Notwithstanding, the best way to conquer your terror might be to try controlled incremental exposure. Start by handling the smallest buttons you can find - for example the ones off a shirt collar or a teddy bear's dungarees - before moving on to gradually handle larger and larger ones. Eventually you will be able to handle a really big button, such as one off an old lady's coat without having an adverse reaction.*

Dear Miriam,

THE SEVEN button has fallen off my calculator and I've got a load of sums to do. I'm worried that if the number seven comes up in one of the sums I won't get the right answer. I'm 33, my husband is 32 and we've been married for 5 years.

Anxious, Basingstoke

Miriam writes: *Don't worry. You can still get the right answers even without the seven button! For adding sums, use three plus four instead of seven, and for take aways use nine minus two. For percentages or decimals do the same but divide your answer by a hundred.*

MIRIAM'S BUTTON HELPLINES

Button come off hubby's shirt	01 811 8055
Button come off wife's blouse	018 118055
Boyfriend keen to try zipping	01 81 18055
Caught by girlfriend doing velcro	018 118 055
Hubby addicted to toggles	01811 8 055
Vaginal dryness tips to drive your man wild	01 81 18055

CORBYN'S A-BOMB THREAT!

A SHOCKING top secret Labour Party document leaked to journalists reveals how, if he becomes Prime Minister in 2020, Jeremy Corbyn intends to launch a devastating nuclear strike within 15 minutes of taking office. But his target won't be a legitimate foreign enemy, such as ISIS, the USSR or asylum seekers... *it will be his own country!*

Despite campaigning against nuclear weapons for years and pledging to scrap Trident, Corbyn is set to initiate a devastating attack against the British people and the institutions he hates, using the country's massive stockpiles of atomic weapons.

"He's adamant that he's going to kill us all and nobody's going to talk him out of it," a Labour source told us.

button

"As soon as he gets inside 10 Downing Street Jeremy's going to press that red button and unleash Hell," the source continued. "The whole country will be flattened within a few minutes and the death toll will run into the tens of millions."

Experts believe that the few who somehow survive the initial blast will migrate underground, living in the sewers to avoid the intense heat of the irradiated nuclear desert above.

planet

These blind, naked mutants, known as "the children of Corbyn" will live in the shadows, covered in festering sores and using their acute hearing to hunt rats that they will then hungrily devour, feasting on their still warm flesh.

telegraph

And if that's not bad enough, when the supply of rats dries up, they will be forced to turn to cannibalism to survive, feeding wretchedly in the darkness on each other's still twitching corpses. And it is this prospect that has caused consternation amongst some Labour MPs.

"Turning Britain into a nation of sewer-dwelling, blind, mutant cannibals was not something we mentioned in our last manifesto," Shadow Cabinet member Diane Abbott told *The Daily Politics*'s Andrew Neil. "And if Jeremy insists on pursuing this controversial policy, I will have no hesitation in starting to think very carefully about whether or not I would wish to retain my position as a member of his front bench team," she added.

However, Shadow Home Secretary Andy Burnham stressed that any government decision to launch a nuclear attack on Britain would not be taken lightly. He told *Mascara World* magazine: "Jeremy won't be making any snap judgements about whether he will or won't press the red button until he has listened carefully to both sides of the argument."

express

"Having said that, as Prime Minister, the final decision will be his, and I will back him in whatever course of action he eventually decides to take," Mr Burnham said.

hut

Corbyn yesterday remained tight-lipped when pressed by reporters to reveal his nuclear armageddon plans. "You'll just have to wait and see," he told *PM*'s Eddie Mair.

Armageddon: *Nuclear blast crater (left above) and a post apocalyptic city (left below). Scenes like these could be commonplace as Corbyn plans to launch nuclear strike on his own country.*

Countdown to DOOMSDAY

How Corbyn's plan to destroy us all will unfold, minute by minute...

MAY 7TH 2020... 22:00
Polls close across the country

MAY 7TH 2020... 22:01
First result in - Sunderland South

MAY 8TH 2020... 07:30
Cameron concedes defeat following landslide victory to Labour

MAY 8TH 2020... 09:30
Jeremy Corbyn arrives at Buckingham Palace

MAY 8TH 2020... 10:00
Queen invites him to form new government

MAY 8TH 2020... 10:30
Corbyn arrives at 10 Downing Street and chats with Downing Street staff and civil servants

MAY 8TH 2020... 10:43
Corbyn requests secret nuclear launch codes

MAY 8TH 2020... 10:44
Corbyn changes all target co-ordinates to cities around Britain

MAY 8TH 2020... 10:45
Corbyn presses button to launch nuclear strike and retreats to underground bunker

MAY 8TH 2020... 11:00
Warheads land simultaneously in 69 UK cities, killing 99% of population in the initial blast

MAY 8TH 2020... 12:00
Corbyn hosts lunchtime champagne reception for Vladimir Putin, Robert Mugabe, Abu Hamza and Sepp Blatter in reinforced concrete bunker

"I won't climb into bed with Murdoch"

LABOUR leader *Jeremy Corbyn* last night snubbed *Sun* owner *Rupert Murdoch* after turning down an invitation to a sleepover his house.

The new Labour leader was playing with his Lego when the millionaire press baron called and asked Corbyn's mum if Jeremy wanted to go for a sleepover at his Chipping Norton mansion.

friends

"Murdoch said he had just got a new PS3 and wondered if Jeremy wanted to come over and play on it,"

said Ada Corbyn, 104. "He was having a few friends over, including Alexander Lebedev and Richard Desmond." Murdoch said that he only had one bed, but if he wanted to sleep over, they could all get in it and make a den.

cheers

However, Mrs Corbyn explained to the humble press baron that Jeremy didn't want to come as he believed it a crime that the monopoly of the media, not the electorate, was instrumental in determining governmental policy, and he had some homework to do on a speech.

~*Corbyn*

Never Mind the Diabolics...
Is Corbyn Beelzebub?

The Lord of Darkness: Could Jeremy Corbyn secretly be the Devil Incarnate?

EVERYBODY agrees that *Jeremy Corbyn* is evil, but could it be that he is actually Satan himself, the Lord of Misrule come up from his infernal abode of Hades to wreak havoc upon the electorate? Now, Devil expert and Archbishop of Canterbury *Dr Justin Welby* sets about examining Corbyn's many diabolical qualities to discover once and for all if the Labour leader is, as many believe, the Devil Incarnate.

BEARD

Like the Devil, Corbyn has a beard. Although the Labour leader's trim, grey face fanny is markedly less pointy than that of his mephistophelian counterpart, it nevertheless puts him in company with a selection of the world's most evil people, including Osama Bin Laden, the Yorkshire Ripper and Saddam Hussain when they found him hiding in that hole.

Mark of the Devil: 555/666

HORNED-NESS

From little bumps to giant, curly ram's horns like Tim Curry had in *Legend*, the Devil is always pictured with horns growing out of his head. Whilst Corbyn apologists would undoubtedly point to the fact that their leader doesn't have horns on his head as evidence that he isn't Satan, note how he often wears a Breton cap: a piece of headwear easily big enough to conceal a small pair of horny protuberances, like off a young Hellboy. The jury's still out on this one.

Mark of the Devil: 333/666

TAIL

The Labour leader's bang to rights on this one, for as a foetus Corbyn possessed a long tail, just like Beelzebub. And it gets worse for the member for North Islington, for he's still the proud owner of a small tail - or coccyx - at the base of his spine. Vestigial, only visible on X-rays and without a triangle on the end it may be, but a tail is a tail.

Mark of the Devil: 444/666

CLOVEN HOOVES

It's impossible to know for certain whether Corby possesses the tell-tale goat-like feet of the purgatorial Master of Abbadon, but all the evidence points towards it. Cloven hooves would be enormously uncomfortable in normal shoes: Is this why Corbyn notoriously favours sandals when out and about on his demonic parliamentary business? Of course, cloven hooves would be visible through his sandals and would give away his true identity, thus harming his political career. Perhaps this is why, rather unfashionably, he wears socks with his sandals.

Mark of the Devil: 555/666

WALKING BACKWARDS

According to *The Book of Revelation*, the Devil walks backwards, whilst on TV footage Corbyn seems to have mastered the technique of walking forwards in order to throw us off his Brimstone-infused scent. However, it is highly likely that he does indeed occasionally walk backwards, such as when carrying a sofa up some steps with a friend who is moving into a flat, or when moving a wardrobe out of a bedroom that is going to be carpeted.

Mark of the Devil: 666/666

REDNESS

All images of the Devil show him as being scarlet red, and red is a colour that has featured prominently throughout Corbyn's life. It's the colour of his political party's flag, his favourite vegetables, tomatoes, and the colour of his favourite football team, Arsenal. Also, if he spends too long in the sun, the opposition leader's skin reverts to a diabolic, bloody hue.

Mark of the Devil: 108.336/666

Corbyn's Satan Ratin':

With a final score of 2661.336 out of a possible 3996, Corbyn's Devil Probability Factor comes out at exactly **66.6%**. Sounds familiar? You bet. For as it is written in the Book of Revelation 13: 11-18: *"Let him that hath understanding count the number of the Beast: for it is the number of a man; and his number is six hundred threescore and six or 66.6%, and his name shall be called Beelzebub who is Lucifer that is called the Devil."*

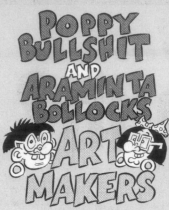

POPPY BULLSHIT AND ARAMINTA BOLLOCKS ART MAKERS

HI ARAMINTA. READY FOR ANOTHER DAY GRAFTING AT THE CREATIVE ARTFACE?

YES, POPPY. AND I'M SURE IT WILL LEAVE ME COMPLETELY DRAINED.

WHAT ARE YOU WORKING ON?

THIS. I SIT ON A BEAN-BAG FOR 5 HOURS WITH MY EYES SHUT.

WOW!

I'M STATICALLY INTERACTING WITH THE BEAN-BAG, SETTING UP A TENSION THAT EXPLORES THE COMPLEX RELATIONSHIP BETWEEN PERSONHOOD AND ENVIRONMENT...

...SOMETHING LIKE THAT, ANYWAY.

HOW'S IT GOING?

WELL, I NEED £25,000 TO TAKE IT TO EDINBURGH...

HOW MUCH HAVE YOU BEEN PLEDGED SO FAR ON YOUR ARTS CROWD-FUNDING SITE?

LET'S SEE...

THREE POUNDS...

...FROM MY MUM.

GOD. I HATE THE PUBLIC. THEY'RE SO BLINKERED.

YES. THEY'RE NOT PREPARED TO FUND US, YET THEY'D SOON COMPLAIN IF THEY FOUND THEMSELVES IN A WORLD WITHOUT ART MAKERS.

I'LL JUST HAVE TO COME UP WITH A NEW PROJECT, I SUPPOSE...

CUP OF TEA?

GOOD IDEA.

I'LL SORT OUT THE ARTS KICKSTARTER WEBSITE AND YOU FILL IN THE ARTS COUNCIL LOTTERY MONEY APPLICATION FORM FOR MATCHING FUNDING.

RIGHT.

SHORTLY... HOW DOES THIS SOUND? "TEA FOR TWO? EXPLORES THE COMPLEX RELATIONSHIP BETWEEN A PAIR OF WOMEN AND A HOT BEVERAGE. IT IS A JOURNEY IN SEARCH OF A DESTINATION THAT AVAILS OF ITSELF WHILST MAKING NO ARGUMENT FOR ITS OWN MEANING."

YOU'RE ALLOWED FORTY WORDS IN THAT BOX, POPPY.

"...IS A DIALECTICALLY METAPHYSICAL JOURNEY IN SEARCH OF A... BLAH-BLAH..." THERE.

I'M FINISHED HERE TOO.

"TEA FOR TWO? IS A THOUGHT-PROVOKING, VENUE-SPECIFIC INSTALLATION THAT CELEBRATES, QUESTIONS AND ULTIMATELY AFFIRMS ORDINARINESS VIA THE MEDIUM OF SHARED HOT DRINKS IN CUPS, WITH MILK AND SUGAR..."

"ART MAKERS POPPY BULLSHIT AND ARAMINTA BOLLOCKS (UK) INDULGE IN A SUPERFICIALLY TRITE DIALOGUE ABOUT THE PREVIOUS NIGHT'S TV, WEAVING COMPLEX LAYERS OF MEANING INTO THEIR VAPID OBSERVATIONS WHILST DRINKING TEA..."

"...THE SEEMING BANALITY OF TWO WOMEN TALKING ABOUT EMMERDALE WHILST DRINKING TEA BELIES AN UNSPOKEN TAPESTRY OF MEANING THAT UNDERPINS THEIR DISCOURSE, CAUSING US ALL TO SIMULTANEOUSLY CHALLENGE, CONFIRM, DENY AND QUESTION THE ASSUMPTIONS UPON WHICH WE CONSTRUCT OUR EXISTENCE."

"WE NEED £25,000 IN THE NEXT 5 MINUTES TO BRING THIS UNIQUE ARTISTIC HAPPENING TO LIFE..."

"...PLEDGE £12,500 OR MORE AND WE'LL GIVE YOU ONE OF THE ACTUAL TEABAGS USED IN THE PERFORMANCE."

CLICK!

RIGHT. THAT'S UP ONLINE NOW.

FIVE MINUTES LATER...

TIME'S UP!

PING!

HOW MUCH HAVE WE MADE, ARAMINTA?

NOTHING. NOT EVEN ANYTHING FROM MY MUM THIS TIME.

THE PHILISTINES! WE PUT SO MUCH INTO THAT BID, TOO.

IT WAS A BOLD VENTURE TO BRING ART FUNDING TO THE MASSES AND THE BASTARDS HAVE FLUNG IT BACK IN OUR FACES, ARAMINTA.

PERHAPS THE PEOPLE OF BRITAIN AREN'T READY FOR SUCH A CHALLENGING, THOUGHT-PROVOKING PIECE. IF THEY CAN'T FRAME IT, THEY CAN'T UNDERSTAND IT... >TSK<

NO, POPPY, IT'S NOT THAT...

I'VE JUST LOOKED IT UP ON GOOGLE AND OUR TEA-DRINKING INSTALLATION HAS ALREADY BEEN MADE BY SOME OTHER FEMALE ARTISTS, IT SEEMS.

REALLY?

YES, LOOK... "TWO GIRLS ONE CUP." THEY'VE EVEN MADE A VIDEO OF THE PERFORMANCE.

LET'S SEE.

SQUIT! PLAARP! PLIPPY-PLOP! GUZZLE! GLUG! RETCH! SLURP!

THE BACH THAT DOGGED IN THE NIGHT

CHRISTMAS EVE 1734...
OI! HAVE YOU FINISHED YOUR CHRISTMAS ORATORIO YET, OUR JOHANN SEBASTIAN?

AYE - NEARLY, LUV!

YOU KNOW IT'S GOT TO BE READY IN TIME FOR YOU TO PLAY IT TO ARCHDUKE FRED TOMORROW, DON'T YOU?

OF COURSE I DO! BUT I'M JUST GOING TO TAKE THE DOG FOR A QUICK WALK - I'LL FINISH IT WHEN I GET BACK!

WALK THE DOG MY BAROQUE ARSE! I'M OFF TO THE NEAREST LAYBY TO WATCH A BIT OF DIRTY ALFRESCO SEX! heh-h eh...

TWO MINUTES LATER...
PHWOOAR! THIS IS THE REAL STUFF ALRIGHT!

UH-UH-UH!

AY - THEY'RE PROPER GOIN' AT IT!

GREAT! THE SHOW'S STARTED! I'M GOING TO GET AS CLOSE TO THE FRONT AS I CAN -- GET A PROPER VIEW OF WHATS GOIN' ON!

'SCUSE ME, 'SCUSE ME! ROYAL COURT COMPOSER COMING THROUGH!

OI!

DO YOU BLOODY MIND?

SHOVE
PUSH

UH-UH-UH..! UH-UH-UH!

GO ON SON! GET IN THERE! GIVE IT SOME WELLY!

HE'S A BIG LAD, ISN'T HE, EH?

I WOULDN'T KNOW! I CAN'T SEE NOWT FOR YOUR BLOODY WIG!

AYE! YOU'RE BLOCKIN' US VIEW!

GERTCHA!

GO ON - HOP IT!

OOYA!

UH-UH! UH-UH! UUHH!!

RAT'S COCKS! I CAN'T SEE A BLOODY THING! AND IT SOUNDS LIKE HE'S GETTING TO THE VINEGAR STROKES AND I'M GOING TO MISS IT THANKS TO THIS STUPID WIG!

WAIT A MINUTE... THAT GIVES ME AN IDEA!

SHORTLY...
GET IN! I'VE GOT A GRANDSTAND VIEW - AND JUST IN TIME! HE'S GOT THE JESTER'S SHOES!

UH-UH-UH! UH-UH!

I'LL JUST LEAN IN FOR A BETTER LOOK AT THE CREAM PIE!

WOOAAHH! CHRIST ON A KLAVIER!

EEK!

PLOK

GO ON - PISS OFF!

KICK

IN FACT, PISS OFF THE LOT OF YOU! YOU'VE BROKEN THE GOLDEN RULE - LOOK BUT DON'T TOUCH!

AW!

ME AND THE MISSIS ARE GOING TO FINISH THIS OFF IN PRIVATE!

SLAM!

JS BACH'S LITTLE KNOWN CONCERTO FOR ONE FINGER

XMAS CONCERT

SPLINK! SPLINK!

YER FOOKIN' RUBBISH! BOO! GERROFF!

VOICE OF HIS EXCELLENCY ARCHDUKE FREDERICK...

George Bestial

The day?

I don't do them by the day.

Two hours then.

Fifty quid well spent sugar.

Time for us to explore.

Just need to find a quiet spot...

Always peaceful and cool under the pier.

Cool but *hot*.

Bollocks.

So

FULCHESTER MALL OPEN 7 DAYS A WEEK

Think might be as well heading off the beach sweetheart...

TOILETS ›

Freshen up, I'll be one minute.

CONDOMS

Anyone got change of a tenner?

CONDOMS

You never know your luck George...

rudex
reasonably safe
FRUIT FLAVOUR
x3 lubricated condoms

Megadrug

Kinky.

Ten minutes later

KNOCK KNOCK

BAM!

134

ARCHAEOLOGISTS UNEARTH ARSE!

ARCHAEOLOGISTS working near Hadrian's Wall in Northumberland were celebrating last night after unearthing the most complete Roman arse ever found in Britain.

Hello cheeky: Bottom was discovered at Hadrian's Wall.

The backside, believed to date back to 150 AD, is in almost perfect condition, with buttocks, nipsy and a tintis.

empire

"The arse we have discovered is almost certainly that of a soldier who was stationed at this most northerly outpost of the Roman Empire nearly two thousand years ago," explained dig leader Dr Diggory Leader of the Vindolanda Project.

carriage

"Judging by the cleanliness of the balloon knot, it belonged to a high ranking soldier who could afford Roman lavatory paper," he continued. "Perhaps a Centurion or a Tribune."

cheek

He told us: "Bits of arse turn up all along the Wall from time to time. A bit of cheek here, a ringpiece there, a pile or two, but we've never unearthed anything

Intact bum found on Roman dig

like this before. This dirtbox really is a once-in-a-lifetime find."

sauce

Dr Leader, who is head of Archaeology at the University of Cambridge, previously hit the headlines in 2004, when he discovered an Anglo Saxon bellend whilst excavating at Sutton Hoo, East Anglia, and in 2009, when he unearthed a pair of 38DD Viking tits on a dig in the Shetland Islands.

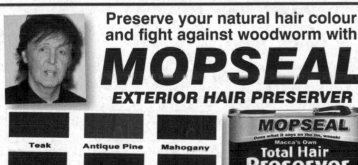

135

137

* WINNER: 2015 PULITZER
PREDICTABLE PUNCHLINE PRIZE

EVERYONE agrees that the National Health Service is the jewel in Britain's crown. When we fall ill, we have the comfort of knowing that, provided we can get past the receptionist, we will be able to get an appointment with the most unpopular doctor at our GP practice within a fortnight. But sometimes we can't wait two weeks, and that's where our local hospital's Accident & Emergency department comes into its own. The waiting room is a hive of activity, with a myriad of busy people each with their own fascinating story to tell. *But who are they? What are they doing? And how long is it since they last slept?* Let's take a peek behind the curtains to find out ...

Who's Who and What?

1 Senior Consultant
This highly experienced trauma specialist is in charge of the whole department. Every decision she makes could make the difference between life and death for an injured patient. She has been on duty for 4 days without sleep and at the moment she is having a conversation with the White Rabbit and the Mad Hatter out of Alice in Wonderland.

2 Chief Administrator
It is this man's job to ensure the smooth running of the hospital; staff have to be paid, expensive medicines have to be bought and buildings and equipment maintained. It is the chief administrator's responsibility to set the budgets and make sure that the books balance. And woe betide him if his health trust fails to meet its financial targets. There will be no second chances. He will be asked to take early retirement with nothing to show for his efforts but an index-linked final salary pension, a generous golden handshake and a knighthood. This will have to tide him over until he is re-hired by the same hospital as a highly-paid management consultant a few weeks later. Health Service budgets are tight, and every financial decision must be thought through carefully. Here, he and several of his senior colleagues are heading to New York to meet a gallery owner to discuss commissioning a sculpture for the hospital foyer.

3 Deputy Chief Administrator

4 Assistant Deputy Chief Administrator

5 Executive Assistant Deputy Chief Administrator

6 Chief Executive Assistant Deputy Chief Administrator

7 Assistant Chief Executive Assistant Deputy Chief Administrator

8 Chief Administrator's Secretary

9 Triage Nurse
It is her job to estimate how quickly you will die if left untreated. Here she is assessing the injuries of a man who has been hit by a car. Rushed in by air ambulance, he now faces a six-hour wait before being seen by a fourth year medical student.

10 Politician
Whichever party he's from, he's here to tell the underpaid, overworked staff that the NHS is safe in his party's hands, and will be dismantled by the opposition. With his shirt sleeves rolled up and his tie tucked in to avoid bringing germs into the hospital, he is accompanied by a mob of Fleet Street's finest, fresh from the pub and dressed in dirty shoes and anoraks.

Can You Spot...?

☐ ● A patient in a gown who has brought his drip down from the Intensive Care Unit to have a fag by the door.

☐ ● The surgeon who will be performing the above patient's heart-lung transplant also having a fag.

☐ ● Medical students being stomach-pumped following a sponsored pub crawl to raise money for a new stomach pump.

☐ ● A man who came in with a broken toe and is now having a heart attack due to worrying about his car getting clamped in the car park.

☐ ● A children's television presenter with a milk bottle stuck up his bottom.

☐ ● A tramp asleep across some chairs.

☐ ● A junior doctor asleep across some chairs.

☐ ● A nurse having her bottom pinched by drunken man.

☐ ● A nurse having her bottom pinched by an ambulance driver.

☐ ● A nurse having her bottom pinched by a senior consultant.

☐ ● A nurse having her bottom pinched by a man whose job it is to stop medical staff being assaulted.

They Do at the A&E Department

139

No Thanks for the Memories!

Pipe dream: Bert Haddock's lifetime ambition of getting his pink oboe played by his missus has been repeatedly thwarted by events.

IMAGINE being able to recount exactly what happened on ANY given day in history! It sounds impossible, but a retired gas worker from Yorkshire has discovered a unique mind trick that allows him to remember what he was doing on some of the biggest days in world history... *by linking them to his failure to get a blow job.*

OAP Bert is Real-life History Man!

During his long life, Keighley-born *Bert Haddock*, 97, has witnessed the key historical events of the the 20th century. From man landing on the moon to the fall of the Berlin Wall and 9/11, he has lived through a turbulent century of world-changing news.

But for him, every momentous date in history is tinged with sadness, as it has always scuppered his plans to experience the unworldy pleasure of mouth-to-penis stimulation.

Paris

"I had always really fancied having one of those blow jobs they talk about," he told us. "One of the blokes at work told me he'd had one in Paris at the end of World War I and it sounded champion."

"Unfortunately though, I must be the unluckiest bloke in the world when it comes to getting noshed off," said Bert. "Me and the wife had first planned to have one in September 1939 and she was just about to get started when war was declared and I got sent to the front line."

"What with all the excitement of me getting conscripted and being posted overseas, we forgot all about my blow job," he added.

Perez

Even at the end of hostilities in 1945, as the rest of Britain celebrated, Bert was still on fellatio rationing. He told us: "It was the same after the war as well. Me and the missus were so busy

Historic events: The Cuban Missile crisis, the assassination of JFK and man taking his first step on the moon. The world watched these events open-mouthed, except Bert's wife, whose mouth remained firmly closed.

making ends meet that we simply didn't have time for chewies, so we decided to leave it for a bit until after the Cuban Missile Crisis."

But even though a nuclear confrontation between East and West had been narrowly averted, the swinging sixties failed to mark the end of the cold war on Bert's cock.

He told us: "On November 22nd 1963, I happened to be on an early finish at the cokeworks and the wife had finally agreed to give it a go. My fly was almost half-unzipped when news came on the TV that the American president had been shot in Dallas."

Hulkenberg

"Typical! I couldn't believe it," said Bert. "The mood didn't seem right after that so we decided to leave it once again."

"Nowadays, when people ask me what I was doing when I heard about JFK, you should see their faces when I tell them I was failing to get sucked off once again!"

After that, what with the Moon landings, the assassination of Bobby Kennedy and the 1970 World Cup, Bert's chances of getting a banjo cleaner were few and far between.

Spidermanenberg

He told us: "It wasn't until the mid-1970s that I decided I would book a few weeks off work and finally get serious about being sucked off."

"I'd locked the front door and my wife had disconnected the phone, but just as we were about to start one, the neighbours shouted through the letterbox that the last American troops had left Vietnam. I tried to ignore it but the moment had gone," he continued.

"January 1982 was the next window in the calendar, but sadly my wife said she no longer felt like sucking me off because Mark Thatcher had gone missing in the Sahara Desert," he added.

Mime Kampf
A. Hitler

DANKE

DANKE

DANKE

WHAT DO YOU THINK IT MEANS?

ER... THAT FROM THE TEARS OF WAR THE DAILY BREAD OF FUTURE GENERATIONS WILL GROW?

OH YEAH! I TOTALLY GET IT NOW!

FRUT'BUNN THE MASTER BAKER & HIS GINGERBREAD SEX DOLLS

FRUBERT, DEAR... WHERE ARE YOU OFF TO AT THIS HOUR.?

ERM... I'VE JUST REMEMBERED THAT I LEFT A SCONE OUT EARLIER AT THE BAKERY. I DON'T WANT IT TO GO STALE OVERNIGHT.

BUT TONIGHT IS LITTLE CHELSEA'S RECORDER RECITAL. SHE'S BEEN PRACTISING FOR WEEKS. SHE WAS SO HOPING YOU'D COME.

OH, SO THAT'S IT, IS IT.? YOU'D LIKE ME TO GET A REPUTATION AS THE KIND OF BAKER WHO SERVES STALE SCONES, WOULD YOU...?!

YOU KNOW WHAT THEY SAY: A STALE SCONE ONE DAY, A REVOKED BAKING LICENCE THE NEXT. I SUPPOSE THAT'S WHAT YOU WANT, IS IT? YOU'D LOVE THAT, WOULDN'T YOU?

NO, FRUBERT. OF COURSE NOT. IT'S JUST...

RIGHT THEN. SEE YOU LATER.

SLAM!

HEH-HEH! DID I BOLLOCKS LEAVE A SCONE OUT! I'M ACTUALLY OFF OUT TO MEET A HOT PASTRY SLUT I'VE HOOKED UP WITH ON "GINGR"— THE NEW BAKER/GINGERBREAD LADY DATING APP... IT'S ACE!

PHWOOAR! SHE'S A BIT OF ALRIGHT AND NO MISTAKE!

gingr
NAME: JESSICA
AGE: 21
VITAL STATISTICS: 36 DD MERINGUE BREASTS
HOBBIES: MODELLING, BLOWJOBS, CASUAL SEX WITH BAKERS

I CAN'T WAIT TO BLOW MY FILTHY HUNDREDS AND THOUSANDS ALL OVER HER INNOCENT YOUNG DOUGHNUT..!

≡SLURP!≡

VROOOOM!

SHORTLY...

SCREEECH!

Red Lion

HALF SEVEN! I'M BANG ON TIME!

WHERE IS SHE?! DON'T TELL ME SHE'S STOOD ME UP, THE B...

AH! THANK GOD FOR THAT... THERE SHE IS, OVER BY THE BAR!

WHY HELLO THERE, MY DEAR... YOU MUST BE...

...JESSICA!?

WHAT THE...?! WHAT THE HELL IS THIS?!

THIS PICTURE MUST HAVE BEEN TAKEN TWO BLOODY DECADES AGO! 21 MY BAKER'S ARSE— YOU'RE 40 IF YOU'RE A DAY!

...AND 36 DOUBLE D..?! I TAKE IT THE DD STANDS FOR "DROOPY DUGS"?! AS FOR THE MODELLING, YOU'D BUCKLE THE BLOODY CATWALK AS SOON AS YOU CLAMBERED ONTO IT..!

YOU'RE LUCKY I'M A REASONABLE MAN, JESSICA. I COULD HAVE YOU UP IN COURT FOR BREACH OF THE TRADES DESCRIPTIONS ACT!

APPS LIKE GINGR ONLY WORK WHEN PEOPLE ARE TOTALLY UP-FRONT ABOUT THEIR APPEARANCE AND PERSONALITY. I AM NOT A SHALLOW BAKER, JESSICA—I LIKE GINGERBREAD TARTS OF ALL SHAPES, SIZES AND AGES—BUT THE ONE THING I CAN'T ABIDE IS DISHONESTY.

gingr
NAME: FRUBERT
AGE: 22
VITAL STATISTICS: 13 INCH COCK
HOBBIES: BODYBUILDING, TANTRIC SEX, OVERSEEING BILLION POUND BUSINESS EMPIRE

141

Scum mothers who'd have 'em

2.47am

BANG BANG BANG BANG BANG

Mum! What a nice surp—

Lemme in.

I need to kip here.

Oh – ah, er, of course, yes, I'll fix up the sofa.

Sofa? Fuck off, I'm your mother!

Who is it at this hour?

Mum, love...

Am fuckin' movin' in!

It's *three* in the morning.

I know, but she'll be asleep soon – she's pissed.

WAAAH!

You'll be nice and comfy mum, is a big sofa...

So... Have you left the B&B for good then?

Yeah, fancied a fuckin' change.

What about Chantelle, your friend across the landing?

I haven't got no friends across fucking nothing.

BANG BANG BANG BANG BANG

If that's that cunt Daz I ain't here.

H-hello Daz.

Where is she?

Not here, I'm afraid.

What the *fuck* do you want?

I didn't fuck Chantelle.

How come she knows about the scars on yer arse then?

Fuck knows, she must've seen me arse somehow.

She said you stuck it up *her* fuckin' arse.

Lying slag.

She said you said cunts were fuckin' shit after prison.

Word for word what you said to me...

Alright I fucked her. Happy?

Soz.

Can you *please* ask them to be *quiet*?

WAAAH!!

Fuckin' bastard!

You dirty fucker!

You dirty fuckin' arse fucker cunt bastard!!

Please mum, can you try and keep it –

DAZAFUCKINLUVYA!!

– down...

LOVE them or hate them, you just can't ignore them. And you might think you know everything there is to know about them. But do you really? Here's...

10 THINGS YOU NEVER KNEW ABOUT PIERS

1 THE world's first pier was begun in Brighton in 1871 by then Lord Mayor Samuel Henry Soper, who intended to build "The Wonder of the Age - A Magnificant and Splendid Walkway to Bestraddle the Sea, Being A Bridge to France." However, he ran out of money after 1,700 feet. But 'Soper's Folly,' as it was known, proved popular with holidaymakers who each paid just a farthing to walk its length and 8 guineas for an ice cream at the end.

2 THE word pier comes from the Scandanavian verb 'piør' which means 'to burn down for insurance purposes.'

3 IN 1992 six-year-old Dilwyn Hughes broke the world record for the biggest post-sweets pier puke. Fuelled by 6 sticks of rock, 15 candy flosses, four ice creams and two bags of greasy fried doughnuts, all washed down with six gallons of milkshake, it clocked in at a massive 224 cubic litres! Prior to being sick, Hughes had been on the bendy slides... *18 times!*

4 THE world's smallest pier was only eighteen inches long. The decking planks were made from matchsticks and a miniature doll's house was used for the end of pier-pub. It was opened by world's smallest man, Calvin Phillips, but sadly was destroyed later that day when it burnt down. The owner went on to collect the world's smallest insurance payout.

5 AT the end of every pier in the UK you'll see men fishing. And if they all look familiar, that's because they all have the same defeated and destroyed souls from years of hopelessly sitting in the same place, contemplating life's miserable trudge. The ennui caused by constantly dashed dreams is reflected in the blankness behind their weatherbeaten faces. None of them has ever caught a fish.

6 THE world's longest-running End of the Pier Show began on Blackpool's North Pier in 1935 with *Eric's Happy Organ Funtime*... and is still going! So far there have been eight different Erics, manning a slightly-too-loud Wurlitzer Organ in shifts. Nearly eight CDs of popular music hall hits have been sold over that period, and an estimated 2.6 million people have winced and shifted their deckchairs a few feet further away from the din.

7 YOU might think that by walking to the end of a pier, you'd get a closer look at the horizon. But you'd be wrong. That's because the horizon is always 27 km away, and however far you walk along a pier, it simply moves back by the same distance. So they are utterly pointless.

8 IT is estimated that enough piers to make a football pitch the size of Wales to the moon and back are burnt down by their owners for insurance purposes every day.

9 BECAUSE of their isolation, piers are a favourite meeting place for people who don't want to be seen. In fact, at any one time, 83% of the people on a pier are either men and women conducting extra-marital affairs, drug dealers or spies.

10 BECAUSE they stick out into the sea, piers are not technically part of the United Kingdom and so are not subject to the same laws as mainland UK. The pier owners can implement any laws they like. Many piers have a year round dog ban, and if you keep your car on the South Pier at Bournemouth, you won't have to pay road tax. On the Queens Pier in the Isle of Man, meanwhile, homosexuality is still illegal and carries a sentence of forty lashes with the birch and up to five years in prison.

BIG VERN

KNOCK! KNOCK!

Hello Vern. Are you moving house?

Too right, Ernie. I'm sellin' ap an' movin' to the Costa del Crime.

In fact, the estate agent's showin' a young couple rahnd the gaff now, Ernie.

As you can see, this property offers plenty of scope for improvement.

For example, you could un block this old chimney breast and make room for an open fire.

Eh!? Wot's 'e on abaht, Ernie? Make room fer a fackin' wot!?

Open fire.

Right you are, chief.

BLAM! BLAM! BLAM! BLAM! BLAM! BLAM!

I'M TOO SEXY FOR MY JOB!

Do ya think I'm sack-sy?: Fred has been fired from every job his local labour exchange has found for him due to the curse of his powerful erotic allure.

A LINCOLNSHIRE man is being forced to claim £130 per week in benefits because he is simply *TOO SEXY* to work. *Fred Mousepractice*, 54, says he has lost *FOURTEEN* jobs in as many months, because his extreme physical magnetism renders him literally unemployable.

The local Job Centre has little difficulty finding jobs for Fred in warehouses, factories and shops, but the 54-year-old manual worker always ends up getting sacked because he is simply too sexy.

"It's ridiculous. I desperately want to work, but I just ooze such eroticism that it's literally impossible for me to hold down a job," Mousepractice told his local paper *The Scrampton Clarion and Bugle*. "Now I've got no choice but to sign on."

doctor

Due to a series of bad backs after an injury he picked up on his last day of school, Fred had been unable to work since the late seventies. He told reporters: "Eventually,

"I'm on benefits and it's not right," says Fred

in 2013 the labour exchange called me in and forced me to have a medical and the doctor said I was fit for work. I was delighted. For the first time in my life I would be off benefits and paying my own way in the world."

mighty

Mousepractice's first job was at a spent fat reclamation plant in Saxilby.

"It was hot work, scraping the congealed fat from big plastic

tubs into the main hopper," he said. "So I decided to strip down to the waist."

"As you can imagine, the grease got everywhere, and the sight of my slippery, oiled-up torso caught the attention of the women in the plant. They couldn't keep their eyes off me, and as a result work went out the window."

"They were all so distracted by my sexiness that they were having erotic fantasies about me and spending half their shifts in the bogs, flicking themselves off," he said.

mickey

The factory foreman, alarmed at the dip in productivity, took Mousepractice to one side and told him he'd have to let him go.

"Officially, I was sacked for stealing money from a charity collecting tin in the canteen. I was gutted. I'd been working

at the place for less than a morning."

"To be fair, I don't deny stealing the money, but it was only around seven quid so it wasn't the real reason I lost my job. The truth of the matter was, I was so sexy that I had simply become a liability in the workplace," he said.

minnie

A similar thing happened in Mousepractice's next job, working the night shift sprinkling cheese onto lasagnas at a factory in Wragby.

"The lasagnas come by on the conveyor belt at a fair old rate, and you've got to be on the ball to get the right amount of cheese on each one," he explained. "But the girls on the production line had something else on their minds... me!"

"It was a skilled job and it required a lot of coordination. You had to drop a handful of grated cheese onto the top of each lasagna as it went past. And to be fair, the girls were very good at it. But when I turned up, all their years of training went to pot."

allegro

"With my muscular arms pumping rhythmically between the cheese bin and the lasagnas, I must have been a sight for sore eyes. In fact I was such a dish that they were like them women off the Coke advert where the bloke comes to mow the lawn, standing there mesmerised, staring at me open-mouthed with undisguised lust."

"A whole night's worth of lasagnas went out without any cheese on," he said.

montego

At the end of the shift, the factory manager came out of his office and handed Fred his cards. But employment law gives workers protection against dismissal for something beyond their control, and Mousepractice's sexiness fell into that category. Another reason was soon drummed up.

"I was told that I was officially

UB Phwooar-ty: Mousepractice is now forced to claim benefits each week because he is simply too sexy to hold down a paid job.

being sacked because I'd been going through the women's lockers when I'd gone for a piss break. Which, in fairness, I had. But both me and the manager knew the real truth."

"I'd only done one shift but once again I was out on my arse."

blue riband

And it was a pattern that was to be repeated. Over the next few months, numerous other employers, alarmed by the way his extreme sexual magnetism disrupted female members of the workforce, also used the excuse of petty theft as a reason to get rid of Mousepractice.

"It was becoming increasingly clear that I was literally too sexy to hold down a job for any length of time," said Fred. "And now my reputation is such that there isn't an employer in the area who'll touch me with a bargepole." As a result the Dunham-on-Trent bachelor has been signing on the dole since November.

banjo wafer

"I suppose I've got no choice. Who's going to employ someone as sexy as me? I'll just have to keep signing on," he added. "You might think that the problem would lessen as I got older, but in fact the opposite is true. When I went grey and a bit thin on top, I just got even sexier than I already was, like George Clooney and Bruce Willis."

"I want nothing more than to be able to work, but I can't see it happening any time soon. This powerful sexiness of mine is a disability," he said.

"In fact, I ought to get extra benefits for it, and a car. And one of them blue badges so I can park on the double yellows outside the betting shop and off licence," he added.

Dripping: The women workers at this fat reclamation plant were too aroused by Mousepractice to work.

144

OUR MILKMAN'S LIBERACE!

The residents of Barnton were the luckiest people in the world, for their milkman was none other than Mr Showbusiness himself...Liberace!

Early one morning, the flamboyant entertainer was making his rounds in his motorised grand piano milk float.

Two pints of gold-top, a carton of Elmlea and a Chopin Nocturne for the Robinsons at number 42. Why, I think that's just sensational, it really is. Isn't that just sensational, ladies and gennelmen.

LIBERACE DIARIES

PLINKY-PLONK! TINKLE-TINKLE!

Morning, Mrs R. Here's your order. It's a delight to serve you folks and I mean that from the bottom of my heart. I really do.

Thank you, Liberace.

Have you seen the news? There was a big bullion robbery at the airport last night.

Oh wow! Gracious me!

Yes. Twenty million pounds worth of gold they got away with.

Twenty million? Why, I've got that much gold on my right hand.

Hnyeh-hnyeh! I'm only kidding, ladies and gennelmen. I'm just messin' with ya.

Yes. The police gave chase, but the robbers just disappeared into the night. Four of them, there were.

My oh my!

Anyway, I gotta be getting on. This milk isn't going to deliver itself, and I mean that most sincerely, I really do.

Liberace set off to make the final delivery of his round - a pint of semi-skimmed and a yoghurt to old Granny Turpin at number 43.

PLINKY-PLONK! TINKLE-TINKLE!

Hello? What's this?

Why, that's odd. That really, really is, ladies and gennelmen.

MILKO, 4 EXTRA PINTS AND 4 EXTRA YOGHURTS PLEASE. Signed Granny Turpin

What would Granny Turpin be wanting with four extra pints and four extra yogurts?

Milko's here.

Smashing. We'll all have a big mug of tea and a bowl of cornflakes.

Mmf! Mmf!

Shut it, lady!

Yeah. As soon as we've all had our breakfast, we'll load this gold up in the motor and scram.

A good milkman develops a sixth sense that tells him when something ain't quite right. And I gotta tell you, ladies and gennelmen, something ain't quite right here.

I just gotta make sure that Granny Turpin's not in some kind of trouble, I really do.

KNOCK-KNOCK!

Yeah, what do you want?

Is Miss Turpin in? I've got a special offer on whipped cream this week - two pots for a pound. I was just wondering if she'd like to place an order.

No, she don't.

I'd kinda like to hear that from Miss Turpin herself, ya know?

Well you're hearing it from us, and we're her grandsons. Now beat it.

It sure was swell meeting you folks, and I'd just like to say...

SLAM!

Hmm. Well, ladies and gennelmen, Granny Turpin's a spinster, so I know that those burly guys were lying when they told me they were her grandsons, but that big pile of gold I spotted through the door tells me who they really are.

*Next Week in **Our Milkman's Liberace:** Mr Showbusiness cracks open a sex trafficking ring whilst delivering a fromage frais to a Bed & Breakfast.*

LETTERBOCKS

DOES anyone know what happened to Golden Grahams? You never see them advertised on telly anymore, and it may possibly be my only claim to fame as my name happens to be Graham. But I suppose, like they say, everyone gets their fifteen minutes of fame.

Graham Jacobssen, London

TODAY, my iron broke and I've got the shits. I don't think the two events are related, however.

John Mason, e-mail

DOES it seem at all fishy to anyone else that Princess Margaret's son calls himself David Linley, even though his mum's surname was Windsor and his dad was the son of the Countess of Rosse, Lord Snowdon, who also used to go by the name Antony Armstrong-Jones? The only other people you see who go around making up loads of different names for themselves like that are on *CrimeWatch*, and the police generally want to speak to them.

B Bloggs, Dulwich

I WANTED to try something new at a recent dinner party, so I decided to serve stuffed peppers having been told they were basically peppers with rice in. However, I misheard and served peppers 'with Ricin.' Fortunately the guests who survived all saw the funny side, particularly as I had burnt the peppers anyway.

Simon Hoffmann, Chichester

"YOU won't fool the children of the revolution" sang Marc Bolan in 1972. He should have told that to my uncle Dave, who made a fortune selling oregano to credulous hippies at the Isle of Wight festival. He also claimed to be a guru, and that his cock had mysterious powers when it was sucked off.

Shane, Belfast

I HAD a close shave the other week. Fortunately, however, it was when I was shaving, so in fact it was exactly what I wanted.

D Cooper, East Grinstead

I WOKE this morning to the wonderful sight of a woodpecker in my garden. By the time I had made myself a cup of tea, it had disappeared. What kind of society do we live in when people are coming into people's gardens and stealing woodpeckers?

JC, e-mail

STAR LETTER

A LOT of people have been outraged recently about that dentist paying thousands of pounds to shoot Cecil the Lion. But for years people have been paying dental fees and lining dentists' pockets, allowing them to afford to pursue these barbaric hobbies. In reality, everyone who has been to the dentist has to share some of the blame for Cecil's death. I have a clean conscience as I have not been to the dentist in 30 years.

Toothless Bob, Whitley Bay

HOW come in olden days, when a couple of blokes were duelling, their 'seconds' would never jump in and say "Come on lads, it ain't worth it," or something like that? They always just stood twirling their moustaches, or whatever.

Lincoln Pratt, Totnes

I KNOW that the ancient Greeks used to put coins over the eyes of their dead to pay the ferryman to take them into the next life. However, I often wonder if they ever came across a right jobsworth bastard if they didn't happen to have the correct change, like what happens a lot with Stagecoach.

Titus Strosin, e-mail

I THINK cricket should cash in on "Harry Potter mania" by giving umpires wands and getting them to wave them about when delivering their decisions during the match. The kids would fucking love it.

Alister Jackson, Dungannon

HOW come, if lions are supposed to be big cats, their young are called cubs, and not kittens? I think some of these "so called" wildlife experts are taking the piss if you ask me.

Jenna Fountain, Luton

WHEN I was younger, I was repeatedly told to respect my elders. Now that I'm 94 you can all go fuck yourself. Apart from Lionel down the road who is 95.

Mr Lewis, Eastliegh

I REMEMBER when I was at school, I once called our history master fatso and got the cane. Thirty or so years later, my son called his deputy head a cunt and got referred for counselling. Just one more example of this country going soft.

P Hall, Dorking

A MATE of mine told me you can earn easy money as one of those blokes holding a 'Golf Sale' sign. So last week I made my own sign and stood all day at the end of the street. I have yet to see a single penny. Can any of your readers help? I've definitely spelled it correctly.

Andy, York

WATCHING an old Frankenstein film the other night where he brings the monster to life, I was appalled by the blatant lack of health and safety. While all the electricity was being generated via the thunderstorm, the roof was leaking badly and water was pouring in. It's a wonder nobody was seriously electrocuted or even killed.

Mary Bish, Totnes

LETTERBOCKS

I OFTEN wonder what would happen if someone suddenly let the air out of a blimp. Someone should try it to see if it whizzes all over the sky making farting noises. Obviously, the pilot would be given a parachute – It's not a completely hare brained scheme, I have actually thought it through.

Gus Kirk, e-mail

I REALLY fancy the actress Sophia Vergara and would like to ask her out. Are any other readers sweet on her or do I get a clear shot?

Roger England, Epsom

MILLIONAIRE presenter Chris Evans recently said he spent £25,000 on an 1966 Alfa Romeo from Italy which he hadn't actually seen, and went on to tell us all "please, never do this." Thanks Chris, I'll bear that in mind when I'm next looking to replace my X-reg Corsa.

Rich Evans, Colwyn Bay

HAS anybody else noticed that all meat that comes from a pig ends in the letter 'n'? Apart from ham. And pork. And sausages. Actually forget about what I just said. I wish I never even mentioned it.

Daniel Charles Lewis, West End

IF camels have to conserve as much water as possible for their epic cross-desert journeys, why do they spit at people who annoy them? Surely a kick in the goolies would be far more water efficient.

Jim Hobson, Blackpool

IT'S all very well having "twelve good men and true," but why not stick a few villains on the jury to even up the odds? They have rights too after all. It's not as if they'd be just acquitting fellow villains, but would also be able to convict innocent men too. Whichever way you look at it, it seems a much fairer system than we have in place at the moment.

Cruz Gibbons, London

IN these times of austerity it really galls me to see mice still eating cheese. I work 48 hours a week, pay my taxes and stamp, and I can't afford to buy cheese.

Brian Flan, Knottingley

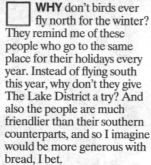

WHY don't birds ever fly north for the winter? They remind me of these people who go to the same place for their holidays every year. Instead of flying south this year, why don't they give The Lake District a try? And also the people are much friendlier than their southern counterparts, and so I imagine would be more generous with bread, I bet.

Jonathan Tovar, Hull

EVERYONE thinks that Marie Antoinette got what she deserved by foolishly suggesting that, in the absence of bread, the starving peasants of Paris eat cake. However, I came home from work starving the other day. I was dying for a sandwich but there was no bread. Then I spotted a piece of Iceland Sticky Toffee Cheesecake left over from Sunday - very nice it was too. So, perhaps she had a point after all.

Earl Akins, Sheffield

I RECKON that all cars should be fitted with a device that detects when all four wheels are off the road, and then plays the *Dukes of Hazzard* air horn music.

I Numnutts, Weymouth

I WENT to see Benedict Cumberbatch playing Hamlet at The Barbican Theatre recently, and it was absolute shite. Seeing as Hamlet was a Dane, I was at least expecting him to have a bash at it in a Danish accent, but he sounded more like an English public schoolboy than a Danish prince. Whenever Danish ex-goalkeeper Peter Schmeichel appears in the media, at least he does a passable Manchester accent.

Vincent Whitley, Notts

IF they were to update the Sisyphus myth to a modern day setting, I think they'd have him folding jumpers in Primark.

Christina Martin, London

MY wife said that giving birth is more painful than having your leg sawn off without anaesthetic, but I'm not convinced. Could any ladies who have given birth and had a leg sawn off without anaesthetic please write in to confirm which was the more painful?

Steve Coulton, Formby

I DON'T know why people refer to getting a wank at the end of a massage as "Happy Endings." I got the wank but then she tried to up the agreed price by a tenner, and a massive argument ensued. An ending certainly, but happy? I think not.

Bryant Bond, London

The MAN in the PUB
Britain's Most Ill-Informed Columnist

I'LL tell you what, did you know there's thirty years worth of undigested meat in your guts. Can you believe it? *Thirty fucking years worth!* Providing you're over thirty, of course. Mate of mine had that colonic irrigation, and when they looked at what come out, there was a beefburger in there that he'd had when he was five.

DID you know you can swim through a blue whale's heart? That's Gospel! And a blue whale's tongue is as big as an elephant. Or a car. An elephant or a car. Biggest animal that's ever lived, your blue whales, fucking massive they are. Bigger than dinosaurs. My brother went swimming with them, in Florida. Cost him a hundred pound for an hour, and if you wanted to take a picture of them in the tank it was extra.

GUESS how many people get ate off sharks every year? Go on, guess. How many people do you reckon get ate by sharks in an average year? 500? A thousand? Ten thousand? I can't remember the exact number, but it's loads less than you'd think. About two hundred, something like that. Maybe three hundred in a bad year. Evil bastards, sharks.

HERE'S a thing. Honey is the only food that doesn't go off. I heard that on Steve Wright. And Burt Reynolds has an eleven inch cock. Right, I'm off for a piss. Any chance of a lift home at closing?

TOP TIPS

CAULIFLOWER heads resting on the surface of glass-topped coffee tables make excellent billowy clouds for earwigs passing beneath.
Nicola Hamilton, Uxbridge

MAKE your postman think he is sexually attractive to dogs by barking wildly behind the door and extending your wife's new lipstick through the letterbox.
David Thompson, Epping

KERB crawlers. Avoid unwanted attention from the law enforcement community by simply driving through your local red light district at 10mph in a hearse.
Iain Devenney, Oxford

TOO frightened to say boo to a goose? Why not start with a pigeon and see how you get on.
Steven Elverrd, Easton

CLEAN and cook dirty new potatoes at the same time by simply putting them in the dishwasher.
Eddie von Burger, Stoke

AVOID embarrassment when falling from a ladder by whistling nonchalantly as you fall to make it look like it was a deliberate action.
John Tunney, Corby

EVERY time you book into a hotel, take a selection of dead light bulbs with you. Then simply swap them with the working ones from your room when you leave to save a fortune on buying new ones for your house.
David Lloyd, High Wycombe

FARMERS. Erect opaque fences to prevent distracted motorists counting your sheep and falling asleep at the wheel.
Spenner, Warrington

COOKING burgers? Don't waste money on expensive frying pans. Simply fill the water nozzle on your clothes iron with cooking oil, set the dial to linen and iron the burger for 2 minutes on each side.
Yabba, Streatham

ROMANTIC comedy filmmakers. Save budget on rain machines for your touching movie climax by filming it in Scotland. Any fucking day is fine.
Peapod Manure, Glasgow

...DEPOSIT PAID, CONTRACTS SIGNED & EXCHANGED, SALE COMPLETE! HERE ARE YOUR KEYS!

OH SHIT! I THINK MY SPARE TYRE HAS GOT A FLAT

149

Many Happy Returns!

RETURNING OFFICER *Reginald Mouseback* has been in charge of election day vote-counting in Rushcliffe, Notts, since the mid-1960s. Over his five decades in the job he has seen many politicians come and go but now, as he prepares to retire, he has decided to put pen to paper and write a humorous account of some of the funniest moments he has experienced during his career. *It Shouldn't Happen to a Duly Appointed Returning Officer* (Sausage Sandwich Books, £0.49 via Amazon download) is an uproarious collection of election day anecdotes that is already in the Top 100 of the South Nottinghamshire Political Non-Fiction e-book charts.

"It's a fantastic job because you only have to work one day every five years," he told us. "Of course, the downside is that the hours are very unsociable; I often don't get home until three or four in the morning."

"And it's also mind-numbingly dull work, endlessly walking round Rushcliffe Leisure Centre with a clipboard, making sure there are no major irregularities in the counting process."

"But there is a lighter side to the job, and that is what my new memoir is about. Once I sat down to start writing, the hilarious memories just came flooding back. There was so much material, my problem wasn't how to fill those sixteen pages, but deciding what to leave out!"

In these exclusive extracts from his book, Mouseback recalls the most hilarious moments from half a century of returning officing.

Key Marginal

❝Election night 1979 is remembered by most people because Mrs Thatcher - perhaps the UK's most divisive Prime Minister - swept to power with a huge majority. But I remember that night for an altogether different reason, and one that still has me splitting my sides with laughter all these years later.

atmosphere

As the polls closed, the atmosphere in the Leisure Centre was electric. The 180 ballot boxes had been brought in from the polling stations across the constituency and were lined up at the front. As returning officer, it was my job to open them so that the count could commence.

I reached for the key in my right hand trouser pocket, but it wasn't there! Immediately, a succession of farcical scenarios began racing through my mind.

bar

Perhaps we'd have to open all the boxes with a tin-opener, or maybe we'd have to embark on a high-speed chase round the borough looking for a set of bolt-cutters. Or would the counting officials be forced to set to trying to fish the ballot papers out through the slot using a butter knife?

Fortunately, I quickly found the keys in the other pocket of my trousers, and was able to open the locks in the usual way. But had they not been there, the scene in that room would have been absolutely hilarious, like something out of *Mr Bean!*"

Squeaking to the Audience

"The most nerve-wracking part of my job is when I have to go up on stage to read out the results of the count on live television. And on the night of the February 1974 general election, I knew that the eyes of the nation were upon me and any embarrassing slip-up would be seen by millions of viewers.

Never mind the ballots: Reginald Mouseback has been a returning officer for half a century.

Election Official Reg Celebrates Fifty Years with Humorous Memoir

It had been a long night. I had only had a couple of sandwiches and some cakes and sausage rolls since tea time and by the time I was due to go on stage and announce the results I was feeling a little faint with hunger.

I must have looked a little peaky, because a St John's Ambulance man standing by the steps asked me if I was okay and gave me a puff from his emergency oxygen bottle.

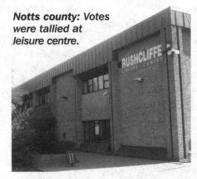

Notts county: Votes were tallied at leisure centre.

The only trouble was, Rushcliffe Leisure Centre was also full of helium cylinders that had been used to inflate all the election night balloons... and it suddenly occurred to me that the bumbling paramedic had accidentally given me a few deep breaths from one of those! My mind raced - I was about to go on live telly to announce the poll results sounding like Mickey Mouse!

To be honest, it was such a hilarious prospect that I was ready to see the funny side and laugh as long and hard as anyone. But in the event, all the helium bottles had been clearly labelled as such, and anyway weren't connected up to a breathing mask like the oxygen cylinder was, so the chances of a mix-up of the sort I had envisaged taking place were in reality almost nonexistent.

pascal

I went up on stage and announced the results - a win for Kenneth Clarke (Conservative) with a majority of 6198 - in my usual voice. But if I had inadvertently taken a few deep breaths of helium first, I'm sure the resulting farcical scene would still be getting re-run on clip-shows today, and probably be as popular as that elephant that did a mess on *Blue Peter*."

Wind of Change

"On election night in Rushcliffe Leisure Centre there will be 70,000 polling papers, all painstakingly counted and arranged into piles for each candidate. So you can only imagine how horrified I was on election night 1997 to spot a giant wind machine in the corner of the room. It had been left over following an indoor kite-flying display earlier in the week, and was frankly an accident waiting to happen.

psi

The consequences of it getting accidentally switched on were only too obvious: 70,000 votes flying everywhere like so much confetti, with 150 desperate counting agents leaping about like dervishes trying to catch them all. Despite the thought of all our hard work going down the drain, I have to admit I was doubled up in laughter at the thought of such a slapstick scene.

Fortunately, the wind machine was safely wrapped up under a tarpaulin and in any case had had the plug taken off. But had that not been the case, and had the device somehow got plugged in and turned on at full power, the chaotic scene would certainly have livened up the BBC's election night coverage.

deadshot

David Dimbleby and Peter Snow would have been unable to read their autocue through their tears of mirth at my side-splittingly shambolic antics as I tried and failed to get near enough to the powerful fan to switch it off. It would have been like a scene from *Total Wipeout* or *Takeshi's Castle* as I was repeatedly blown off my feet and sent sliding helplessly across the shiny floor of Rushcliffe Leisure Centre. ❞

Next week: "Election night 1970 - Oops! The belt holding my trousers snaps just as I step on the stage to announce the poll results on live television in front of millions of viewers. Luckily I am also wearing braces so nothing happens."

The Tea Party's Over

Chimps now prefer cappuccinos to cuppas, say experts

Party animals: Traditional chimps enjoyed a cuppa in the afternoon.

CHIMPANZEES are increasingly choosing to drink COFFEE at their parties rather than the usual tea, according to a new report released this week by the British Zookeepers' Association.

In the past, chimpanzees dressed in children's clothes would happily guzzle down pot after pot of good, strong builder's tea to the amusement of the zoo-going public. But these days, the upsettingly-bottomed apes are increasingly ditching their traditional afternoon cuppa in favour of sophisticated coffee blends popularised by high street chains such as Starbucks, Costa and Caffe Nero.

"Our chimp house now has its own Nespresso barista machine," said Twycross Zoo's Head of Primate Ecology Spanky Chipperfield. "Between the twelve bonobos in our flange, they currently get through about sixty cups a day, and a dozen of the decaff last thing at night. They just seem to love the flavour."

telly

Chipperfield believes that his chimpanzees first got the idea to try coffee from a television commercial. "They have a telly in their sleeping quarters and one night they saw the advert with George Clooney in the middle of Emmerdale,"

George v the jungle: Chimps may be set for showdown with Clooney as the face of premium coffee machine brand.

he told us. "The next day they wouldn't touch their tea. When we got the pot out, they got very agitated. They were leaping about, screaming and baring their teeth and horrible gums."

heroin

"It took us a few minutes to realise that they wanted coffee instead of tea. The head keeper brewed them up a cafetiere of Blue Mountain in his hut and they loved it," Chipperfield said.

system

Over the following weeks, as they tried a variety of different coffee blends, the chimpanzees' taste in coffee became increasingly sophisticated. Eventually, zoo bosses relented and bought them their own £100 Nespresso machine.

"Their favourite blends

are Caramelito, Ristoranto and Vivalto Lungo," said Chipperfield. "And they insist on

using the full-price coffee pods so it's costing us a fortune."

"If you try to fob them off with the cheap knock-off ones from the cash & carry, they'll bite your fucking face off," he added.

cistern

The Twycross apes' coffee-drinking antics have proved such a hit with the zoo-going public that Nespresso have now expressed an interest in featuring them in a forthcoming TV advertising campaign.

A company spokesperson confirmed that, although they were keen to retain Clooney as the face of the brand, a preliminary approach had been made with a view to possibly starring the chimpanzees in a television commercial. "A script has been written," she told us.

u-bend

"If George Clooney can match the chimps' price, the ad will feature him in a bowler hat, moving a piano down some stairs," she added.

GAME OF THRONES WEB LEAK SHOCK!

HBO drama pirated before it's even made

THE eagerly-anticipated eighth season of historical fantasy series *Game of Thrones* has been LEAKED ONLINE before filming has even started. The ten hour-long episodes, which are not even scheduled to begin production until later in the year, were made available online last night, causing huge excitement amongst the show's viewers.

"These episodes weren't even going to be filmed until September, and not broadcast until next Summer, so to see them now is like Christmas coming early," said one *GoT* fan, who said he had watched the whole, as-yet-unmade series back-to-back in a single sitting.

pride

But producer Raggedy Fiveskin said he was deeply disappointed by the uploading of the shows onto a streaming website. "Game of Thrones is a high profile show, and we at HBO pride ourselves on keeping all the twists and turns in the plot secret until the official

Serial thriller: Game of Thrones fans reacted with excitement at news that entire unfilmed season had been leaked online.

broadcast date," he told NBC's French Letterman. "So to have the whole next series pirated in its entirety and posted online before we even start shooting is a big blow for everyone who works so hard on the show."

flange

And director Rip Tarsehole said that the leaking of the next season would undoubtedly put a dampener on proceedings when filming finally gets underway in September. "The actors will be shooting scenes that they know the fans have already watched online," he told E!Online's Clit Squirter. "It will be hard for them to get motivated enough to give their best performance."

But critics had nothing but praise for the leaked shows. "The GoT cast should take heart," said imdb's Ample Labia. "The series that they are about to shoot is the best ever, with some fantastic performances and great plots."

hoop

HBO head Scrotal Pearson said that security would now be tightened up to prevent future *Game of Thrones* series being leaked. "Seasons seven and eight haven't even been written yet, and we'd hate for them to join series six being streamed on one of these pirate sites," he said.

snatch

"You'd think it would be quite easy to protect footage that hadn't even been filmed, but these pirates are a clever and determined bunch," he added.

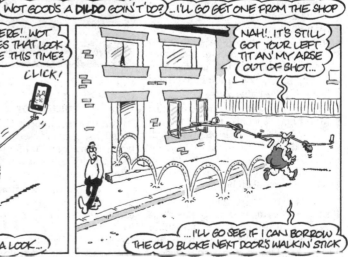

US COPS 'UP IN ARMS' OVER AGE HIKE

POLICE STATIONS across America were in uproar yesterday after the US government announced plans to raise the age at which officers become too old for this shit.

Previously, international police law stated that policemen were automatically deemed too old for this shit at 52. But new legislation set to be introduced throughout the States next week will see that age rise to a whopping 57, with immediate effect.

statement

In a press statement released this morning, US Police Chief of Staff, Sgt Manny Ramdoyal, claimed: "The decision to raise the age at which officers can officially be regarded as too old for this shit is not one we have taken lightly."

"However, there has been widespread feeling over the past few years that officers are becoming better equipped to cope with this

By our US Correspondent
Spiro Paramecium

shit as they enter their mid, and even late, forties."

manager

Ramdoyal continued: "I have personally spoken to several officers who told me they still felt about the right age for this shit well into their fifties."

"We simply cannot afford to lose good men, who are still perfectly capable of dealing with this shit, due to long-outdated and frankly archaic legislation," he added.

However, there has been angry opposition to the move from lawmen across the States.

Detroit detective Hank McMurdoch-Murphy, 51, was one of many embittered, recently divorced, former alcoholic police officers to speak out publicly against the new legislation.

focus

"It's a goddam outrage, plain and simple," McMurdoch-Murphy told reporters outside his office this morning. "I've spent the last few years working in good faith under the assumption that I had just 12 months of this shit left. Now I find I have put up with another six years of it. Jeez!"

***Copper bolt (left):** Shock as age at which US police officers deemed too old for this shit raised by five years and (above) a donut shop.*

He continued: "When I was in my thirties, I used to quite enjoy dangling suspects off tower blocks by their arms and regularly having the DA on my ass."

"These days, though, my lumbago is giving me constant grief and I've got piles like a bag of Babybels. I am simply too old to spend every weekday directly disobeying orders whilst drinking machine-made coffee from a Styrofoam cup."

hawkwind

At a press conference in a donut shop on 53rd and Main, New York cops expressed their outrage to the new proposals. "Why, those up-state pen-pushers have got a god damn noive, sitting on their fat asses all day. I'd like to see them come and put up with this shit like I gotta," said 49 year old Sgt Patrick O'Hoolihan. "Boy, those bozos wouldn't last five god damn minutes," he added.

One Out, All Out!

Splitting heirs: Minor royals planning work to rule.

BRITAIN'S minor royals are planning to launch a series of wildcat strikes over the summer, timed to cause maximum disruption to fetes, country fayres and horticultural shows. *David Carnegie*, Earl of Southesk and General Secretary of NUMRHTIA - the National Union of Minor Royals, Heirs to the Throne and Irrelevant Aristocrats - said his members had been driven to industrial action by unacceptable changes in their work, pay and conditions.

"Many of my members work up to two hours a week attending charity banquets, handing out cups at sporting events and shaking hands," said the Earl, who is 67th in the line of succession. "In addition, we are often expected to work nights, sitting in the royal box at the opera or attending theatre premieres and formal dinners for no extra pay."

butlers

"This action is long overdue. NUMRHTIA members have never gone on strike before, but enough is enough," he continued. "It is time to get our butlers to draw a line in the sand for us and say, 'This far and no more'."

"We're not asking for much, just the abolition of inheritance tax for estates valued at over £100 million and a reduction in the minimum wage to 95p an hour for all domestic

EXCLUSIVE!

staff," he added.

If the first planned strike goes ahead on September 16th, widespread disruption is expected throughout the country, including:

- *Polo matches at the Hurlingham Club unattended by Earls*
- *Prestigious Harrogate Garden Show left patronless*
- *Ceremonial dinners at Sandhurst forced to go ahead without anyone to toast*

But sporadic strike action had already begun last night. In London, the Hon. Alexander Lascelles, Lady Rose Gilman and the Earl of St Andrews mounted a flying picket in an attempt to prevent scab minor royals attending a charity ball at Kensington Palace in aid of the Prince's

Minors' strike timed to turn screw over Summer fete season

Trust. Standing around a solid gold brazier in which they were burning Chippendale furniture, the strikers blocked Rolls Royces trying to deliver guests through the ornamental gates of the 600-room mansion.

blakeys

Several limousines were forced to turn back, unable to deliver their chinless cargoes to the red carpet as the angry protestors gathered round with shouts of 'Poor show', 'It really is appalling' and 'Not an awfully good idea, what-what'. The Marquess of Glencoe was later arrested after a lump of concrete was dropped off a motorway bridge onto the bonnet of a Bentley carrying the Earl and Countess of Redesdale to the Henley Regatta.

Top o' the Mourning

The Hilarious World of Funerals
with the late *Sir Terry Wogan*

● **THE FUNERAL** of 88-year-old Leeds man *Albert Truncheon* was going without a hitch until funeral director Ernest Stoops removed his top hat at the graveside as a mark of respect. As a keen amateur magician - performing under the name of The Amazing Stupendo - the undertaker had that morning accidentally picked up the wrong top hat. As a result, 40 white rabbits leapt out and started hopping around the coffin and mourners. Naturally upset by chaotic scene, the deceased man's widow, Ada Truncheon, burst into tears, and Stoops offered her his handkerchief to dry her eyes. However, he had also put on the wrong tailcoat that morning, and instead handed her the end of a 60-foot long string of multi-coloured handkerchiefs.

● **MOURNERS** gathered to pay their respects in the parlour of 78-year-old *Dolly Urmston* couldn't believe their eyes when a fully-grown polar bear walked into the front room of her terraced house in Guisborough, North Yorkshire. The hungry 12-foot beast had been on the run for three days after escaping from nearby Flamingoland and was extremely hungry. The bear proceeded to go on the rampage, dismembering and eating several mourners before the vicar finally drove it off by hitting it on the head with his thurible. What little remained of the bear's victims was wrapped in napkins and popped in the coffin with Dolly by the undertaker, who also gave the family a 30% discount for a bulk burial.

● **IN THE SAME** way that sailors are often buried at sea in lead coffins, airline pilot *Frank Winchester* left a request in his will that he wanted to be buried at sky. At a solemn funeral ceremony, Frank's family, friends and loved ones gathered at 35,000 feet in a DC10 as his body, placed in a balsa wood coffin filled with helium, was pushed out of the cargo door and floated up into the heavens never to be seen again.

THE BOY WHO CRIED

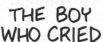

MILF!

ONE DAY... LADS! HOLLY WILLOUGHBY'S JOGGING DOWN OUR STREET IN AN ILL-FITTING TOP AND BRA!!

HA!HA!! SUCKERS!

LATER... LADS! LADS! MYLEENE KLASS HAS JUST GOT CAUGHT IN A SHOWER. YOU CAN SEE RIGHT THROUGH HER DELICATE FLORAL DRESS FROM M&S!!

HA!HA! YOUR FACES! I CAN'T BELIEVE YOU FELL FOR THAT AGAIN!

UNTIL... LADS! YOU WON'T BELIEVE THIS! LORRAINE KELLY IN A LOW-CUT TOP, SWEATING LIGHTLY AND BENT OVER SOME SHOPPING BAGS!

YEAH, RIGHT.

FUCK OFF.

SIGH!

OCH, I WISH SOMEONE WOULD HELP ME WITH MA HEAVY MELONS!

THE QUESTION that has split the nation into three warring factions... just *WHO IS* the *BEST JK*? Story lovers side with *Harry Potter* author *Rowling*, economists throw their weight behind eminent fiscal theorist *Galbraith* and acid jazz fans plump for the Cat in the Hat *out of Jamiroquai*. But who is right? Which one is the best? We've put all three contenders head to head to hat for a no-holds-barred cage fight to the death in a bid to put this raging debate to bed once and for all. It's time to finally find out the *TRUTH*...

·········· ROWLING ··········

······ out of JA[M]

ROUND 1

TALLNESS FOR SOMEONE who has sold between 400 and 450 million books, Rowling is of remarkably average height, tipping the scales at a mere 5'5". To put that in context, the *Harry Potter* writer shares her altitude with German Chancellor Angela Merkel, twerking pop star Miley Cyrus and unorthodox step-parent Woody Allen. And in a bizarre twist of fate, she is also exactly the same height as actress Emma Watson, who plays Hermione Grainger in the *Harry Potter* movies! **Score 8**

TALLNESS CLOCKING IN at an unremarkable 5'9" in his stockinged feet, you might imagine that this would be a mediocre round for the Grammy Award-winning UK chart-topper. But since he's rarely seen without his trademark

ROUND 2

HATS JK ROWLING famously wrote about a hat in her *Harry Potter* books - the "Sorting Hat" that allocated new Hogwarts pupils to their various school houses on a frankly quixotic and dictatorial basis. However, this hat doesn't actually exist and was re-created using CGI trick photography for the movies. When it comes to real life hats, Rowling is only believed to own one - a blue one with a bit of net at the front which she wears for weddings. **Score 7**

HATS THE *VIRTUAL INSANITY* singer well earns his reputation as the Cat in the Hat thanks to his massive collection of over sixty assorted hats, caps and titfers in a bewildering selection of styles. But unlike most middle-aged pop stars, who wear hats in a fruitless attempt to hide the fact that they

ROUND 3

CARS AS A PENNILESS young author, Rowling used to get around in a rusting N-reg Datsun Cherry. "There was always something wrong with that car," she told NBC's French Letterman. "It was forever breaking down or failing its MOT and I could never afford to get it fixed properly." However, thanks to the success of the *Harry Potter* series of books, Rowling has now been able to afford to put a new exhaust on the car, get the sills welded and fit new pads and discs at the front. **Score 6**

CARS A KEEN DRIVER, the *Cosmic Girl* singer keeps more than sixty high performance motors in the garage at his Essex mansion - in fact, he has exactly the same number of cars as hats. And each one of his Ferraris, Porsches and Maseratis has been specially customised to match one

ROUND 4

NOBEL PRIZES for ECONOMICS THANKS TO royalties from her books, Rowling is now richer than the Queen. But she also knows what it's like to scrimp and save; as a penniless young single mum on benefits, she learnt the values of thrift, prudence and careful budgeting. It's certainly not as far-fetched as a *Harry Potter* story to imagine that she might one day find herself winning the Nobel Prize for Economics. **Score 7**

NOBEL PRIZES for ECONOMICS KAY HAS MADE millions from his funk-lite records, but he famously spends his cash as quickly as he earns it on flash cars, big hats and drugs. With such a checkered financial history it's unlikely that the committee

ROUND 5

FUNKABILITY AS A TEENAGER growing up in Gloucestershire in the 1970s, Rowling was not exposed to funk, soul or R&B jazz fusion music, preferring to listen to records by Donny Osmond, David Cassidy, David Essex and Test Department. Indeed, throughout all of the *Harry Potter* books she has made little or no reference to complex grooves featuring electric guitar, electric bass, Hammond organ and drums playing interlocking rhythms, placing particular emphasis on the first beat of every bar. **Score 5**

FUNKABILITY IF YOU LOOK up "funk" in the dictionary, you will find just one word: Jay Kay out of Jamiroquai. In fact it would no exaggeration to say that, with the release of his first single *When You Gonna Learn* in 1992, Jay Kay invented funk music. And it's a genre that he has tirelessly championed in the intervening years, culminating with his 2011

ROUND 6

WRITING HER *HARRY POTTER* books about a school for wizards set the publishing world alight, becoming the most sucessful series of children's stories ever written. The books have sold millions of copies translated into 67 languages and have spawned 8 blockbuster movies with a star-studded cast list that reads like a *Who's Who* of showbiz royalty. But with a tally of just seven novels in the series, it's a disappointing final furlong for Rowling in the JK Stakes. **Score 7**

WRITING HE MAY HAVE sold more than 35 million albums and written hundreds of funky songs, but the Acid Jazz Space Cowboy only appears to have written one book - a frankly lacklustre tome called *Jamiroquai; Piano/Vocal/Guitar* - which is available for 1p in the

HOW DID THEY DO?

ROWLING ········

Expelliarmus! Despite the closest Celebrity Face-off finish in Viz history, the Harry Potter author was unable to weave enough magic to prevent herself coming third. **40**

out of JA[M] **41**

or OUT OF JAMIROQUAI...

E BEST JK?

...MIROQUAI

GALBRAITH

ROUND 1

10" tall hat on his head, he actually tops out at a practically unbeatable 6'7" - the same height as towering man mountain basketball star Dennis Rodman. Jay's going to be just about impossible to beat in this round. **Score 9**

TALLNESS JAY KAY out of Jamiroquai can put the celebratory champagne back on ice, because it turns out that JK Galbraith was an unbelievable 6'8" - exactly the same height as American slam dunk legend Earvin "Magic" Johnson - thus winning this round by the narrowest of margins... *a single inch!* **Score 10**

ROUND 2

are going bald, Kay still has a lustrous, healthy head of hair and his hat-wearing is merely a twattish affectation. **Score 10**

HATS ALWAYS self-conscious about his towering height, Galbraith consciously eschewed hats throughout his life, as he did platform shoes when they became all the rage in the seventies, fearing they would push him over the seven-foot mark. Indeed, the only hat he would have worn would have been a Jewish skullcap or yarmulke, were he ever to have visited a Synagogue. Fitting closely to the back of his head, this would not have added to his height. **Score 1**

ROUND 3

of the hats in his collection. Sadly, as they are too high to fit under the sleek sports car rooflines of his vehicles, when he goes out for a drive with girlfriend Denise Van Outen he has to take his hats off and put them in the boot. **Score 8**

CARS IT'S A LOW-SCORING round for the eminent economist as throughout his life he found it difficult to fit into normal-sized cars due to his height, and so drove everywhere on a motorbike. Indeed as a young man, whilst researching and writing his first book *American Capitalism: The Concept of Countervailing Power*, Galbraith earned his living as a speedway rider for Bradford Tudors, racing each Wednesday night at Odsal Stadium. His best year was 1956, when he finished fourth behind Arthur Forrest in the world final. **Score 0**

ROUND 4

of the Alfred Nobel Foundation will ever elect to award him the highest honour in Economics. But in a world where Bono is a UN Adviser, Kevin out of the Backstreet Boys is invited to address the US Senate and Will.I.Am is a keynote speaker at the World Economic Forum in Davos, anything is possible. **Score 3**

NOBEL PRIZES for ECONOMICS THROUGHOUT his long and illustrious career, awards and honours were heaped on Galbraith until they were coming out his arse. Dozens of honorary degrees, laureates and doctorates, Presidential Medals of Freedom, a citation from the President of India and the Order of Canada... the list goes on and on. But Galbraith never received the Nobel Prize for Economics and, since he died in 2006 and therefore fails the first test for eligibility, it is an honour that will forever elude his grasp. **Score 0**

ROUND 5

smash hit *Lifeline*, which peaked at number 99 in the charts with a bullet. **Score 10**

FUNKABILITY BEING BORN to a middle class Canadian family at the turn of the century would be an inauspicious start to any putative funk career, and choosing to take a PhD. in Agricultural Economics at the University of California, Berkeley wouldn't do anything to improve matters. But that's just what JK did, further confounding the situation by deciding to become a Harvard lecturer in Economics between 1934 and 1939 - *three decades before funk was invented!* In fact, it's only Galbraith's six month sabbatical playing slap bass for San Francisco-based soul funksters Sly and the Family Stone on their 1971 "Family Affair" world tour that saves him from scoring a big fat zero in this round. **Score 1**

ROUND 6

Amazon marketplace and is currently languishing at number 1,622,954 in the bestsellers list. It's a humiliating fall at the last fence for the Cat in the Hat. **Score 1**

WRITING THROUGHOUT his long and distinguished career, Galbraith was a prolific writer, penning an amazing *thirty books* on subjects as diverse as Post-Keynesian Economics, Oligopolistic Capitalism and Price Control Theory. The fact that probably nobody has ever read one all the way through, and that none of them have been turned into blockbuster movies is neither here nor there, so it's an impressive last gasp push for victory for Galbraith in the JK Handicap. **Score 30**

...MIROQUAI

Funk his luck! The Space Cowboy may have been quick on the draw in the early rounds, but in the final analysis he just couldn't pull a win out of his stupid giant fucking hat.

GALBRAITH

A Capital performance! Once all the profits and losses were accounted for in this epic three-way clash of the JKs, the lanky, late Economics guru came out at the top of the balance sheet. **42**

Next week: *Dirty* v *Dragons* **Who's the Best Den?**

The Polar Mayor

A Stirring tale of Endurance and Bravery beyond the Call of Civic Duty

IN JANUARY 1912, following a gruelling 800-mile trek, Captain Scott finally reached the South Pole only to discover that Antarctic explorer Roald Amundsen had beaten him by mere days. Although bitterly disappointed, Scott was determined to claw back some honour for his King and Country and challenged his Norwegian rival to a snowman building contest.

THE TEAMS worked on their snowmen for hours, battling blizzards, freezing temperatures and frostbite. When the two entries were finished, one question remained: Who would decide which one was the best? Someone was needed who was capable of taking such a decision, and Scott and Amundsen knew there was only one man for the job.

ALDERMAN Ernest Tonks had been Mayor of Blackpool for 30 years, and was a veteran judge of countless snowman, sand castle, large vegetable and glamorous granny contests. When the call from the Pole came through, he didn't hesitate for a moment. Postponing a Parks Committee meeting, he immediately set off on his 10,000 mile Antarctic odyssey.

A CROWD of wellwishers gathered along the golden sands of Blackpool beach to give Councillor Tonks and his wife the Lady Mayoress a proper send-off. The municipal brass band struck up a rousing chorus of *Oh! I Do Like to Be Beside the Seaside* as the pair set sail towards the horizon on the first leg of their mammoth civic trip to the icy wastes of Antarctica.

THE VOYAGE to the South Pole was long and arduous. As they traversed the heavy seas off Tierra del Fuego, the Mayor's hat blew off and his wife was forced to jump into the water to retrieve it. Their tiny, vulnerable boat came close to capsising many times as they rounded Cape Horn amidst a violent maelstrom of 100 foot waves and 200mph winds.

EVENTUALLY, the exhausted Mayor and Lady Mayoress reached Antarctica, making landfall at Evans Point. But there was no time for them to rest; they immediately began the next, even more hazardous stage of their epic journey. Between them and the snowman contest lay 800 miles of ice, snow, unscalable mountains and bottomless crevasses.

AFTER AN adventure-filled trek during which the Mayor's hat once again blew off and his wife was forced to climb down a 1000-foot deep ice chasm to retrieve it, the pair finally reached the South Pole. As they arrived, they were greeted warmly by Amundsen, Scott and their men, who were anxious to find out once and for all whose snowman was the best.

THE MAYOR wasted no time, judging each snowman for technical skill, use of materials and lovability. Eventually he awarded the prize for Best Snowman at the South Pole to the British entry. Scott was delighted with his prize - a stick of rock, 2 tickets to see Charlie Cairoli at the Tower Ballroom and a day pass for the Big Dipper at the Pleasure Beach.

Next week - Councillor Tonks and the Lady Mayoress trek overland to Nepal and scale Mount Everest to judge a knobbly knees contest between George Mallory and Andrew Irvine.

VIRGIN DEATH MINCER "up & running by 2019"

VIRGIN boss *RICHARD BRANSON* says he is confident that his much heralded Death Mincer will be up and running and turning customers to bloody pulp some time in the next two years.

Extra strong mince: Branson promises his lates scheme will give members of the public chance to be reduced to bloody mush in a giant machine.

~ Branson

The giant steel machine, which has been ten years in development, will offer paying members of the public the opportunity to be agonisingly rendered into a fleshy mush similar to that used to make beefburgers.

blades

Even with an eye-watering six figure ticket price, the rich and famous are already queuing up to be amongst the first into the hopper to experience its razor sharp whirring blades and toothed grinding drums.

"A ride in the Virgin Death Mincer promises to be the experience of a lifetime," Branson, 64, told reporters gathered at the Nevada desert test facility where the $1bn device is being developed.

owls

"And to demonstrate my confidence in this amazing new technology, in 2017 I shall be the first person to be puréed into a fleshy slurry when we fire it up for the first time."

millers

The project, which was originally planned to begin mincing

Bearded Billionaire Promises Ride of a Lifetime in Giant Human Rendering Machine

customers in 2008, has suffered a series of setbacks and is now running more than six years behind schedule.

The latest hiccup occurred just before Christmas when 25 pigs emerged from the Death Mincer completely unscathed after a test run.

wife of baths

Following the failed tryout a number of celebrity customers, including Madonna, Olly Murs and Ed "Stewpot" Stewart, reportedly asked for refunds on their £200,000 advance tickets.

Pensioners in Winter Pulled Pork Poverty

MILLIONS of pensioners will find themselves in fuel poverty this winter. And if that was not worrying enough, according to a recent report around 98% of them still have no idea what pulled pork is.

The charity Help the Elderly say that as we head into winter, many old people who have worked hard and paid taxes all their lives may only be able to afford to heat one room and will be completely in the dark about pulled pork.

price

"The rise in price of domestic fuel and changes to British food have simply been too fast for pensioners to keep up with," explained Help the Elderly's Keith Pratt.

Fork: Some pork being pulled, yesterday

"Pensioners are only just getting to grips with ranch dressing and double-cooked chips and now they are expected to understand pulled pork," he added.

ladd

The charity recently started running a scheme which showed the elderly how to heat their homes efficiently and how to get to grips with the ordering process in Subway. But they are angry that the food industry is piling on the new terminology and they fear that many pensioners will not be able to keep up.

baker

One pensioner, who had never had her dinner served on a piece of slate, or a knife and fork provided in a small silver bucket until she was 92, said she was confused by what it meant. "Is it luncheon meat?" she asked. "Or spam?"

It's NUTS!

BARMY *Green Party* tree-huggers have vowed to give the VOTE to squirrels, badgers, rabbits and other woodland creatures if they win the next general election. According to a *Daily Mail* journalist who had been drinking heavily for several days, the manifesto pledge would be trialled on local government polls before being implemented nationwide in time for the next general election.

Nutjob Green leader *Caroline Lucas* was playing her cards close to her chest when asked whether the controversial plan to extend the franchise to woodland mammals was officially part of the Greens' policy. "No, absolutely not," she said evasively. And she also refused to be drawn on whether she also planned to give the vote to birds, insects and reptiles such as frogs. "No, absolutely not," she said, refusing point blank to answer the question.

The bonkers party, who want to replace millionaires with trees, ban women from shaving their legs and force everyone to sell their cars and walk around in their bare feet,

Squirrels to get vote by 2020 under crackpot Green manifesto

recently hit the headlines when a *Daily Mail* journalist who had been drinking heavily for several days imagined a top secret Green Party document outlining plans to flood Buckingham Palace with a million gallons of water and convert it into a whale sanctuary with unsightly solar panels on the roof.

What do the Stars Think?

Mike Read,
Radio 1 Breakfast DJ

"I don't mind squirrels getting the vote as long as it's proper, British red squirrels. I don't think grey squirrels should be entitled to come over here and have a say in how our country is run. It's about time we pulled up the drawbridge and said enough is enough. Britain's oak trees are full."

Gemma Collins,
TOWIE star

"I really like squirrels because, they're like mammals or something with all like fluffy tails, and I think that all fluffy things should be able to vote, like baby rabbits and kittens and that and them like puppies what do the like toilet roll adverts because it's just really like nice."

Len Goodman,
Strictly judge

"It's just political correctness gone mad. Squirrels don't let us vote in their elections, so why should we let them vote in ours? We may live in a democracy, but democracy's got to have limits. What's sauce for the goose should be sauce for the gander. And that's as true for squirrels as it is for geese."

Jeremy Clarkson,
Top Gear controversialist

"The only views of squirrels I'm interested in are the ones I get through the windscreen of my Aston Martin DB9 Vantage - the V12 version with uprated suspension, supercharger and flappy paddle gearbox - as I drive over them at 100mph on the Chipping Norton bypass."

Andy Murray,
tennis Scotsman

"I can't see anything wrong in principle with extending the franchise to squirrels. But, like us, they should only be allowed to cast a vote when they're eighteen, and as they only live to the age of about four years in the wild I can't really see them influencing the outcome of general elections much."

Bear Grylls,
survival expert

"I often eat live squirrels for my lunch when I'm lost in the woods. I would hate to think that by chomping down on a bushy-tailed snack I had disrupted the operation of the democratic process, so if squirrels do get the vote, I'll probably just have a Greggs Steak Bake instead."

CLOONEY'S CASH

Heart-throb actor **George Clooney** answers *your* financial questions.

Q **I'VE RECENTLY** had my hours cut at work, and my wife and I are finding it increasingly hard to make ends meet. We have a young child, and with the nights drawing in and the temperatures dropping, we're both concerned about how we're going to afford our utility bills. Have you any advice on how we can make sure that we're not left out in the cold?
Barry, West Yorkshire

George says: IT'S CERTAINLY understandable that you're worried about gas and electricity bills. The experts are saying that this year may well be the coldest on record! My advice is to get a starring role in a film and use the money to spend winter abroad, possibly somewhere like Egypt. It should be nice and warm there. This is what I did after making *Ocean's Eleven* with Steven Soderbergh in 2001. Hope this helps.

£P£P£P£P£P£P£P£P£P£P£P£P£P£P£P£P£P£P£

Q **I HAD A BAD** month in which my washing machine broke, my car failed its MOT and I dropped my mobile phone in the toilet. I had to take out a loan with a pay-day lender so I could afford to get everything fixed, but I didn't read the small print and now I owe the company over £12,000, rising on a daily basis. I'm at my wits' end - what can I do to break the debt cycle?
Martha, East Sussex

George says: PAY-DAY LOAN companies can seem like a godsend when you're in trouble, but always read the small print before taking out an agreement, and make sure that you can afford to pay the loan off before it snowballs out of control. I myself had a large bill to pay one month - my wife and I bought an island residence in the Thames for around £10m - and I was racking my brains to think how I could pay for it. Thankfully, I remembered that I'd received $20m in salary and revenue share for *Gravity* in 2013, so I easily had enough money to pay for it outright. I suggest you get a starring role in a film and use the money you earn to pay off the debt.

£P£P£P£P£P£P£P£P£P£P£P£P£P£P£P£P£P£P£

Q **I BOUGHT** a house with my partner at the height of the property boom, but we've recently split up and when looking to sell the house we've discovered we're in negative equity and would lose around £30,000 if we sell at the market value. Neither of us can afford to lose this much money, and it's causing even more arguments between us. Do you think there's any way we can sell up without losing everything?
Sara, Ayrshire

George says: ENDING a relationship is hard at the best of times, and things can really turn ugly when money is involved. The good news is that house prices are creeping back up again, so those who are in it for the long haul should be able to recoup what they paid out. However, when you need to sell a property quickly, it can be hard to get what you need as your bargaining power is low. My advice would be to get a starring role in a film like I did with 2003's *Intolerable Cruelty*, for which I earned around $15m. Then you should use the money you make from that to buy out your ex-partner, keeping hold of the property as an asset as it will eventually pay off in the next economic boom. Think of the long-term and you'll come out of this a winner.

More helpful tips from George next week!

MANATEE ABOUT THE HOUSE

Sid the Sexist

TITS OOT!

TYNESIDE'S SILVER-TONGUED CAVALIER

IN THE PUB...

HOW, LADS.

HOW SID.

HANG ABOOT! WOT THE FUCK'S CANNIN' ON 'ERE!? WHY D'YUZ LOOK LIKE A FUCKIN' ZZ TOP TRIBUTE BAND?

GET WITH THE TIMES, SID MAN. IT'S TWO THOOSAND AN' FIFTEEN! EVERY SELF-RESPECTIN' BLURK'S GORRA BEARD NOO.

AYE. BORDS WINVEN'T EVEN LOOK AT YUZ IF YUZ'RE NOT SPORTIN' FACIAL FUZZ, LIKE.

HADAWAY AN' SHITE, MAN! AS IF THE BLART'S GANNA BE INTERESTED IN A LURD O'FUCKIN' CAPTAIN BIRDSEYES!

YUZ'LL SEE, SID. THESE CHIN FANNIES ARE FANNY MAGNETS.

HI THERE, LADS. SEXY BEARDS.

CHEERS PET.

DO YOU LOT FANCY COMING BACK TO OUR PLACE?

AYE. SOONDS CANNY

HAD ON - THEZ FOUR OF US AN' AANLY THREE OF YEEZ.

YES... WELL... ONCE YOU'VE STARTED PUBERTY YOU CAN GIVE US A CALL.

SEE YOU LATER, BABYFACE.

BOLLOCKS!

2 WEEKS LATER...

FUCK'S SAKE, MAN! NEE SHAVIN' FERRA FORTNEET AN' AH'VE STILL GORRA CHIN LIKE ALAN SHEARER'S FUCKIN' HEED!

SIDNEY! ARE YOU ALREET IN THERE, SON? YOU'VE NOT LEFT THE HOUSE FOR WEEKS, AND YOU'RE SPENDING A LOT OF TIME IN THE BATHROOM. IT'S NOT THAT EXPLOSIVE DIARRHOEA AGAIN, IS IT?

LEAVE US ALAIRN, MAM! AH'M TRYIN' T'GROW A BEARD IN 'ERE!

WELL I NEED TO GET IN THERE FOR A MINUTE TO CLEAN UP, LUV. YOUR AUNTIE VI'S SHOWER BROKE THIS MORNING SO SHE CAME OVER TO SHAVE HER LEGS. I'VE NOT HAD A CHANCE TO WASH OUT THE PLUGHOLE YET.

LATER THAT DAY...

TELL Y'WOT, LADS... THESE BEARDS SHOULD COME WI'A FUCKIN' 'EALTH WARNIN'. AH'M WORRIED ME COCK MIGHT DROP OFF IF I DEE MUCH MORE SHAGGIN'!

AYE. ME AN'AALL.

AN' ME.

HOW LADS.

AALREET, SID. NOT SEEN YOU FORRA COUPLE O' WEEKS.

AYE, WELL... AH'VE BEEN BUSY SQUEEZIN' OOT THIS FUCKER, 'AVEN'T I?

AYE... THAT'S AN IMPRESSIVE EFFORT, THAT, SID. VERY WIRY.

IT LOOKS A BIT... GUNKY, LIKE, SID.

WELL THAT'S WOT THE BORDS GAN FOR THESE DAYS, MAN, HURBUR CHIC, THEY CAALL IT.

LOOKS LIKE IT'S GOT PRITT-STICK IN IT, SID.

NAH MAN BOB. THAT'S URNLY... ERM...BEARD WAX.

HI THERE. I LIKE YOUR BEARD.

AH DIVVEN'T BLAME YUZ, PET.

FANCY COMING BACK TO MINE..?

ERM... AYE! AALREET THEN!

SHORTLY...

TELL YOU WHAT... WHY DON'T I GIVE YOU A NICE, RELAXING, EROTIC BACK MASSAGE TO GET YOU IN THE MOOD..?

AYE. SOONDS BELTA, PET.

OIL

JUST TAKE YOUR TOP OFF AND LIE DOWN ON YOUR FRONT ON THE BED.

I'LL JUST TURN UP THE HEAT A BIT... GET IT REALLY HOT AND STEAMY IN HERE!

AYE, THAT'S CANNY HOT, PET. AH'M SWEATIN' LIKE A FAT LASS IN THE QUEUE AT GREGGS.

RIGHT! THAT'S ENOUGH FOREPLAY... I'M ABSOLUTELY GAGGING FOR IT! TAKE ME NOW, YOU SEXY, BEARDED STUD.

ROLLOVER JACKPOT

AALREET PET... LET'S GET DOON AN' DORTY...!

NEXT DAY...

GOOD NEWS, MR. SMUTT. THE SWELLING FROM THE KICK YOU RECIEVED TO THE GROIN SHOULD SUBSIDE IN A MONTH OR SO...

...AS FOR THE BRUISES ALL OVER YOUR FACE, THEY'LL FADE IN A FEW WEEKS. BUT IN THE MEANTIME, YOU COULD THINK ABOUT GROWING A BEARD TO COVER THEM UP.

GUMPH!

HA! HA!

HO! HO!

HA! HA!

MICKEY'S MINIATURE GRANDPA

ADVENTURE WAS NEVER FAR AWAY FOR YOUNG MICKEY MARSTON ~ FOR HIS GRANDFATHER WAS CONVINCED THAT A GYPSY'S CURSE HAD SHRUNK HIM TO AN INCREDIBLE TWO INCHES IN HEIGHT!

D.J '15

THE MARSTONS ARE ON HOLIDAY IN SPAIN

HAVE YOU SEEN YOUR GRANDPA AROUND, MICKEY?

I MANAGED TO FIND A FARMACIA WHICH SELLS HIS TENA INCONTINENCE PANTS.

TORO! TORO!

HEY, LOOK AT ME, MICKEY ~ I'M A BULLFIGHTER!

WHEN YOU'RE TWO INCHES TALL LIKE ME, A **STAG BEETLE** MAKES A FEARSOME BULL!

AND I'LL DEFEND MYSELF WITH THIS COCKTAIL STICK AND A RED POSTAGE STAMP ~ THE IDEAL SWORD AND CAPE FOR A MINIATURE MATADOR!

OH NO! A GUST OF WIND HAS SNATCHED THE "CAPE" OUT OF MY HAND!

AND THAT STAG BEETLE IS POUNDING ITS HOOF AGAINST THE GROUND ~ IT'S GETTING READY TO CHARGE!

SHRIEK! I MUST ESCAPE BEFORE IT GORES MY TINY BODY WITH ITS MIGHTY PINCERS!

OH DEAR.

IT'S NOT EVEN A BEETLE, MUM ~ IT'S JUST A LEAF.

GASP! PERHAPS I CAN BOUNCE OFF THIS CHILD'S INFLATABLE ARM-BAND AND REACH THE SAFETY OF THAT SUNBED!

THE ARM-BAND IS AS BIG AS A BOUNCY CASTLE TO ME!

POP!

HMM!

COME ON DAD, LET'S GET YOU INTO THE SHADE ~ YOU'VE BEEN IN THE SUN TOO LONG.

I'LL BUY YOU AN ICE CREAM SUNDAE AND YOU CAN TAKE YOUR PILL.

SHORTLY

PHEWF, IT IS HOT! I COULD DO WITH A SWIM TO COOL MYSELF DOWN.

BUT THE HOTEL POOL IS TOO VAST FOR SOMEONE OF MY "STUART LITTLE" STATURE!

AND SO

I'VE CREATED MY OWN PINT-SIZED SWIMMING POOL OUT OF THIS EMPTY ICE CREAM SUNDAE DISH.

A COUPLE MORE THIMBLES-FULL OF WATER SHOULD DO IT!

AND I'VE JAMMED A LOLLY-STICK INTO A CRACK IN THE WALL TO MAKE MYSELF A SUPER DIVING BOARD!

HEY MICKEY WATCH THIS DIVE!

GRANDPA, DON'T...!

CRACK!

SORRY MICKEY, I THINK WE SHOULD PACK UP AND FLY HOME EARLY

AWW MUM!

I THOUGHT THE SUNSHINE MIGHT HELP YOUR GRANDPA'S CONDITION, BUT IT'S JUST MAKING HIM MORE DOOLALLY THAN EVER.

SHORTLY, IN THE HOTEL ROOM

OH NO, THAT'S TORN IT!

FOR SOME REASON YOUR GRANDAD RIPPED ALL THE PAGES OUT OF HIS PASSPORT!

YES, HE WAS USING THE COVER AS AN "IDEAL MIDGET-SIZED TENT" ON THE BEACH YESTERDAY.

OH DEAR! HOW ARE WE GOING TO GET GRANDPA HOME WITHOUT A VALID PASSPORT?

WE'D BETTER GO AND SEE THE BRITISH CONSULATE.

BRITISH EMBASSY ESPANA

I'M SURE THEY HAVE TO DEAL WITH THIS SORT OF SITUATION ALL THE TIME.

...YES MRS MARSTON, THE CONSULATE IS EMPOWERED TO OFFER ASSISTANCE IN CASES OF MEDICAL EMERGENCY.

CONSUL

AND AS YOUR FATHER IS CLEARLY TOTALLY GAGA WE'LL DO EVERYTHING WE CAN TO HELP.

I WILL PERSONALLY ACCOMPANY YOU TO THE AIRPORT AND ENSURE THAT YOUR FATHER RETURNS SAFELY HOME TO BRITAIN.

CONSUL

THANK YOU SO MUCH!

AT THE AIRPORT

PASSPORTS

OUCH! OOYAH! DON'T WORRY MRS MARSTON ~ I WILL SMUGGLE YOUR FATHER THROUGH PASSPORT CONTROL WITH NO PROBLEM.

HIS ~OOYAH! ~ MINISCULE SIZE MEANS THAT I CAN ~OUCH~ CONCEAL HIM INSIDE MY RECTUM WITHOUT ANY ~ACK!~ DIFFICULTY AT ALL!

BIG VERN

HELLO AND WELCOME TO MASTERCHEF. IT'S A BREAKFAST SPECIAL THIS WEEK.

OUR CONTESTANTS HAVE JUST FIVE MINUTES TO KNOCK UP A TRULY OUTSTANDING AND ORIGINAL MORNING MEAL! COOKING DOESN'T GET TOUGHER THAN THIS!

LET'S MEET THE CONTESTANTS. FIRST UP IS VERN DAKIN FROM BETHNAL GREEN. WELCOME TO THE SHOW, VERN. WOTCHA GREGG.

WHAT ARE YOU GOING TO DO FOR US THIS MORNING THEN, VERN..? I'M KEEPIN' FINGS NICE AND SIMPLE...

...FRESHLY GRAHND SCOTTISH WHOLE-GRAIN OATS BOILED IN RICH, FULL-FAT MILK AND SERVED WITH A MEDLEY OF WILD BERRIES... PUKKA. SOUNDS GREAT, VERN.

AND NOW LET'S MEET OUR SECOND CONTESTANT... ERNIE.

TELL ME, ERNIE... WHAT'S ON YOUR MASTERCHEF MENU? WELL, GREGG...I'LL BE ATTEMPTING SOMETHING A LITTLE MORE AMBITIOUS...

MY DISH IS SMOKED ALASKAN SALMON WITH SCRAMBLED EGGS, SICILIAN LEMON-CHOPPED DILL... SOUNDS GREAT.

...AND - FOR THE PIÈCE de RÉSISTANCE - I'VE GLAZED A SINGLE, FRESHLY-SALTED CAPER ONTO THE TOP OF THE SALMON FILLET, TO GIVE IT THAT SHARP, MEDITERRANEAN TANG. OH DEAR, OH DEAR, ERNIE.

WHAT IS IT, GREGG? WELL, THAT DOES SOUND LOVELY AND ALL ... BUT I'M AFRAID MR TORODE HERE IS ALLERGIC TO CAPERS!

IT'S TRUE. IF I EAT ONE SINGLE CAPER, ERNIE, I'LL HAVE A REACTION AND DIE. OH CRUMBS... WELL... WHAT SHOULD I DO? I COULD TRY TO REMOVE THE CAPER...

GOOD IDEA. BUT DON'T WORRY...IF THE CAPER DOESN'T COME OFF, WE'LL JUST GET VERN TO DO THE PORRIDGE FOR US. DO FACKIN' WOT?

I AIN'T DOIN' NO PORRIDGE FOR FACKIN' NOBODY! YOU AIN'T SENDIN' ME DAHN, YOU CAHNTS!

BLAM! BLAM!

BLAM! BLAM! BLAM!

I'M SORRY, ERNIE! I NEVAH MEANT FOR YOU TO GET MIXED UP IN THIS!

BLAM!

BLIMEY... I TOLD YOU COOKING DIDN'T GET TOUGHER THAN THIS.

BLAM!

OH, LORDY! IT'S *the* **FAT** (TRAY) (SAN) **SLAGS**

TATOO FIXERS

WE TATTOO:
ARMS
LEGS

HI! HOW CAN WE HELP YOU?

I WANT T' GET A REALLY AWFUL TATTOO FIXED

YES?.. WELL YOU'VE COME TO THE RIGHT PLACE

RECEPION

OKAY... WHAT'S THE STORY?

WELL, I WAS PISSED IN A CLUB IN MAGALUF, AN' I THOUGHT OF A GREAT TATTOO F'MESELF.

YEAH... SO MANY PEOPLE GET A TATTOO WHEN THEY'RE DRUNK

NO, I WAS ONLY PISSED WHEN I THOUGHT IT UP... I WENT T' GET IT DONE NEXT MORNIN WHEN I'D SOBERED UP A BIT

I REGRETTED IT SOON AS I 'AD IT DONE, DIDN'T I, TRAY.. REALLY EMBARRASSIN', AN' TROUBLE IS, IT'S ON A BIT O' ME BODY THAT EVERYONE CAN SEE.

WHERE IS IT?

JUST ABOVE ME FANNY

LOADS O' PEOPLE GET T' SEE THAT, DON'T THEY, SAN

THEY DO...

...SIX OR SEVEN LAST NIGHT

WELL, I SUPPOSE WE'D BETTER HAVE A LOOK

AYE... 'OLD ON... I'LL JUST GET ME KIT OFF

I ♥ 10 INCH COCKS IN ↓ HERE

OH, **WOW!** THAT IS SOME **BAD INK!**

I KNOW... I DON'T KNOW WOT I WAS THINKIN' OF

WELL, DON'T WORRY, BECAUSE THAT'S AN EASY FIX, AND I THINK WE'VE ALL GOT A FEW IDEAS OF WHAT WE CAN DO...

RECEPI

SO... I THOUGHT PERHAPS A **PHOENIX**... IT REPRESENTS A **NEW START**... IT'S DRAWING A LINE UNDER PAST MISTAKES

THAT'S GOOD, IN'T IT, SAN? THEM FLAMES LOOK TOP

NO, I DON'T LIKE BIRDS... THEY SHIT EVERYWHERE

OKAY... HOW ABOUT THIS ONE? A **TIGER?** A SYMBOL OF POWER AND INDEPENDENCE

NO, I DON'T LIKE CATS... THEY SHIT EVERYWHERE

OKAY... HOW ABOUT THIS TRADITIONAL **JAPANESE CARP?** IT REPRESENTS CALM AND TRANQUILITY.

THAT'S NICE, SAN... AN' FISH DON'T SHIT EVERYWHERE

I'M NOT 'AVIN' A BIG **FISH** TATTOO ABOVE ME FANNY, Y' KNOW WOT BLOKES ARE LIKE... THEY'D MAKE A CRUDE REMARK EVERY TIME THEY WENT DOWN T' GIVE ME A NOSH

AYE... I S'POSE YER RIGHT

LOOK, I 'AD AN IDEA MESELF OF A DESIGN I'D LIKE..

OKAY... WELL- LET'S HAVE A LOOK

IT SAYS A LOT ABOUT ME...'OW I'VE CHANGED...'OW I'M NOT THE SAME PERSON WHO 'AD THAT TATTOO DONE.. I'VE MOVED ON... I'M DIFFERENT...

CAN Y' DO THAT?

ER...YES..

SO...

BZZZZ! BZZZZ!

TATOO FIXERS

WE TATTOO:
ARMS
LEGS
HANDS
BODY
NECK
INTIMATE
(TITS, FANNIES)
NO FACES

THERE WE GO... ALL DONE

THAT W' QUICK

THAT'S BETTER... I CAN WEAR ME THONG ON THE BEACH AGAIN NOW WI' OUT FEELIN' EMBARRASSED

I ♥ 18 INCH COCKS IN ↓ HERE

Take a Shit

WINNER
MAGAZINE OF THE YEAR
~Take a Shit Magazine of the Year Awards

Paul the Midwife!

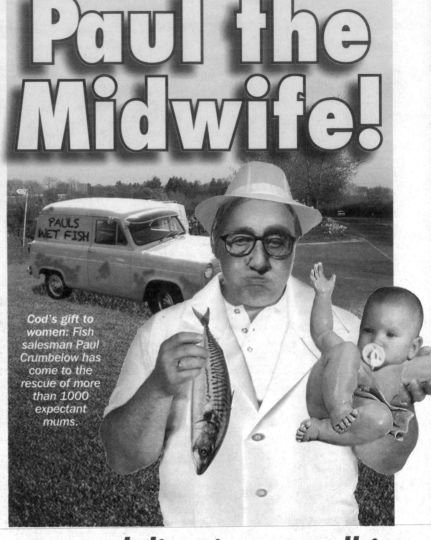

Cod's gift to women: Fish salesman Paul Crumbelow has come to the rescue of more than 1000 expectant mums.

As told to
Vaginia Discharge

WITH maternity-based TV series such as *One Born Every Minute, A Baby Story* and *Call the Midwife* riding high in the ratings, midwifery has suddenly become the career of choice for Britain's youngsters. But competition for the limited number of places available on university training courses is fierce, and only the lucky few student nurses eventually make it through to become fully-fledged midwives, witnessing the wonderful miracle of birth on a daily basis.

But one man who has delivered over a **THOUSAND** babies has never been near a college of midwifery in his life. What's more, many of the expectant mothers that door-to-door frozen fish hawker Paul Crumbelow, 58, has helped through tricky births have been showbiz stars! "I've got no medical training," he told us. "I just always seem to be in the right place at the right time when heavily pregnant celebrities go into labour."

Now Channel 5 are set to immortalise Paul's incredible career in a big budget 10-part drama series, *Paul the Midwife*, provisionally starring either Liam Neeson or *Hi de Hi's* Jeffrey Holland in the title role. Paul told *Take a Shit* magazine: "Seeing my life being acted out on the screen by the biggest stars in the world is amazing, but not nearly so amazing as the real life experiences that inspired it."

JUST like a proper, qualified midwife, Paul says he'll never forget the first baby he delivered ... not least because the mother was none other than POSH SPICE!

"I was selling my wares round a fancy estate in Syston. It was a hot day and the compressor on the freezer in my van had gone tits up. The fish was starting to thaw out in the back so I was trying to flog it off quickly before the smell got too bad and the flies found me. Believe you me, there's nothing worse for business than trying to charge top dollar for frozen fish when you've just turned up in a cloud of bluebottles.

I went up a long gravel drive and rang the bell of a mock Tudor mansion. I nearly fell backwards off the step when the door was answered by **DAVID BECKHAM**. He told me I'd called at rather a bad time, but I'd got my foot in the door and launched into my sales patter, telling him about my vanload of flash-frozen Atlantic lobster tails, jumbo crab sticks and line caught haddock Kievs.

Halfway through my spiel, from inside the house I heard a screech that was tuneless and very harsh on the ear. I recognised it immediately as the voice of Beckham's wife Victoria. I followed him into the living room where we found the former Spice Girl lying on the floor, doubled up in pain. She'd gone into labour with their first child Brooklyn.

Becks might have a cool head when it comes to taking penalties or appearing in adverts for anything, but right then and there he went to pieces, I can tell you. He was like a headless chicken, running round the room and panicking. Somebody had

Home deliveries are all in a day's work for celebrity mobile fishmonger

to take charge and that someone was me.

I sent the England captain off to fetch some towels and hot water while I checked Posh to see how dilated she was. She was already 8cm and the baby was coming. There was no time to call an ambulance. There was nothing for it - I was going to have to deliver it myself.

Luckily, Victoria wasn't too posh to push, and after five minutes of gritting her teeth and squeezing, the baby popped out. I immediately hung it upside down by its feet, slapped it on the arse and weighed it, and then turned to the proud father to tell him it was a boy. But Becks was nowhere to be seen. He had gone to Harrods to order a set of Louis Vuitton silk towels, with

> *...I checked Posh to see how dilated she was. She was already 8cm and the baby was coming...*

the monogrammed initials "V&D" in Swarovski crystals in each corner.

By the time he got back, mother and baby Brooklyn were both doing well, happily tucked up and fast asleep. I thought my job was done, but Becks asked me if I wouldn't mind sticking round while he popped out again on another important errand. He was back an hour later with a tissue sellotaped across his buttocks where he'd just had his newborn son's name tattooed across his arse in Olde English capital letters.

I told him I really had to go now as I'd already lost three hours of my round. But Beckham was so grateful for what I'd done for him and Posh that he agreed to buy all the remaining stock out of my van - a cool £250 worth. As I piled the quickly defrosting boxes of fish products on the step, I couldn't imagine how he was going to fit them all in his freezer. But it wasn't my problem. I'd already been paid in cash and I don't do returns."

AFTER his experience with the Beckhams, Paul assumed that delivering a celebrity baby whilst delivering frozen fish was a one-off. But he couldn't have been more wrong, because over the following years he found himself being forced to act as emergency midwife at a rollcall of star births that reads like a Who's Who of expectant A-listers, including

• Delivering **MADONNA**'s first child Lourdes whilst selling breaded fish bits door to door in her exclusive Notting Hill neighbourhood.

• Taking charge of the birth of X-Files star **GILLIAN ANDERSON**'s second child when hawking battered hakeballs door to door in Richmond upon Thames.

• Amazingly, delivering all of **HOLLY WILLOUGHBY**'s children, after knocking on her door selling frozen whitebait mince all three times her waters had just broken.

But the most high profile birth at which Paul was forced to take charge was that of third in line to the throne **PRINCE GEORGE**. And the delivery came about when Crumbelow called in at the prestigious St Mary's Hospital in Paddington.

I'd bought a job lot of blow-frozen Cambodian lobster tails from an importer on a retail park in Oadby who'd gone bust. They were an expensive, premium quality item so there was no point trying to hawk them door-to-door on the estates round Leicester. My usual customers round there wouldn't know a quality seafood delicacy if it bit them on the bollocks, so I packed my van and headed for the posh bit of London.

I tried to flog them in a few restaurant kitchens but drew a blank. I was getting desperate. In a last ditch effort to offload my stock, I decided to try my luck in St Mary's - a fancy maternity clinic where I was sure the high class private patients would appreciate gourmet products like lobster. I took a couple of boxes as samples, got in the lift and pressed the button for the basement kitchens.

Just as the door closed, a regal hand pushed through the gap and held it open. I couldn't believe my eyes when I saw who bustled in. It was **PRINCE WILLIAM**, and it was obvious that his heavily pregnant wife **KATE MIDDLETON** was in the final stages of labour. She was puffing her cheeks out, gripping her swollen stomach and making all groaning noises. William pressed the button for the top floor delivery suite and the lift started to go up.

As we rose past floor after floor, Wills chatted to me informally, asking me what I did for a living and how long

I'd done it. He was very interested in my work and also very well informed about the frozen fish retail business. He seemed relaxed but all that changed when the lift suddenly juddered to a halt between two floors. At this point, his demeanour changed - in fact I've never seen a man panic so much. He may be cool as a cucumber when he's doing his day job as an airsea rescue helicopter pilot, but he was like a headless chicken in that lift and it was left to yours truly to take charge of the situation.

I told him to ring security on the emergency phone, and he was told the good news that the engineers had already been called. The bad news was they had another couple of jobs to go to first, so they wouldn't be at the hospital for another two hours at least.

By that time I'd delivered enough babies to know that in two hours the country would have a new Prince, and it was going to be down to ME to deliver him. I'd already checked and Kate was 8cm dilated. Baby was on his way alright ... right there in the lift!

It was a routine birth. I told Kate to push and breathe for a bit and then do one big final push, and out he popped. I lifted him up by his feet and slapped his arse, which could, I suppose, be construed as treason. But his proud mum and dad were so pleased with their little bundle of royal joy that they decided to overlook my transgression.

In fact, William was so pleased with the loyal service I had rendered that he agreed to buy all the stock of lobster tails I had with me in the lift - half a gross. That was quite a weight off my mind as, after the best part of three hours out of the freezer they had started to thaw out and were on the turn.

When the engineers finally winched us up and got the lift doors open, the happy couple went out onto the steps

to show the new Prince to the press whilst I was whisked away by royal protection officers. They explained that because I had seen Kate's intimate areas whilst midwifing the birth, I would have to sign the Official Secrets Act, promising never to reveal what they looked like or how bushy they were. Of course I immediately complied - I didn't dare consider what the consequences of refusing to sign would be.

IN 2005, following a series of food poisoning outbreaks and a critical article about his frozen fish business in the Leicester Mercury, Crumbelow's found his door-to-door sales slowing down. Determined to halt the decline, he decided to test new markets further afield.

I took my refrigerated van across the pond to Hollywood. Like many frozen fish salesmen, Tinseltown has always held an exotic allure for me. I knew the stars of the silver screen are sods for a bit of fish, so naturally I was excited when I walked up the drive to my first cold call - a sprawling 3-swimming pool mansion on Sunset Strip surrounded by high walls. I'd got a pallet of Estonian pollock that I was selling as Atlantic cod, because it looks exactly the same when it's frozen. You can only tell you've been had when the stuff's cooked and in your mouth, and by that time I'd be long gone.

The door was answered by a Spanish maid. She seemed pleased to see me and invited me in straight away, which was odd because I

usually have to force my way in by sticking a foot in the door and then pushing. She led me through the palatial, marble-floored hall and into a bedroom where I found a woman who was clearly having contraptions. It was **BRITNEY SPEARS**, who I recognised from her videos.

"Doctor's here, Miss Britney," said the maid. She had seen my white fishmonger's coat, blue rubber gloves and wellingtons, and leapt to the conclusion that I was an emergency obstetrician.

I didn't have time to explain that she had made a mistake. I had already checked how dilated Britney was and it was 8cm. The baby was on its way, and once again yours truly was going to have to deliver it. I sent the maid for some hot water and towels and got down to work. I'd delivered more babies than I'd had cold fish, but this one was to prove very unusual. In between her puffs and gasps, Spears explained that she wanted a trendy water birth, so I helped her outside and we went down the steps into one of the swimming pools.

I held her hand and timed her contraptions that were now coming just seconds apart. Britney gritted her teeth and gave one final big push. The baby popped out and bobbed up to the surface. As usual, I picked it up and slapped it on the arse. It was probably something to do with being born underwater, but the little fellow still didn't cry. "Quick," said Britney. "Hit my baby one more time." I often wonder whether that was when Britney got the idea for the title of her 1999 hit record. I slapped the baby again, and this time he let out an ear-splitting, tuneless shriek. There was no doubting he was his mother's son.

The maid eventually turned up with the towels and we climbed out of the pool, dried ourselves and put the baby to sleep in its cot. It was then that I revealed my secret - I was a door-to-door fish salesman, not a doctor. Spears burst into ear-splitting, tuneless shrieks of laughter and said that she had to find some way of repaying me. In the end she bought 20 boxes of frozen pollock fillets at cod prices. Needless to say I'd hightailed it safely back to the UK before she had the chance to cook any of them and discover my cheeky little ruse.

> *...because I had seen Kate's intimate areas whilst midwifing the birth, I would have to sign the Official Secrets Act...*

> *...I held her hand and timed her contraptions that were now coming just seconds apart...*

Load of pollocks: Paul was hawking frozen fish when he found himself delivering Britney's baby.

Next week: "How I delivered a pair of twins for **JENNIFER LOPEZ** the same day as doing Caesarians on all of the **PUSSYCAT DOLLS**. And **ATOMIC KITTEN**."

LETTERbOCKS

Viz Comic
P.O. Box 841
Whitley Bay
NE26 9EQ
letters@viz.co.uk

STAR LETTERS

HAVING just been to see *Legend*, the film about the Kray twins, I have to say that I was pleasantly surprised. In one scene, Reggie Kray was actually wearing a seatbelt when he set off to a pub to shoot somebody. So, perhaps he was not quite the lawless gangster that history would have us believe.

Sheldon Chips, Hull

I'M fed up with people keep telling me "If you change nothing, nothing changes." Well I can tell you, I haven't changed my underpants for two weeks now and the smell from my arse and gusset region has changed considerably.

C Moxon, Barnsley

I JUST passed a van that did 'tyre fitting on the move'. Can any of your readers think of a more pointlessly complicated and dangerous profession?

Pat Carpets, Lancaster

LOCAL authorities should move cycle lanes from the kerb side of the road to the centre. Then we'd see how those smug gits cope with a bit of proper traffic instead of their usual bobbing and weaving and creeping up the inside, frightening the life out of me.

T O'Neill, Glasgow

I DON'T know why the contestants on *Dragons' Den* get so nervous and tongue-tied. If these so-called business magnates are so shit-hot, how come they're working out of a dirty old warehouse and not a plush suite of offices in the city? I'd tell them "I'm out," and they can shove their investments up their arses.

Richard Blofeld, Totnes

IF James Bond has a licence to kill, does that mean that if he killed someone while he was pissed he would lose it? Also, while he was on the provisional licence, could he only beat someone up badly rather than actually doing them in? I certainly hope MI6 don't come trying to recruit me as it's all far too complicated.

Tarquin Balls, Oxford

I WAS going to race that Mo Farah bloke once and I reckon I would have beaten him easily. But on the day of the race I forgot my plimsolls. Have any readers had similarly life-ruining experiences?

D Hayes, Merthyr Tydfil

THEY say that if you can remember the sixties, you weren't there. By this rationale, anyone who can't remember the sixties was there. My daughter is eighteen years old and has absolutely no recollection of that particular decade, but I know for a fact that she definitely wasn't around because I hadn't even reached puberty myself.

Marjorie Whalebones, Deal

I RECKON if Bin Laden had wanted to soften his reputation a bit and have people view him without so much dread and hatred, he could have done a lot worse than changing his name slightly. I think a pipe-smoking, trilby-wearing Osama 'Bing' Laden would have been more palatable and maybe even have made him a more likeable character in the eyes of the west. But as he was shot in the head, I guess we'll never know.

Vic Unilever, Nottingham

I RECENTLY met a man who claimed he could communicate with the dead, but it turned out he was just full of shit. Have any other readers met someone who claimed they could communicate with the dead but turned out to be full of shit?

Tony Chalk, Rhostyllen

THE other day I walked past a plant in the park which smelled like man juice. After some online research it turns out that this offensive plant is called Callery Pear, which is fine by me. However its Latin name is, disappointingly, *Pyrus calleryana* and not *Spunkarus jizzyana* as it should be. Have these scientists got no imagination?

Tim, St Albans

TYPE 'falconry' into Google and then click the 'images' tab. Unless of course you're not interested in pictures of falconry, in which case don't bother.

Gus, London

INSTEAD of having fashion models walk up and down the catwalk, why not simply use a contraption similar to an airport luggage carousel? This would ensure that the audience could get a proper look at the frocks, and the models wouldn't keep going arse over tit like they always do. Not only that, the fifteen-minute wait for the carousel to start up would add to the suspense and excitement of the whole glittering event.

Clark Somerset, Somerset

WITH reference to Mr Somerset's Star Letter (*above*). Although this is a good idea in principle, I think it would be impractical. The people behind the scenes loading the models onto the carousel would more than likely open up their dresses, rifle through them and steal their underwear. Some of the models may go missing altogether.

Hector Chrome, Hull

IF people want to make money betting, why don't they simply put money on the horse which will win the race? Time after time, I see people betting on horses which don't win, and losing their money. It makes no sense to me. The same goes for dog racing.

Alan Farley, Garn

SCIENTISTS have uncovered evidence that chimpanzees have evolved to such an extent that they have entered the Stone Age. Let's hope that they will soon start making mammoth skin clothes instead of displaying their private parts all over the jungle like hairy sex perverts.

D Attenborough, Redruth

TOP

NUCLEAR physicists. Want to split the atom? Simply stick one in a box and mail it to yourself using the Royal Mail's 'Parcelforce' service. It is guaranteed not to arrive in one piece. For splitting subatomic protons and neutrons into quarks, simply mark the box 'Fragile. Handle with care.'

B Brady, Compton Bishop

GENTS. Next time you go to a wife swapping party and spot a wife with whom you would like to sleep, slip her your car keys before everyone else puts their key into the bowl. She can then pretend to pick yours out.

Su Norton, Lydney

TWO chocolate digestives with jam and marshmallow squashed in-between make an excellent 'artisan' Wagon Wheel.

Seamus Geilguid, Liverpool

WHENEVER you drink milk, you should consider that an innocent cow has been sexually molested.

David Craik, Hull

I ONCE raced that Usain Bolt and I was beating him easily but I had to pull up 10 yards from the line because one of my shoelaces came undone and I didn't want to trip.

D Hayes, Merthyr Tydfil

MY mother told me I shouldn't get crumpets out of a toaster with a knife as it was dangerous. I told her it wasn't dangerous if you were careful not to let the knife touch the elements, advice she ignored with fatal consequences when she next had a crumpet. So please could I strongly remind all your readers to make sure the knife doesn't touch the element when getting crumpets out of a toaster.

Tim Tom, Lancaster

LADIES. If a man slips you his car keys at a wife swapping party, take them. If he's a hunk, you can pretend to take them out of the bowl. If he looks like Shane MacGowan's less attractive brother, you can surreptitiously drop them back in for some other poor sod to pick out.

H Monkbottle, Fulchester

MAKE people think you've got an invisible trumpet by pretending to play it every time you fart.

Bury Bob, Bury

DRIVERS. When in a car park, avoid putting those little plastic tokens in your mouth when you pick them out of the machine at the barrier. I always rub my cheesy bell end on them before leaving, so you never know when you might get one of my old ones.

Squatting Dog, Aberdeen

I WAS travelling on the tube the other day and as we pulled into Green Park station, the driver made the announcement "Change here for Buckingham Palace." I realise that the Queen has served this country for longer than any other monarch and deserves our respect, but to get personalised announcements for her house seems a step too far. Plus, I doubt she would take the tube anyway.

T Gate, e-mail

HAVE any other readers seen that American wrestling? It's not like our football. I saw a match the other day and one of the wrestlers kicked his opponent in the head and then hit him with a chair and he didn't get sent off. Then another bloke pretended to be really injured but was blatantly putting it on and there was no yellow card for simulation. I have to say, the ref was having an absolute shocker.

Neil Johnson, Durham

WHERE did the term 'shit through the eye of a needle' come from? I had a dicky tum recently and I couldn't even shit through the eye of the toilet when I was sitting on it.

Mat (one T), Edinburgh

WHEN my granny was alive, she would say that all gay men were very house-proud. I used to think that this was just a rather unhelpful, if well-intentioned, generalisation that stereotyped gay men into one category. However, when I visited a gay friend of mine last week, I noticed that his flat was particularly tidy, so maybe my granny was right after all.

Miles Fibreboard, Luton

I'M afraid Mr Fibreboard *(above letter)* is gravely mistaken. Knowing one gay man with a tidy flat does not mean that all gay men are tidy. He should do a control experiment, whereby he visits a heterosexual friend to check that his flat is a tip to confirm the theory.

Lembit Spoons, Carlisle

HAS Mr Spoons *(above letter)* no idea of how statistics work? The samples are simply so small as to make the results meaningless. What if he visited his gay friend the day after his hoover had broken. Or imagine he dropped in on his straight pal the day after his mum came round and did a spring clean. What Mr Fibreboard should do is visit the flats of 500 gay and 500 straight friends and mark them out of 10 for tidiness to see if there is any statistically significant difference in the state of their flats.

Dr Jules Overcoat, Leeds

OH, dear. I'm afraid Dr Overcoat *(above letter)* is guilty of the 'bad science' prevalent amongst academics today. Knowing whether the flat belonged to a straight or gay man before he marked them for cleanliness might lead him, unconsciously, to sway the results. The best methodology to employ would be to choose 1000 men at random from the phone book, visit their flats and mark them out of 100 on their overall tidiness. The visits should be repeated at least five times over a set time period, any outlying results eliminated, and the average score for each flat taken. Only then, after these results were obtained, should the flat owners be questioned about their sexual orientation.

Dr Ben Goldacre, London

I THINK that a very poor choice of models for the pictures on Pioneer 10 and 11 is the reason we have not been visited by extra-terrestrial life. If an alien saw that, they would think that all earth women had tits like two asprins on an ironing board. I can't blame them for not visiting us. I wouldn't cross half the known galaxy unless the women of the planet I was going to were 38DDs at least.

Brampton Feldspar, Oakham

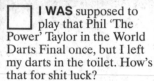

RECENTLY a seagull shat on my head as it flew over, an event my mother used to say was lucky. I'm not usually one for superstitions, but I thought I'd try my luck on the lottery. After buying 16 tickets and 12 scratch cards, I was amazed to later find out I had won £25. Maybe there's more to this world than what meets the eye.

Richard Dawkins, Oxford

WHILST buying a lovely woollen jumper for the coming winter from my local Marks and Spencer, a ridiculously attractive lady at the checkout asked me for my email address. Naturally, I was extremely flattered and somewhat excited at the prospect of her emailing me to arrange a date. That was two weeks ago and I still haven't heard anything from her. All I get is M&S sending me notifications of their latest sales. I'm starting to think M&S have stolen my email address from my checkout angel.

Jockey Scotsman, Monton

I WAS supposed to play that Phil 'The Power' Taylor in the World Darts Final once, but I left my darts in the toilet. How's that for shit luck?

D Hayes, Merthyr Tydfil

"NEVER regret anything that made you smile," wrote 19th century wit and novelist Mark Twain. This would hold a lot more water with me if I hadn't have been pissing myself laughing whilst I shat in a pint glass in Magaluf in 2003.

Jack Gray, Cheltenham

WHATEVER happened to scuba divers getting their flippers caught in giant clams' mouths? Nowadays it's all great white sharks. Come on, the sea, where's your sense of nostalgia?

Guy Venables, West Dean

After his entire family were eaten by a shark, marine biologist Dr Dick Hymensnapper vowed that no one else from Hammerhead Bay would ever perish in the jaws of one of these evil man-eating monsters. Now, together with his colleagues Billy-Bob Prepuce and Shania Perineum, he tirelessly patrols the waterfront in search of these killers of the deep. They are...

THE SHARK HUNTERS OF HAMMERHEAD BAY!

At Shark Patrol HQ.

WHOOP-WHOOP!

WHOOP-WHOOP!

SHARK PATROL

Shark alert! A Great White's been spotted in the harbour!

Quick, let's get down there!

Hymensnapper fired up the Shark Patrol jeep and the team set off.

Minutes later, the intrepid hunters arrived at the seafront car park...

My God! It must be twenty-five foot!

We're going to need all the firepower we can muster to kill that brute!

Come on, let's get parked. Can anybody see a space?

There's one!

No, that's disabled.

Look at that. Parked across two spaces so no one dunches his doors.

Selfish bastard. I hope he gets a ticket.

Stop, Dick. Someone going there, look!

Great!

Come on, woman, come on!

What's she doing?

Come on, you can put your seatbelt on later, woman. Jesus. We've got a man-eating shark to kill here.

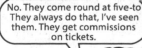

GILBERT RATCHET

GOLLY! I WANTED TO BUY DAD A FUNNY CARD FOR HIS BIRTHDAY..

GREETIN

BIRTHDAY CARDS £1·99

BUT I CAN'T AFFORD THESE PRICES!

NEVER MIND — I'VE INVENTED THIS 'HUMOROUS-BIRTHDAY-GREETING-O-MATIC' WHICH WILL BATTER DAD OVER THE HEAD WITH A TOMBSTONE WHILST CRUELLY MOCKING HIS ADVANCING AGE.

BLEEP HA HA, YOU'RE NEARLY DEAD, YOU OLD GIT!

THAT'S ODD — DAD DOESN'T SEEM PARTICULARLY AMUSED BY MY HUMOROUS BIRTHDAY GREETING O MATIC.

HA HA! YOU'RE FALLING TO BITS, YOU DECREPIT OLD TWAT!

SIGH SORRY GILBERT. I'M FEELING A BIT GLUM ABOUT GETTING OLD.

THE YEARS SEEM TO BE WHIZZING PAST MUCH TOO QUICKLY.

NOT TO WORRY DAD — I'LL CONSTRUCT A MACHINE THAT WILL SLOW DOWN THE PASSAGE OF TIME FOR YOU!

SEE, THIS DEVICE WILL SIMULATE THE EFFECT OF WAITING FOR A TRAIN CONNECTION AT LLANDUDNO JUNCTION WHILST A DRUNKEN JIM DAVIDSON EXPLAINS TO YOU THE SHORTCOMINGS OF HIS EX-WIVES, IN THE RAIN.

THE MINUTES WILL CRAWL BY AT A SNAIL'S PACE!

UH-OH! TIME IS PASSING SO SLOWLY FOR DAD THAT THE MASS OF HIS BODY IS INCREASING, IN ACCORDANCE WITH EINSTEIN'S SPECIAL THEORY OF RELATIVITY! *

* PLEASE ADDRESS ALL CORRESPONDENCE TO: VIZ COMPLAINTS DEPT. C/O PROF BRIAN COX, UNIVERSITY OF MANCHESTER.

YOW! DAD HAS BECOME SO HEAVY THAT THE PLATFORM HAS COLLAPSED UNDER HIS WEIGHT!

CRASH!

OOYAH! I ACHE ALL OVER!

THANKS A BUNCH GILBERT — NOW I FEEL MORE OLD AND DECREPIT THAN EVER!

THE KEY TO FEELING YOUNG IS LOOKING YOUNG, DAD...

I'LL RIG UP A GADGET THAT WILL HELP YOU ACHIEVE JUST THAT!

SEE, MY AUTOMATIC UNDERPANT EXPOSER WILL KEEP YOUR TROUSERS PULLED HALFWAY DOWN YOUR ARSE, IN THE YOUTHFUL FASHION!

WOW, YES! JUST LIKE A YOUNG PERSON!

OH-EM-GEE, GILBERT! THIS DEVICE OF YOURS IS EFF-TEE-DOUBLEYOU!

I TOTES FEEL THIRTY YEARS YOUNGER, INNIT?

BELLOW!

CHARGE!

LOOK OUT DAD!

THE SIGHT OF YOUR RED SPOTTED UNDERPANTS HAS ENRAGED THAT TRADITIONAL CARTOON BULL!

CRASH!

EEYOW!

OOOH! THAT MUST'VE HURT!

THE BULL HAS SPEARED DAD RIGHT THROUGH THE NETHER REGIONS!

CLONK!

SNORT!

YIKES! NOW DAD'S BEEN TOSSED HEAD-FIRST INTO A WASPS' NEST!

ANGRY BUZZ!

AARGH! MY FACE IS GETTING STUNG TO SMITHEREENS!

OO-ER! DAD IS SURE TO BE CROSS WITH ME NOW!

CROSS?! I'VE GOT UNSIGHTLY BIG RED LUMPS ALL OVER MY FACE AND AN UNCOMFORTABLE HORN WHICH SEEMS TO BE PERMANENTLY STUCK IN MY PANTS...

...IT'S JUST LIKE BEING A TEENAGER AGAIN! CHEERS GILBERT — YOU'VE REGAINED MY LOST YOUTH FOR ME!

REMOTE CONTROL PUNCHLINE-O-MATIC

BADUM TISH!

Where the Hell's Roger?

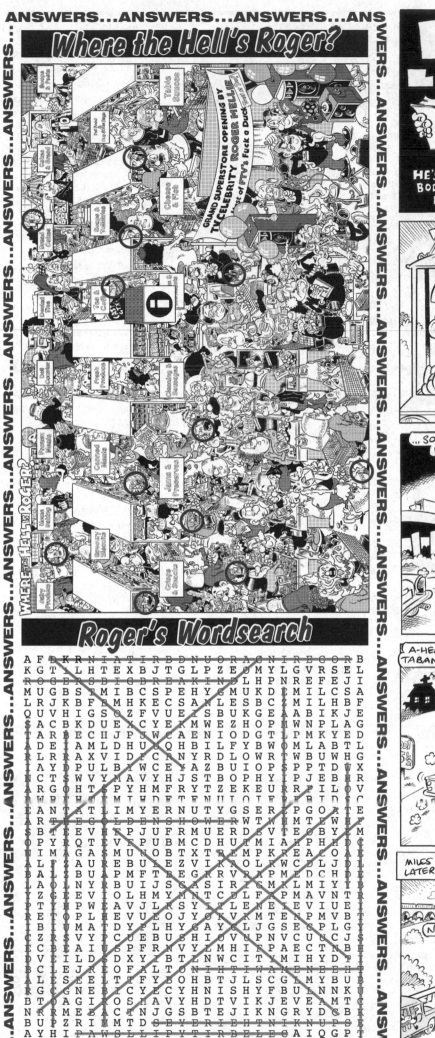

Roger's Wordsearch

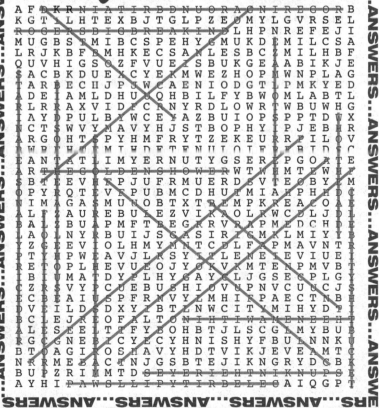

...ANSWERS...ANSWERS...ANSWERS...ANSWERS...ANSWERS...ANSWERS...

SHAME, SET & MATCH!

Undercover reporter exposes disgrace of behind-the-scenes bullying at Wimbledon

Court shorts: 63-year-old Perkin Parmit posed as a ball boy.

THE WIMBLEDON tournament is the jewel in the crown of the British sporting calendar. Each summer, the leafy West London suburb opens its ivy-clad doors and welcomes the best tennis players from around the world to compete in the prestigious Grand Slam championship. For a fortnight, the All England Club echoes to the grunts of the competitors, the cheers of the crowd and the gasps of people looking at the price of the strawberries.

But one sound you'll never hear on Centre Court is a "please" or "thank-you" from a player. For, despite being handed balls, towels and drinks of barley water up to 500 times during an average match, competitors consistently fail to utter a single courteous pleasantry in return to the ball boys and girls who dance attendance on them throughout the tournament.

And the stars' lack of respect for their on-court underlings was thrown into stark relief at this year's tournament, when top seed Novak Djokovic reduced a ball girl to tears with an angry outburst over a towel.

But if you think the players' on-court behaviour is bad, behind the scenes the Wimbledon stars degenerate even further and they become out and out **BULLIES**. To prove it, during this year's championships veteran *Daily Express* sports hack **PERKIN PARMIT** went undercover as a ball boy to expose top-ranking players such as Roger Federer, Serena Williams and Novak Djokovic. "If you think they're bullies on-court, you should see what they're like off-court," he told us.

SHOCKING UNDERCOVER REPORT!

"What I uncovered about the top tennis stars during my two weeks as a ball boy shocked me and will shock every right-minded person in Britain," added Parmit.

THIS YEAR'S men's champion Novak Djokovic made headlines when his angry Centre Court outburst during a fourth round match against Stan Wawrinka apparently left a ball girl sobbing. But what viewers might not have realised was that the number one seed had already brought tears to Parmit's eyes before the game even started.

❝Just before the match, I was helping Novak prepare in the Wimbledon dressing room, packing spare racquets and wristbands into his Adidas bag. I thought I'd done a good job, but Djokovic had other ideas, and whacked me round the back of the head with his racquet. He can serve at nearly 150mph, so the wallop came keen. Shocked, stunned and upset, I asked him what the matter was. *"You stupid little bellender, you've forgotten my bananas!"* he screamed in my face. I could feel his spit on my cheek.

bananas

I quickly got a bunch of bananas from the bowl on the side, and tried to squeeze them into the bag, but there was no room. I asked Djokovic if I should take a couple of racquets out to make room for them and he just went mental. His outburst was unprintable. *"If you don't get those bananas in that fucking bag, I'll shove them up your fucking arse, you titting ballsack!"* he yelled. His eyes were bulging and his face was purple with rage.

sleeper

I couldn't believe what was happening. How could a big star treat a small boy like this? My bottom lip started to tremble and I felt the tears welling in my eyes. When he saw that I was upset, Djokovic laughed at my distress and kicked me repeatedly up the shorts, calling me a big crybaby and a gaylord. By now sobbing uncontrollably, and with Djokovic's taunts echoing in my ears, I somehow managed to squeeze the bananas into the sports bag and carried it out for him.

love & death

Once on Centre Court, Djokovic was all sweetness and light, smiling for the cameras and waving to the crowds. But if the celebrities in the Royal Box had been able to see how he'd been treating me just moments before, I'm sure their cheers would have been replaced by boos. ❞

THIS YEAR'S losing finalist Roger Federer has won the Wimbledon Championships seven times and is a firm favourite with the Centre Court crowds and tennis fans around the world. But, says Parmit, the Swiss tennis star's bullying ways behind the scenes have won him few friends amongst the ball boys and girls who are the constant butts of his cruel jibes and taunts when the cameras are off.

❝I was sent to the dressing rooms to take Federer some barley water when play was suspended halfway through the third set because of a shower of rain during his quarter final against Gilles Simon. I handed him the glass and turned to leave. *"Where do you think you're going, you pathetic squirt?"* he said. *"Kiss my shoes. Go on, kiss them."*

zelig

I thought he must be joking, but when I looked in his face and saw his lip drawn back in a cruel sneer, it was obvious he meant business. *"Are you deaf or stupid or what?"* he taunted. *"Kiss my shoes or I'll smash your fat face in."*

Tennis the menace: Top stars like Novak Djokovic (left) and Roger Federer (right) are big bullies, says Perkin.

It was utterly humiliating, but I just wanted to get out of that dressing room in one piece, so I kneeled down and kissed Federer's trainers. I thought I'd got away with it but Federer hadn't even started. What he did next turned my stomach.

nose

Reaching down the back of his shorts, he broke wind into his hand before clasping it across my nose and mouth, holding it there tightly until I had no choice but to breathe in. "That's disgusting," I choked. "You ought to be ashamed of yourself Federer, you big bully." His expression changed to one of mock concern. *"Aw diddums,"* he jeered, sticking out his bottom lip. *"Let me help you wash your face."*

Next thing I knew, he was pushing my head into the lavatory and flushing it, kneeing me in the backside as he did so. Above the gurgle of the water I could hear Federer's mocking laughter and his repeated taunts of: *"Drink it, fartface. Drink it!"*

blow

Fortunately, at that moment the referee announced on the tannoy that the rain had stopped and it was time for the match to re-start. Federer let me go and I pulled my head out of the toilet. As he left to go back out on court he threatened me, leaving me in no doubt that if I told on him, he'd get me after the match and kick my face in. I dried myself off as best I could with a paper towel and returned back to the court for the last few games of the final set.

drain

It was an easy win for Federer against the French 12th seed, and as he left Centre Court, the crowd cheered him to the rafters. But I couldn't hear their applause. My ears were still burning with the humiliation of what I had suffered during the rain break. And also they were still full of toilet water.

YOU MIGHT think that bullying is a predominantly male pursuit, and that girls are too sensitive to indulge in such cruel, tormenting behaviour. But amazingly, says Parmit, the stars of the ladies' tennis circuit are every bit as bad as their men counterparts.

" It was the day of the ladies' semi-finals and my mum had given me fifty pence to get some crisps. I was on my way to the ball boys' tuck shop by Centre Court when I noticed four girls in tennis dresses gathered by the lockers. My heart sank as I recognised them as Serena Williams and the other semi-finalists. They were hanging around killing time as their games didn't start for another twenty minutes. I didn't want any trouble, so I stared at the floor and tried not to meet their eyes as I tried to sneak past them and get through the door. But a muscular

> ## *Reaching down the back of his shorts, Federer broke wind into his hand before clasping it across my nose and mouth...*

leg was blocking my way. "Where are you going, you virgin?" I immediately recognised the mocking voice as belonging to Serena Williams. The other girls laughed, egging her on. "Yeah, bumfluff. Where are you going?" they chorused. "Are you going to the toilets for a wank?" I could feel my face reddening with embarrassment as their spiteful cackles echoed down the corridor.

New balls please: ladies semi-finalists teased embarrassed Perkin that he hadn't attained puberty and shut him in cramped locker.

"No he's not," taunted Serena. "He can't have a wank because he hasn't got any pubes." All four of them burst out in peals of mocking laughter as I burnt up with shame. "Look!" cackled Agnieszka Radwanska, noticing my scarlet cheeks. "He's got a cherry on. Bumfluff boy's got a cherry on!" They licked their fingers, touched my cheeks and hissed, pretending they were so hot that the water was boiling off them.

horn

I tried to push past my tormentors to get away but Serena was now standing in my way with her sneering sidekicks standing beside her. "Oh no, you don't get away that easily," she announced. "Get him, girls." The next thing I knew I'd been pushed to the ground and they were going through my pockets, stealing the fifty pence my mum had given me for my crisps, my asthma inhaler - which they stamped on - and some Panini football stickers that they proceeded to rip up in front of me.

My tears welled up as I looked at the shreds of my best stickers lying on the floor, but Williams and her gang of bullies hadn't finished with me yet. Before I knew what was happening, the laughing foursome had picked me up and stuffed me into Serena's locker and turned the key. "We'll be back for you later, baldy-bollocks!" they called as they all left to play their semi-finals.

bag

Serena crushed Sharapova in straight sets, so it was less than an hour later when she returned and unlocked the door. I leapt out of the locker and made my escape, dodging past her and heading for the dressing room exit as fast as my legs would carry me. I didn't dare look behind me, and ran all the way home and up to my bedroom. My mum asked me if I'd enjoyed my crisps, and I just burst into tears. "

ALTHOUGH firm favourites with the Wimbledon crowds, the Murray brothers, Andy and Jamie, have a reputation at the championships for making their subordinates' lives a misery, meting out Chinese burns, barbers' scrubs and dead legs to any ball boy unfortunate enough to cross their path. So when Perkin found out he was scheduled to be in charge of providing dressing room towels on men's quarter-finals day when they were both playing, he went to desperate lengths to avoid being on the receiving end of their bullying.

" I pretended to have a tummy ache at breakfast and told my mum that I was too poorly to go into Wimbledon that day. But she was having none of it. She dosed me up with cod liver oil before dropping me off at the gates of the All England Club, watching me till I went inside to make sure I didn't nick off.

job

When I got to the changing rooms, the Murrays were waiting for me. "Where've you been, you wee bumboy?" they scoffed. When I hotly protested that I wasn't a bumboy, Andy grabbed me in a half-Nelson and twisted my arm up my back. The pain was excruciating. "Say you're a bumboy," he growled. "Say it! Say you're a bumboy." "Okay," I replied. "You're a bumboy." It felt good to fight back, but I knew that cheeking the Murrays would only make things worse.

"Let's make him eat a dog dirt," said Jamie, and the brothers grabbed me and dragged me outside and round the back of the BBC commentary box. There, in the gutter, was an old dog turd

Doubles trouble: Murray brothers made ball boys' lives a misery.

with a lolly stick stuck in it. Andy picked it up by the stick and waved it under my nose. The smell filled my nostrils and I heaved as the British number one pushed the stinking number two closer and closer to my face. "Come on," he mocked. "Eat up your nice lolly. It's shite flavour, your favourite."

tool

Jamie had his arm round my neck and he pinched my nose to make me open my mouth. As luck would have it, just at that moment the tournament referee Mr Jarrett came round the corner. "What on earth is going on here?" he demanded. Jamie released me immediately and Andy threw the turd onto the commentary box roof. "We were just playing a game of hide and seek with this ball boy, sir," said Andy, innocently. "Isn't that right, sonny?" I felt Jamie's knuckle pressing into the small of my back and nodded mutely.

"Where should you be?" said Mr Jarrett, looking sternly over his glasses at the Scots pair. "Getting warmed up for our matches, sir," replied Andy. "Well why aren't you?" said Jarrett. "Don't know, sir," they mumbled. "Well go and do it," said the referee. "And don't let me catch you again mucking around here when you should be practising." Andy and Jamie slinked off, but I knew they'd be back to get me later, as soon as Jarrett's back was turned.

> ## *Let's make him eat a dog dirt," said Jamie, and the brothers grabbed me and dragged me outside...*

Then the referee asked me why I wasn't in the dressing room sorting out towels. I could have told him about how the Murrays tried to make me eat a dog dirt, but they would have denied it.

It would have been a lowly ball boy's word against the darling of British tennis and his brother. In any case, their mum, Judy Murray, was always at Wimbledon, and I knew if I'd told on them, she would have gone in to see the referee and told him that her sons weren't bullies and they didn't tell lies. It would have been me that ended up getting done off old Jarrett. "

Minn's SPIES

"Hi Readers, Minnie Driver here. You may know me best for... erm... erm... I'll come back to that. But when I'm not doing that, whatever it is, I'm mad about the world of espionage. I just can't get enough of spies, intelligence gathering and secret services. Of course, I'm not a spy myself (although if I was, that's exactly what I would say, so maybe I am). But I'm not one. Or am I? Anyway, whether I am or not, judging by the size of my *Minn's Spies* postbag, *Viz* readers are just as mad about spies and spying as I am. Here's a selection of some of the best letters I've received this week... *for your eyes only!*" *Minnie xx*

IF I had a licence to kill like James Bond, I don't think I'd use it very much. Just my brother-in-law and the man who sits by the fruit machine in the pub and only goes on it and wins after I've put a load of money in it. But I wouldn't use it much after that, because killing is wrong. Oh, and the taxi driver who comes for the bloke next door at four in the morning and blows his horn. And the man off the Cillit Bang adverts. But that's it.

Terry Spermwhale, Hull

MY wife would make a terrible spy as she can't keep a secret for the life of her. She told everyone in the post office when I got a septic anal fissure, that I have a spent conviction for indecent exposure and that I caught VD off a prostitute in Nottingham a couple of years ago. Honestly, if she got a job at MI5 the Russians would know all our ruddy state secrets by teatime.

Frank Ballspond, Hull

MY husband worked as an intelligence agent in MI6 for many years, and it always used to make him laugh when he watched James Bond films, because the reality of his job was nothing like the picture presented onscreen. He did have a fountain pen with a laser gun in it and a watch that could undo the zip on my dress, but apart from that his working life was as far removed from the movie spy fantasy as it is possible to imagine.

Ada Rimmer, Braintree

FURTHER to my previous letter, my husband also had a company car with missile launchers behind the bumper bars, and he once drove it into the sea and it turned into a submarine. But apart from that, the picture of the intelligence services presented in James Bond films is simply nonsense.

Ada Rimmer, Braintree

WHENEVER someone is exposed as a double agent working for the Russians, they invariably turn out to be Cambridge-educated homosexuals, eg. Burgess, Maclean, Blunt etc. Why don't MI6 simply stop employing Cambridge graduates and homosexuals? Come on, this is basic stuff.

Glenda Spite, Jarrow

I'D lovo to bo a spy, and I'vo invontod my own socret codo. This lottor will appoar gibborish unloss you can crack it! To dociphor it, roplaco all tho o's with o's.

Oddio McAtoor, Onfiold

IF anyone from the secret service is reading this, I'd just like to say that I'd love to be a spy and go on secret missions etc. I'll be sat on a bench in the National Gallery next Tuesday afternoon looking at Turner's *Fighting Temeraire*, and if you want to make contact, sit down next to me and say: "The spring has come early in Berlin." I will reply: "Yes, and the geese are flying high this year," and we'll take it from there.

Denis Plaxton, Monmouth

WHY, when secret agents make contact with one another, do they do it in a park where there are lots of people around, walking their dogs, jogging and taking the air? They ought to buy a couple of tickets for Sting's Broadway musical *The Last Ship*, where they will be guaranteed complete privacy.

A Pantin Harrogate

WHEN I was six, I met a real-life spy in the park. He didn't look anything like James Bond, he was shabbily dressed with stains down the front of his tracksuit bottoms. He offered me sweets and asked me if I wanted to go back to his spying headquarters for a play with all his gadgets. But unfortunately it was my tea-time so I wan't able to go with him. I still regret my missed opportunity, as it would have been fascinating to take a close-up peek at the hidden world of espionage.

Seth Hargreaves, Deal

I RECENTLY watched that movie *Tinker Tailor Soldier Spy* starring Gary Oldman, but I must say it was quite a disappointment, as it was 100% about spying, which doesn't particularly interest me. From the title, I would have expected it to be 75% about tinkering, tailoring and

---

YOU SEE THEM every day in films and on TV, but if you passed one on the street you'd never know. They're all around but they're completely invisible, lurking in the shadows. Your next door neighbour, or even your wife or husband could be one and you wouldn't know. They're spies, and here's a dossier of Top Secret Titbits about these undercover spooks with a licence to kill.

I spy with my little eye...

007 Things You Never Knew about SPIES

001 SECRET agents fearlessly stare death in the face every day, but amazingly they are terrified of wasps. "I don't know what it is about wasps that shits spies right up," MI6 head **Stella Rimmington** told *Take a Break* magazine. "But if one of them stripy little bastards comes in the room, they're all jumping out the windows on their Union Jack parachutes before you can say Jack Robinson."

002 THE smallest spy ever to be recruited by MI6 was **Calvin Phillips**. His official agent number was 00.007, and he was issued with a Scalextric-sized Aston Martin complete with miniature machine guns, a tiny ejector seat and launchers that could fire missiles the size of biro tops a distance of up to four feet.

003 EVER since the so-called "fourth man" **Sir Anthony Blunt** was outed as a Russian spy in 1979, the hunt has been on to identify the so-called "fifth man". Many possible names have been put forward, including Foreign Office civil servant **John Cairncross**, *Ground Force* handyman **Tommy Walsh**, Basil Brush sidekick **Mr Roy**, football pundit **Jimmy Hill** and performance artists **Gilbert & George**.

soldiering, all subjects that I am fascinated by. Another example of rip-off Britain.

Mrs Audrey Dogspenis, Godalming

FURTHER to my previous letters, my husband once went to space in order to destroy a giant diamond-coated reflector that a man with a cat and a scar was going to use to focus the sun's rays on the United Nations, and on his way back he got thrown out of a plane by a man with metal teeth and had to run across some crocodiles. But apart from that, he said his job in the intelligence service mainly involved a lot of boring paperwork and form-filling.

Ada Rimmer, Braintree

SPIES have to blend into their surroundings, so anyone who stands out in a crowd due to being exceptionally tall would make a very bad secret agent. For this reason, nobody would expect the CIA to recruit them, so ironically they are perfectly suited to being spies. If the Russians are smart, they would ban the Harlem Globetrotters from visiting the Kremlin, except Meadowlark Lemon who is only 5 foot 8.

Dr M Tinwhistle, Bakerwhistle

I WOULDN'T want a car with an ejector seat in it. If the electronics controlling it were anything like as temperamental as the "Blind Spot Information System" on my Volvo XC90, it would be going off and firing my passengers out the roof every five minutes.

Spud, Luton

"MY dad's a spy!" my six-year-old son boasted to a pal in the school playground. I had to laugh, because I'm not a spy at all, I'm a travelling salesman for a company that makes pressure valves for the gas industry. I do spend a lot of time travelling in eastern Europe, but I'm definitely not a spy, I can assure you of that. The reason I don't talk about my work and tend to change the subject if someone brings it up, is that my work is very technical and really quite boring. Anyway, I've already said too much. Did anyone see the football last night?

John Smith (not my real name), London

JUST like a spy, I am unable to come home in the evening and discuss my day at work with my family. It's not that doing so would endanger national security, it's just that I'm a pipe fitter and I've been unemployed for the last five years.

Frank Plywood, Tooting

'SPIES like us' sang Paul McCartney in 1986. I don't know much about the world of espionage, but I would imagine releasing a Top 20 song about the fact that you are a spy is a good way to blow your cover.

Maynard Pickpocket, Hull

MI5iam

DR MI5IAM STOPPARD ANSWERS YOUR PROBLEMS

Is My Hubby a Spook?

Dear M,

I THINK my husband might be working for the Russians. He says he isn't, but then that's exactly what he would say if he was. I am 33, my husband is 35 and we have been married for 8 years.

He works in a chipboard plant in Northumberland, and he has access to information about the woodchip making and hot glue processes used in the factory, and I am worried that he has been passing these secrets on to his KGB handlers.

He's never been to Russia, but then neither had Kim Philby, so that proves nothing. He could easily be meeting Soviet agents in Wentworth car park in Hexham on his lunch hour, handing them plans and microfilms. His friends say he never leaves the factory and spends his lunchtime in the canteen, but they may be double agents too, corroborating his story like Burgess and Maclean did with Philby.

Worried, Northumberland

Dear Worried,

I wouldn't be too concerned. The Russians have been manufacturing chipboard since the 1940s and their technology is far more advanced than our own. It is unlikely that your husband could be passing anything of interest to the Kremlin. It is far more probable that he is working as a handler, procuring secrets from a double agent embedded in a Soviet chipboard factory for his Northumberland-based paymasters.

Whatever you do, don't be tempted to share your concerns with your husband. If he fears his cover is about to be blown, he may stab you with a ricin-tipped umbrella or spike your tea with pollonium.

MI5iam

Dear M,

I'M WORRIED that my husband is having an affair. I am 33, my husband is 35 and we have been married for 8 years. He's a manager for Blandford AA1 Ltd., a Lancashire-based commercial crockery hire business.

We were happily married until a couple of months ago when he hired a very attractive, 20-year-old new secretary. Soon after taking her on, my husband started staying late at work every evening. When he did come home, late at night, he was always tired and went straight to bed.

The other day I found a pair of skimpy black lace knickers in his pocket and a receipt for a stay at a nearby hotel for a weekend when he told me he was away on a sales conference. My husband has become cold and distant, and I can't remember the last time we made love. I am certain he is carrying on with this woman. Please help me, MI5iam. What can I do to save my marriage?

Wendy, Ackrington

Dear Wendy,

It sounds to me like your husband is a spy and his business is merely a front for British Intelligence. His new "secretary" is almost certainly a glamorous Russian agent, planted by the KGB as a honey-trap to glean confidential military secrets from your husband during sex.

However, there is no need to worry, as your husband is undoubtedly feeding her false information. Only by sleeping with her is he able to convince her that the information he is feeding her is trustworthy. As soon as she has outlived her usefulness and passed on the maguffins to her Soviet handlers, after fucking her one last time he will dispassionately kill her by painting her gold. Then you can draw a line under this whole episode and start to work on putting your marriage back together.

MI5iam

004 SPYING isn't merely confined to sinister international intelligence agencies. Industrial espionage is also big business. In 2006, a man was caught snooping around the headquarters of Kentucky Fried Chicken, attempting to photograph the company's secret recipe of eleven herbs and spices. He later broke down under interrogation and admitted he was working for Nandos before being strapped to a table and cut in two using a giant laser beam.

005 IN 1968, at the height of the Cold War, an MI6 select XI captained by *Sir Nicholas Elliott* played a game of cricket against a KGB team led by Soviet deputy director of intelligence *Viktor Chebrikov*. However, details of the British team's batting order and bowling strategy were passed to the Russian side by a double agent working deep undercover, and the KGB won the match by an innings and 56 runs. The traitor's identity has never been discovered although many possible names have since been put forward, including former Chancellor *Sir Rab Butler*, BBC royal correpondent *Nicholas Witchell*, Basil Brush sidekick *Mr Howard* and *Kung Fu Fighting* singer *Carl Douglas*.

006 IF YOU'RE harbouring thoughts of joining the British Secret Service and you're left-handed you can forget it. That's because Q designs all his gadgets, such as suitcases with helicopters in them, cigarette lighter poison dart firers and cheesewire garotte cufflinks, for right-handed spies only. Also, in Monte Carlo, all the ladies' dresses fasten on the right hand side, making magnetic watches worn on the right wrist useless for pulling the zips down.

007 IN 1992, MI5 received intelligence that *Thunderbirds* Tracey Island was going to be that Christmas's must-have toy. However, a mole working for the KGB passed this information to his Kremlin paymasters. The Russians then managed to buy up more or less the entire world's stock of the playset, leaving children throughout Britain in tears on Christmas morning. The double agent responsible was never identified, but over the years several possible names have been put forward, including BBC Director General *Sir Hugh Carleton-Greene*, *TOWIE's* **Joey Essex**, Basil Brush sidekick *Mr Derek* and former Newcastle striker *Les Ferdinand*.

Then & Now

with Jack Then & Fred Now
This Week:
The High Street

BRITAIN is an ever-changing place, and nothing illustrates this better than our high streets. Whilst staying quintessentially the same, they are forever re-inventing themselves to keep up with the latest modern trends in shopping and lifestyle. Let's take a stroll down the high street of a typical, bustling market town from the mid-1970s and again down that exact same street today to see some of the fascinating changes that have taken place over the intervening forty years.

① The Butcher

BACK in the 1970s, the friendly local butcher knew all of his customers by name. And he didn't just sell them meat, pies and sausage rolls; he offered a proper service, preparing joints, making up orders and offering cooking advice to busy mums.

He would also make sure that his regular customers got the very best prime cuts and weren't given the meat that he had sexually interfered with in the back room of his shop.

FAST forward to the high street of today and the family butcher is long gone, forced out of business by competition from the supermarkets. However the meat connection remains, as his old premises have now been transformed into a pastie and pie franchise. The food on sale is only warmed up on site; all the meat is butchered, prepared and sexually interfered with at the company's main plant on an out-of-town industrial estate.

② The Grocer

FOUR decades ago, housewives bought fruit and vegetables from their cheery local greengrocer, a familiar figure on every high street with his brown dustcoat and a pencil stuck behind his ear. In those days, shoppers weren't allowed to handle the produce, giving the shopkeeper the opportunity to slip damaged, bruised and squashed items into their orders. He would also routinely put his thumb onto the weighing scales so he could overcharge his customers.

THESE charming customs of yesteryear have all but died out now, since people are now able to select, handle and weigh out their own fruit and veg at the supermarket. Indeed, the boot's now on the other foot, because not only can customers select the best produce for themselves, they can also cheekily push the scales back up with their thumb when weighing out their purchases at the self service tills.

③ The Shoe Shop

FORTY years ago, every town had at least one shoe shop. This specialised in flip-flops, school plimsolls and sensible school shoes, which were piled up in boxes in a back room behind a curtain. Of course, in such a small establishment there was a limit to how much stock could be held, but the shoe shop manager somehow always made sure that they had the style the customer wanted, but not in their size, or the size they wanted but not in the right colour.

TODAY, the shoe shop has long gone, replaced by one of the ubiquitous charity shops that have sprung up all over our town centres. Ironically, taking pride of place in the window amongst the James Last LPs, Dan Brown books and 'antique' knick-knacks, is a pair of dead man's shoes that were purchased as new in this exact shop back in the 1970s. Unfortunately they are still not in the right size or colour.

④ The Sex Shop

BACK in the day, every town had its own sex shop - an establishment where private requisites, marital aids and erotica were available for purchase by discerning adults. Of course, legal restrictions meant that the material on offer was heavily censored; the really hardcore material was only available from Scandanavia or under the counter following a muttered, cryptic conversation. In the days before mobile phone cameras and camcorders, the proprietors also offered a tactful, discreet film processing service, running off duplicate copies of their customers' amateur XXX efforts to swap and share with their fellow managers around the country.

INTERNET pornography is an inescapable fact of modern life. It's unavoidable, especially when feverishly searching for it online whilst the wife is at the shops, and its prevalence has led to a marked decline in the number of adult shops to be found in Britain's town centres. These days the sex shop

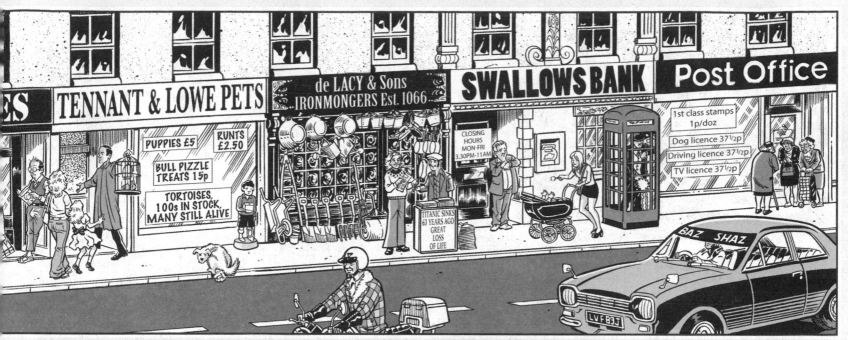

has become a taxi cab office, where really, really hardcore pornography is available from under the counter following a muttered, cryptic conversation with the man at the desk.

5 The Pet Shop

BRITAIN is both a nation of animal lovers and shopkeepers, and the old-fashioned pet shop - a familiar fixture on every high street - managed to combine these two elements perfectly. In the days before animal welfare busybodies, a visit to a pet shop was a fascinating experience, with a bewildering array of cages to peer into, each one piled high with budgies, kittens, puppies and baby rabbits, all happily playing in a mixture of sawdust and their own foulage. Exotic animals were shipped in from all over the world packed into crates, keeping costs down so that schoolboys could buy a tortoise with their pocket money. Anyone wanting one these days would be forced to shell out the thick end of £500 for a "humanely-bred" example.

TRAGICALLY, rising prices have closed down many of the country's traditional pet shops. This one has been replaced with a tattoo and piercing parlour.

6 The Ironmonger

THE old-fashioned ironmongers was a wonderland of household hardware. From a safety pin to a tin bath, from a mousetrap to a bag of cement, everything the customer might possibly have needed was available from one of these fascinating little shops. Behind the counter stood a man smoking a pipe, who immediately knew where to find anything he was asked for amongst his myriad of shelves piled high with dusty cardboard boxes and intriguing drawers full of useful treasures.

SADLY, the vast majority of traditional ironmongers have been forced out of business. The exact same stock that they used to carry is now available from vast, out-of-town superstores a thousand times as large, where the staff hide from customers in case they want to find out where anything is. The old ironmonger's shop is now an upmarket pawnbrokers where people who have got bored with their gold can exchange it for a small amount of money.

7 The Bank

IN the days before credit cards, debit cards and internet banking, the bank was the only place where people could get hold of the cash they needed to do their shopping. For added convenience, they closed at half-past three and didn't open at all at weekends.

THESE days, most high street branches have been closed, and account holders now use the ATM when they need to get hold of their money, for example to pay a mugger. For the customer's convenience, this cashpoint is covered in sick and has a tramp living underneath it in a sleeping bag.

8 The Post Office

IN the 1970s, the post office was the hub of the community - a centre where local news and gossip could be passed from old lady to old lady to old lady, like an olden-times Facebook or Twitter. Topics could quickly start "trending" and go "viral" in the queue for pensions and stamps... Is her from number twelve's baby really her husband's? You'll never guess who my sister saw going into the VD clinic. Have you heard? The butcher's been caught fucking his poultry again.

THANKS to emails and text-messaging, post offices have become a thing of the past. This one has become a betting shop - a new social hub where sports lovers can spend the day enjoying a frantic series of harmless flutters. The customers treat it all as a bit of fun, gambling responsibly and sensibly, setting themselves a strict limit of all their money. But even if they have a losing streak there's no need to worry, because they can just nip next door and sell some of their clothes to raise the stake money they need to win it all back.

9 The Telephone Box

SIR Giles Gilbert Scott's classic K6 design was a feature of every high street from 1926 onwards when the coin-operated handset inside was the only way to keep in touch whilst out and about. The red kiosks also doubled up as impromptu gentleman's lavatories, prostitute advertising spaces and a handy cover for a smoker to enjoy a cigarette in the rain.

IN these days of mobile phones, public space smoking bans and convenient call girl contact sites on the internet, telephone boxes are long gone, and people are now forced to piss in shop doorways instead.

1975 or 2015: Can you spot...?

- A young lad getting a good-natured clip round the ear off a bobby on the beat after getting caught pinching an apple.
- A young lad getting a good-natured searching after getting caught being black.
- A man in a pac-a-mac returning a dead parrot to the pet shop.
- A newspaper seller who lost an arm in the war.
- A youth paid to deliver free newspapers dumping his entire stock in a bin.
- A dog simply doing its business in the gutter.
- A modern, responsible dog owner scooping his pet's foulage up in a bag and leaving it on a pillar box.

- A tramp asking for 10p for a cup of tea.
- A modern artisan café asking £4.50 for a cup of tea.
- A massage parlour offering specialised gentlemen's lower abdominal stress relief treatments.
- A schoolboy coming out of a sweet shop after asking the old lady behind the counter to get a jar of Kola Kubes down from the top shelf.
- A fibreglass child with a caliper on his leg and a slot in his head.
- A child running off with a fibreglass child with a caliper on his leg and a slot in his head, under his arm.

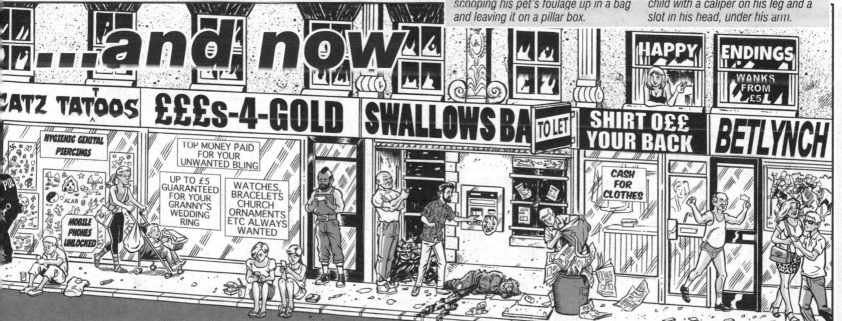

Next week - Then & Now: *The Mortuary at Leeds General Infirmary*

185

Hammond Unveils New Deficit Strategy

CHANCELLOR of the Exchequer *Phillip Hammond* has outlined his latest plan to get the country's economy back on track, and says he is now confident the UK will be able to wipe out its £90 billion-plus deficit before the next general election. In his Spring statement, the Chancellor said that he would be implementing a "bold new strategy" to pay off the burgeoning national debt.

"I was sat watching *Storage Wars* on Dave the other afternoon when I had the idea," he told MPs. "This bloke was on and he paid about two hundred dollars for the contents of a storage locker. When he got in it, there was a beach buggy under a sheet and it was worth eight thousand dollars."

pistols

"In the same programme, other lockers contained a pair of antique duelling pistols, a life size model Alien that had been used in a film and a cowboy hat belonging to Buffalo Bill. All these items were then sold on for profits running into thousands of dollars."

"In another episode, there was a unit that contained a load of valuable snakes, and a man came along and gave them two-and-a-half-thousand dollars cash for them," said Mr Hammond.

"There is money to be made in storage locker auctions, " he continued. "And it's about time Britain started to benefit from this hugely lucrative revenue stream."

Lock up Tsar: Darrell 'The Gambler' Sheets is set to sort out UK economy

To this end, Mr Hammond said that he intends to appoint one of the show's stars - Darrell Sheets - as an official *"Lock-up Auction Tsar"* to head up a national storage hunting taskforce. "Mr Sheets has a sort of sixth sense for spotting the valuable lots that the other bidders miss," said Hammond. "He is just the man we need to lead our country out of recession and kick-start the green shoots of economic growth."

case

But Shadow Chancellor John McDonnell slammed Hammond's plan. "As usual, the Chancellor is living in cloud cuckoo land," he said. "He is naive beyond belief if he imagines that buying up abandoned storage lockers is going to get us out of the economic mess that his financial mismanagement has got us into."

& the city

And McDonnell accused Hammond of being selective with his facts. "I too have seen the programme the Chancellor outlined in his statement to the house, but what he failed to point out is that in the very next episode, Brandon and Lori paid three thousand dollars for a lock-up that turned out to contain nothing more exciting than several boxes full of broken china, some old tyres and a pile of mouldy blankets," he said.

offenders register

The Shadow Chancellor set out his own strategy to clear the country's deficit. "We've got to be realistic," he said. "We must work on a sustainable economic budgetary plan to free this country from the unprecedented mountain of debt that we find ourselves facing. Hard choices have to be made, and sooner rather than later."

"It's about time we faced facts and started buying up unclaimed airline luggage," said Mr McDonnell. "There's this programme on the Travel Channel called *Baggage Battles*, and this bloke on it bought a suitcase and when he looked inside it had a pair of Harry Houdini's handcuffs in it."

"He only paid two hundred for the bag and the handcuffs were worth ten thousand dollars easy," added Mr. McDonnell.

TOMMY 'BANANA' JOHNSON: GOGGLEBOX EDITION

HE'S GOT A BIG BANANA!

I THINK I'LL GO TO THE PARK TODAY!

WHAT'S THIS?

I DUNNO, SOMEBODY WITH A BANANA OR SOMETHING.

OH DEAR! THIS PAINT IS STILL WET AND IT LOOKS LIKE IT'S GOING TO RAIN.

BEEN ON BEFORE THIS. LOADS OF TIMES. IT'S ALL REPEATS.

HEY, MISTER! WHY NOT USE MY BANANA AS A GIANT HAIR DRYER TO DRY THE PAINT?

WHAT'S HE DOIN'?

I DUNNO, BABES, I THINK HE'S GOING TO DRY PAINT WITH IT.

PISS OFF, AND TAKE YOUR GIANT FRIGGIN' BANANA WITH YA!

HAAAAAAA! HA! HA! HA!

ALRIGHT. I'M GOING.

HAVE YOU SEEN MY LITTLE DOG ANYWHERE? HE'S GONE MISSING.

WHAT DER FOCK IS DIS? IT'S SHIZER.

I'VE SEEN THIS BEFORE. HE USES IT AS A TELESCOPE OR SOMETHING.

NO, BUT WHY NOT USE MY BANANA AS A LARGE TELESCOPE TO LOOK FOR HIM?

TOLD YA!

GO ON, FUCK OFF!

HAAAAAAA! HA! HA! HA! HA! HA! HA! HA!

BLOODY BANANA TELESCOPE...

IT'S ALL SWEARING, ISN'T IT. THERE'S NO NEED FOR IT.

WHO WRITES THIS FACKING SHIT?

GOD KNOWS. SOME COMPLETE FACKING HALF-WIT.

OH, HERE'S THE POLICE. WHAT'S GOING TO HAPPEN NOW?

DOH! THE DOG'S MADE ME SPILL ME TEA.

HEY, TOMMY.

THAT BANANA IS JUST WHAT I'M LOOKING FOR! COULD I BORROW IT FOR A SECOND?

WHAT'S HE GOING TO DO WITH IT?

DON'T KNOW.

AGGH! MY BOTTOM!

AAAAAAH! HA! HA! HAAAA! HA! HA! HA!

WHAAAH, BABES! HE'S STUCK IT UP HIS ARSE! HA! HA! HA! HA! HA!

THAT SHOULD PUT A STOP TO YOUR BANANA PRANKS, EH TOMMY? HO! HO! HO!

STAR LETTER

A COLLEAGUE of mine drops his wife off at her workplace each morning before continuing his commute. Every day he says he holds a huge, smelly fart in until she gets out of the car, and then lets rip. He then laughs about this for the rest of his journey, wondering what her reaction would be. I was just wondering if any of your other readers have quirky commuting stories they would like to share.

G Bennett, Auckland

I KNOW mad people traditionally think they're the Emperor Napoleon, but what if one of them thought they were the Emperor Nero who was actually mad himself? Would a mad person thinking they were another mad person actually be a double negative, and mean they were actually sane?

Hamilton Charteris, Crewe

I NEVER think putting the clocks back is very sensible as so many things could go wrong. For instance, what if they went forward during the Le Mans 24 hour race? If the driver in last place with an hour to go crosses the line just as the clocks go forward, he could suddenly find that the race is over and he has won.

Les Broadchair, Hull

WHATEVER happened to dead hedgehogs flattened like pancakes along the highways and byways of Britain? Back in the 70s and 80s you used to see loads of them, but nowadays I can drive to London and back and not see one of the spiky wankers. Come on hedgehogs, get your act together. No wonder you're slipping out of the public consciousness.

Matthew Tennant, Newport

WHEN I was a child, I used to hate having a nap and getting spanked. Now I'm an adult I love it.

Ross, Snodland

I WENT to see the new Bond film the other night. About an hour into it, I really needed to take a piss, so I shouted, "Cut!" in order to get the film stopped while I went to the loo. When the film didn't stop, I shouted again. Eventually, a couple of staff members arrived to escort me from the cinema for causing a disturbance. It appears that there's one set of rules for the film director and another for the film audience members. Typical Hollywood bullshit.

Rudy Twotoot, Barnsley

DO ANY READERS know of a more ridiculous use of double yellow lines than this example in Hanley, Stoke on Trent? I mean, how in God's name would you get out of your car?

Lee 'Moz' Morrall, Hednesford

I once had a free black pudding at a Little Chef by pretending my uncle was Worzel Gummidge.

Greg Pertwee, Derby

DOES anyone know why my fridge has 'security glass' written on the shelves? Presumably burglars are not going to break into my house via the fridge, and I can't see it being to prevent the food making good its escape. Come on fridge manufacturing boffins of this world, explain yourselves.

Tim Buktu, Timbuktu

THE POPE has described homosexuality as the result of disordered thinking. Well, I'd like to inform his holiness that I recently watched a 23 minute film featuring two homosexual women, and far from being disorderly they seemed to know exactly what they were doing and did it extremely efficiently. Perhaps it's time to re-examine the concept of papal infallibility.

H Oxtail-Soup, Bodmin

WHY do pigs have a reputation for being dirty animals? It's not as if sheep make any more effort, what with all the shite hanging off their arse-wool.

Tommy C, Bristol

WITH reference to the point Tommy C makes *(previous letter)*, as a chef I am constantly advised by the Food Standards Agency to regularly wash my hands whilst preparing meat. Yet cows and sheep wander around in fields littered with their own dung and pigs roll around in it. When these animals wash their hooves, I'll wash my hands before cooking them. In the meantime, the Food Standards Agency can go and fuck themselves.

N Lyon, email

WHY, when asked "how old were you in 1982?" for example, do people only give one age? Unless they were born on January 1st I think you'll find everybody else was two ages.

John Mason, e-mail

THOSE 'all-butter' croissants are a rip-off. According to the ingredients list, there's flour and stuff in them too.

Craig Scott, East Calder

STAR LETTER

I WRITE with reference to Mr Bennett's Star Letter *(above left)*. Rather than being a quirky anecdote, I find this a rather heartwarming story. These days, many a man would simply let rip and force his wife to suffer the consequences. He would probably even disable the passenger side window and laugh. These same men will often break wind in bed and force their wives under the covers, giggling to themselves as their poor partners retch. The courtesy and respect that Mr Bennett's friend shows his wife is truly commendable and sadly all too often lacking in marriage these days.

T Fintim, Limbim

Dear Father Coxmas...

You pose YOUR out-of-this-world question to Particle Physicist out of D:Ream **Professor Brian Cox**

Dear Brian I know that time slows down as things approach the speed of light, and that consequently the Apollo astronauts had aged slightly on their return to earth. I have a large wine collection which will improve and so become more valuable with age, so I was wondering that if I went into space and reached the speed of light, how much older would my wine be when I got back?

Hampton Judd, Warwickshire

● **I'M AFRAID** you've got that all arse about face, Mr Judd. It would be your wine that would have to be sent into space and accelerated to near light speed if you wanted it to age. If you sent it out to the nearest star and back, you would be 8 years older when it got back, but your tipple would have aged by 4000 years. As you say, this would make it more valuable, but the bill from NASA for such a venture would run into billions of pounds, depending on how many bottles you sent up. *Bri x*

THE WORLD'S HARDEST SNOWMAN

MY mate told me we should all buy milk from farm shops since, although it costs an extra 32p, it gives the farmers a fair wage. Unfortunately there are no farm shops near me, so I buy my milk from Tesco and when I pass a farm on the way home I sellotape 32p to a cow.

Dave, Leeds

WHAT is it with these so-called 'Canadians' and the way they carry on? I mean, are they British, French or American? Come on, Canadians. Make your minds up.

Theodore Tramp, e-mail

WHAT the fuck is up with these rugby players when they take a place kick, with their stupid *Karate Kid* poses and faces like they're doing long division in their head? In a game with such complicated rules and nuanced tactics, surely hoofing the ball over the bar is the simplest thing that can happen. Why make it look like avant-garde theatre?

Fuzzel, Tulse Hill

THEY say a sure fire way of knowing if a girl is interested in you is that they make strong eye contact and hold your gaze for longer than a second or two. Well I was at the opticians the other day and picking up on the signs, I reciprocated by giving the pretty optometrist a firm slap on the arse and a cheeky wink. Needless to say the police were called and I'm not allowed back there. These body language experts speak a load of shite if you ask me.

Sammy, e-mail

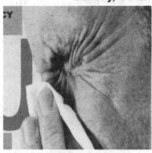

WELL done to the graphic designer for covertly slipping a huge 'barking spider' into this 'flu vaccination' poster.

Ronan McCarthy, Kent

IT has been so long since I have driven a car that I have forgotten which side of the road we drive on in this country. Fortunately, my wife has knitted me a sweatband that I permanently keep on my left wrist as a handy reminder.

WP Frith, Erith

TOP TIPS

LADIES. Ironing can be really dull. Why not spend that time fantasising about the amazing career you could have had? Like a sexy vet or a 1960s jewellery thief in a cat suit.

Ben, Berkhamsted

BIG families. Use one of those dog ball launchers to dish out mashed potato for people sitting at the far end of the table.

Papa Walton, Lisbon

APPEAR taller than you are by talking very quietly as people approach, thus sounding further away.

A Darricott, e-mail

DRESS your dog up as a horse before you take him for a walk so you don't have to pick up the shit.

James Wallace, Belper

WINDOW cleaners. Wear cat collars with bells on around your wrists in order to give an audible warning of your presence to naked customers in their bedrooms.

David Craik, Hull

CONVINCE strangers in the pub toilet that you are an eminent surgeon by thoroughly washing your hands after a piss and then turning the taps off with your elbows.

Iain Cochrane, Brighton

PORN makers. Add a bit of realism by showing a scantily clad lady answering the door to find the workman has left a "sorry you weren't in" card and fucked off after knocking once.

Mal Alcock, e-mail

EXTEND the battery life on your mobile phone by turning it off and placing it in a drawer.

Keith Queef, Llanllyfni

CONVINCE your wife that you were on shandy all night, whilst maintaining a clear conscience, by drinking 12 pints of lager and downing a litre bottle of lemonade on your way home from the pub.

Arthur Mugabe, Monifeith

GUINNESS Drinkers. Use your hangovers to benefit the community by shitting into potholes.

Steve Wetherell, Corby

PARTY planners. Remember to put 'Happy Birthday' banners up at a jaunty angle. It'll give the party a better atmosphere.

Gary Christie, Dundee

EMPTY Smarties tubes make ideal receptacles for keeping Skittles or Minstrels in.

Jarl O'Mog, Nantwich

DESPITE most of your cartoon characters uttering it, I've never heard anyone actually say "rats' cocks" in real life, and I've been to the north of England twice. Three times if you count looking at it out of the train window that time we went to Scotland. If you're wondering, I slept on the way back, so that probably doesn't count.

Matt, London

I'M an American. How 'bout a picture of some guy kissing a broad on her fanny?

Herb Oysterburger, New York

✱ *Sure thing, Herb*

ONCE we're in the year 2360, people will no longer be able to look at a 24-hour digital clock and pretend it's showing the date advancing into the future at a year a minute. I don't know about you, but losing this little pleasure makes me cold to the bone. I'm glad I won't be alive in 2360. It sounds a very miserable place.

Ian Andrews, Hastings

MAY I be the 1000th reader to point out that in the story *Bombs Over Bremenhaven (page 12)*, the Lancaster bomber was incorrectly depicted with side guns. This sloppy attention to detail spoiled an otherwise thrilling and highly plausible story.

Ray Norshine, Timbuktu

DO farts taste of anything? I'm asking from a theoretical perspective, you understand, as I'd rather not get involved in any practical attempts to determine the answer.

Roger Todger, Dodge

I'M AFRAID that I have found the bouncers in strip clubs to be sexist. I was in my local Spearmint Rhino with some friends and decided to get naked and dance seductively around them, only to find myself being promptly ejected, with my pants round my ankles and sporting a semi. It was absolutely appalling, and just goes to prove that it's one rule for attractive women and another for us hard-working blokes.

James Wallace, Belper

I WAS reading that fleas can jump 350 times their own body length. Well, big deal. Fleas are tiny, and so 350 times their body length only amounts to a few inches. I can jump a lot further than that, even when I've had a skinful.

Craig Scott, East Calder

ASK THE FAMILY ABOUT BUTTONS
WITH THE REANIMATED ZOMBIE OF ROBERT ROBINSON

The first question is for mother and eldest child:

● Here's a picture of a clothes-fastening device viewed from a rather unusual angle.

What is it?

ANS: A Button

Now a question for father and ugliest child:

● Here are five buttons, labelled A, B, C, D and E. How is it possible to remove two of the buttons to leave three? You may move any button.

ANS: Remove buttons A & C. Replace button A in the gap left by C, and then remove button E leaving buttons A, B & D.

This is a question for specciest son and most sexually frigid parent:

● A bath is being filled with buttons at a rate of six gallons of buttons every fifteen minutes, whilst a hole in the bath means it is simultaneously leaking buttons at a rate of twenty-four pints of buttons every hour. If the bath takes one hour twenty minutes to fill to the brim, what is the volume of the bath in quarts of buttons?

ANS: The bath holds 112 quarts of buttons.

The Ghost of Greytowers

Pretty young Bunty Twinkle arrived for the first day of term at Greytowers Student Nurse Training College. She had never been away from home before, so she was nervous yet excited about what lay ahead...

On the steps, she was met by the college caretaker, Mr Onan...

Good morning. I'm student nurse Twinkle. It's my first day.

Is it now? Phwooar! You're a pretty little thing.

Come in, I'll show you up to your dormitory.

Gosh! What a magnificent house. It must be hundreds of years old!

Gaw! Look at that! Slobber!

This is your bed.

My, what a lovely room. And my own chest of drawers!

Now when you get up in the morning and you take your nightie off, you've got to stand on that cross.

Oh? Why?

Because it's the rule, that's why. You don't want to get in trouble with matron.

Oh, hello Mr Onan.

Oh, look at you. You two been playing tennis? I dare say you'll be wanting a shower.

We certainly do. We've worked up quite a sweat.

Ohhhhh-h-h.

Just give me a couple of minutes, ladies, to sort the boiler out.

Hi, you must be Bunty, our new roommate. I'm Jackie and this is Mandy.

We're student nurses too.

Isn't this a lovely house?

It is, but it's a bit spooky.

Yes, it's haunted...by the Ghost of Greytowers!

Well I don't believe in ghosts.

Neither did I till I came here. You can hear him moaning and groaning every morning when we're getting dressed.

It's true. The noise seems to come from behind that picture.

Anyway, do you want to come and have a shower with us?

You must be hot after your long journey.

Sure, I'd love to.

Bunty and her new friends made their way to the communal bathroom...

You girls off to take that shower, then, are you? All together, all three of you at once?

That's right, Mr Onan.

CARETAKER

SHOWER STUDENT NURSES ONLY

Gaw! I like it! Dribble!

So tell me, how often does the ghost appear?

Every day, Bunty!

Three or four times, usually.

By the way, you have to get undressed here, by this cross on the floor.

Why?

Mr Onan says it's the rule.

Oh, right.

Some say the ghost is the first owner of the house, who was killed in a duel in the 1600s.

Others say it's a highwayman who was hanged off the big oak tree by the lake.

Ooh, how spooky!

Ooh, yeah, you dirty bitch!

Did you hear that?

A voice that seemed to come from nowhere!

That's the ghost alright. Let's take our showers and get out of here!

Brrr! The water's freezing!

It's always like that, Bunty.

Poor Mr Onan can't seem to fix the boiler.

Shortly...

ETAKER

Enjoy your shower, then, eh, girls?

Not really, Mr Onan. There was no hot water again.

Yes, it was freeezing cold.

Oooh, you don't want that, do you? Gets 'em standing up like jelly babies, eh? Froth!

CARETAKER

Well, if you could have a look at the heating system, that would be super.

Dirty! Dirty! **Dirty** bitches!

I've even heard the ghost's moans and groans when I've been spending a penny in the toilet cubicle.

Me too, the one at the end?

Yes, the one with the portrait of Oliver Cromwell on the wall.

The next day, the pals returned from their classes ...

Gosh, what an interesting lecture about giving a bedpan to someone with a slipped disc.

Yes. Come on, let's get out of these nurses' uniforms.

Good idea.

But...

Oh no! What's happened?

The Ghost of Greytowers has struck again!

That's the fifth time this week!

The phantom often haunts the dormitories while we're away at lectures and steals our underwear.

It's almost as if he knows when we won't be here.

That's spooky.

Eurgh! He's left ectoplasm all over one of my brassieres!

Oh no, not again. I don't know how we're going to get rid of this pesky ghost.

I do! My uncle's the vicar of the next village. He could come over with a bible and some holy water and cast this spook out once and for all!

Great idea!

An exorcism! How exciting!

I'll go and get him right away.

But as she raced to fetch her uncle, Bunty noticed something poking out under the boiler room door...

Hello? What's this? A pair of frilly knickers?

BOILER HOUSE STRICTLY NO ENTRY

Oh my word!

The Ghost of Greytowers is hiding our underwear in Mr Onan's boiler room!

This mystery is getting deeper and deeper!

191

More spooky goings-on next week when the Ghost of Greytowers starts stealing saddles from the nurses' home bike sheds...

SCIENTISTS HAIL CLEAN POWER BREAKTHROUGH

SCIENTISTS at Cambridge University's Maxwell Crabtree Research Institute last night announced a major breakthrough in cold fission technology that promises to lead to free, limitless, non-polluting energy. The revolutionary technology uses low temperatures to split silicon crystals, releasing the massive amounts of latent energy stored in their atomic bonds.

New fuel cell promises clean, free energy for all

Project head **Professor Bradley Piper** told reporters: "The only fuel needed for this process is sand and seawater, which are easily available in practically unlimited quantities. No greenhouse gases are released, and the only by-products of the process are clean drinking water and smaller grains of sand."

"It's such a simple, cheap technology," Professor Piper continued. "There is literally no reason why everyone on earth should not have access to limitless, free, renewable, clean energy by the end of this decade."

fission

The professor also believes that the new breakthrough will stop global warming in its tracks. "Man-made climate change will become a thing of the past," he announced. "It is not overstating the case to say that the cold fission system we have developed could solve many of the world's most pressing problems at a stroke."

By our Science Corespondent
Dr Stanley Jordan

But the statement was overshadowed by controversy over Dr Piper's clothing, as journalists began to question him about his attire. A correspondent for *Scientific American* pressed him about his choice of a blue tie, pale green shirt and brown jacket for such an important announcement.

"What message is the professor sending out by sporting such an uncoordinated array of apparel?" he asked. "This is undoubtedly the most important scientific breakthrough for a hundred years, but are trainers really the sort of shoes that a leading scientist should be wearing for public appearances?"

silicon

Professor Piper attempted to steer the conversation back to the subject of particle physics, but was interrupted by Sebastian de Rigeur, fashion editor of *Theoretical Physics*

Fission victim: Lead researcher Professor Bradley Piper was subject of widespread attacks for his poor choice of outfit at press conference announcing revolutionary scientific discovery

Abstracts magazine, who took him to task over the cut of his jacket. "Your lapels are too wide, you've got double vents in the back and two button, non-working cuffs," Mr de Rigeur said. "Honestly, what do you think you look like?"

poker

New Scientist Renewable Energy correspondent Dr Gigi Wang later slammed Professor Piper's outfit, singling out his glasses for particular criticism for being "so last year". "Geek chic has its place," said Dr Wang. "But it's time for the scientific community to wake up

and smell the test-tubes. Over 85% of people going into science are just drab. We need to attract more people who have a feel for fabrics and how to successfully coordinate an ensemble."

"Professor Piper's clothes were bad. And by bad, I don't mean good, I mean old school bad," said Dr Wang. "He may have moved cold fission forwards, but he's moved hot fashion back to the dark ages."

whizzer and

"A patterned skinny tie with Harris tweed? I mean... like... *hello!?*" he added.

THANKS to the success of hit shows such as *The Big Bang Theory* and boffin role models such as Brian Cox out of D:Ream and Patrick Moore, more kids than ever before are choosing to pursue a career in science. But is it all excitement and test tubes, or is there a more mundane side to the job? What it's *really* like working at the cutting edge of Physics, Chemistry or Biology? Let's take a peek inside the fume cupboard to see a typical...

DAY *in the* LIFE *of a* SCIENTIST

07:30 **THE SCIENTIST** rises early, and before he sets off for work he has to decide what he's going to wear for the day. If he's going to be peering down a microscope at cells or holding a test-tube of brightly-coloured liquid over a Bunsen burner, he may pick a pair of casual **cargo pants** and a collarless **grandad shirt** for comfort. Because he'll be on his feet all day, a stylish, comfortable shoe is needed, such as a *Dr Marten 1460* or an *Airwalk hi-top*. But if he's got departmental meetings to

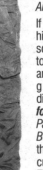

discuss grant applications or funding for his research work, he may choose a pair of smart/casual **chinos**, an **open-necked shirt** and a smart **jacket**, plus a pair of smart but comfortable **loafers** by *Gel Anatomique* or *Ecco*.

If our boffin is addressing a high-powered international scientific conference to present a paper or announce his latest ground-breaking discoveries, a **formal suit** by *Paul Smith* or *Hugo Boss* is the order of the day. He might team this with a *Jasper Conran* **dress shirt** with cutaway collar and contrasting **silk tie** by *Thomas Pink* to provide an oh-so-daring

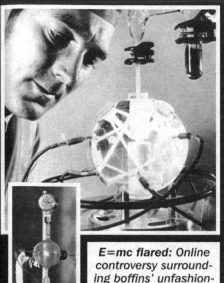

E=mc flared: Online controversy surrounding boffins' unfashionable clothing choices may be overshadowing important scientific breakthroughs and discouraging more stylish students from pursuing careers in physics, chemistry and the life sciences.

A Brief History of Fashion

BRADLEY PIPER isn't the first boffin to have broken the Laws of Fashion Physics. Throughout history, scientists have been meddling with things they don't understand and getting their outfits wrong. Here, theoretical physicist and fashion guru *Professor Stephen Hawking* takes us on a trip down a black hole of *science fashion faux passes.*

● Isaac Newton

Where to start? The father of modern Physics is rightly regarded as one of the greatest geniuses who ever lived, but when it comes to fashion sense he's at the bottom of the class. He may have invented gravity, but honestly - *a knee-length waistcoat paired with a ruched velvet frock-coat with set-in three-quarter sleeves and dress breeches?!* And don't get me started on those petticoat tail cuffs and that chemisiere. Something heavier than an apple must have fallen on his head to make him think that going out in that ensemble was a good idea.

● Marie Curie

This Polish-French radioactivity pioneer was the first female scientist to become a Nobel Laureate, but she certainly wouldn't be winning any prizes for this drab outfit. She died in 1934 of aplastic anaemia brought on by radiation, but it's a wonder that she didn't die of shame first... for going out in this humdrum, dreary get-up. You don't need the 1907 Actonian Prize from the Royal Institution to know that you simply don't team leg-of-mutton sleeves with an Empire-line gathered waist gaberdine skirt and Peter Pan collar. She should Geiger-count herself lucky that she got so far in Science whilst dolled-up in such a Chernobyl-scale fashion disaster.

● Albert Einstein

Einstein had perhaps the greatest brain of the modern scientific era... pity he didn't use it when he was getting dressed in the morning. Because from whichever side of the space-time continuum you look at it, Albert's wardrobe here is a relative disaster. Everything about it screams amateur hour. No wonder he couldn't

resolve the Einstein-Podolsky-Rosen Paradox if he couldn't even work out that you don't tuck a polo shirt into a pair of mid-length flannelette culottes. And as for those shoes! In which unified field would they be a good choice?

● Carl Sagan

Where in the Cosmos to start on Professor Sagan's dress-sense? A teal turtle-neck sweater might go with a mustard corduroy blazer in one of the infinite multiverses out there, but not this one, sister. And when you team that up with his trademark Oxford waistband Farah flares, snake belt and Cuban-heeled suede brogue boots, you've got one Big Bang of a fashion disaster brewing. Sagan was a pioneer in the search for extra-terrestrial intelligence, but we can only hope that we never find any aliens. Because once the little green men on Mars get a load of this clown's astronomical fashion fiasco, we'll be the laughing stock of the whole galaxy.

● Jonas Salk

Poli-Oh No! Virologist Salk developed the first successful deactivated poliomyelitis vaccine and gave his discovery away for the benefit of mankind, but it's a pity his nearest and dearest weren't as generous with their fashion advice. Seriously, Jonas? A pyjama-cut seersucker suit with patch pockets and dart lapels?! *Is this guy for real?* And if that's not bad enough, he sets this horror show 2-piece off with a diagonal striped-tie on a plain white shirt with button down collar. Okay, he may have been a great humanitarian whose selfless scientific work saved millions around the world from paralysis and death, but he himself was clearly immune to the latest menswear trends. This guy's fashion sense needs a shot in the arm... *and quick!*

See you next time, Sci-Fash Fans

Steve X

And the online science community was quick to join in the criticism, with many outraged boffins taking to Twitter to call for Piper to go.

goodbye mr

"Hang ur head in shame," wrote UMIST Astrophysicist **Professor Brian Cox.** *"What's wrong with a slim-fitting military-style blouson with epaulettes? It's not #rocketscience!"*

And Emeritus Professor of Energy Conversion at Newcastle University **Dr Ian Fells** was equally scathing. *"Those trousers!!!!!"* he tweeted to his 68 million followers. *"Puh-lease!!!!!"*

crinkle cut

Despite issuing an abject apology, Professor Piper was later released from his post at the Maxwell Crabtree Institute. A Cambridge University spokesman told us: "This discovery may have been one of the greatest in our history, and a shoo-in for the Nobel Prize, but in that démodé couture, he just had to go, girl."

---

dash of colour. A pair of classic leather-soled *brogues* by *Church's* or a traditional handmade *dress shoe* by *Loakes* of London to finish off the ensemble is always a good choice.

09:00 **OUR SCIENTIST** arrives at the lab and dons his *lab coat* - he can choose between a short, mid-thigh-length version or a slightly longer knee-length coat with a single darted vent and non-working cuffs. Both are tailored from crisp white linen or cotton-polyester mix and feature three square-cut patch pockets, notched lapel and either three-button or press-stud front fastening.

09:01 - 17:30 **THE SCIENTIST** farts around in the lab doing experiments with chemicals, centrifuges, oscilloscopes and isotope ratio mass spectrometers.

17:30 **AT THE END** of another day working hard at the cutting edge of knowledge, he goes home. His choice of clothes now depends on how he intends to spend the rest of the evening. If he's simply going to put his feet up in front of the telly whilst going through some scientific papers, he might slip into a pair of *jogging bottoms* and a roomy *sweatshirt*

with the name of his alma mater on the front. If he's going out, perhaps to the pictures or ten-pin bowling, he may decide to don *slacks*, a *T-shirt*, a *John Smedley jumper* and his favourite casual *Converse* shoes.

But if it's a more formal occasion, such as a posh meal out or to accept the Nobel Prize for Physics or Chemistry, he'll probably opt for a formal *dress suit* featuring either shawl or peak lapels, a pleated *Marcela shirt* with front placket and double cuffs with a black grosgrain silk *dickie-bow tie*, black, flat-fronted *trousers* with no turn-ups, black cashmere *socks* and patent leather slip-on *pumps*.

11:30 **AFTER A** long day pushing back the boundaries of human knowledge, it's time for our scientist to go to bed. He's got an early start tomorrow, pushing back the boundaries of human knowledge even further, so it's important he gets a comfortable night's sleep. Like most scientists, he'll opt for a pair of loose-fitting *lounge pants* and a comfortable grey *T-shirt* or traditional, crisp-tailored striped poplin *pyjamas* with open fly, drawstring waist and contrast piping on the collar. Of course, in these days of equality some scientists are women, and they would probably wear a *baby-doll nightie* or a peep-hole see-through *negligée.*

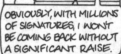

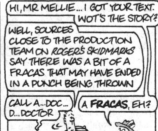

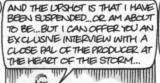

...ANYWAY, THE GOOD NEWS IS, FANS HAVE SET UP AN ONLINE PETITION TO GET THE POPULAR PRESENTER AND SKIDMARKS BACK ON AIR... AND IT'S ALREADY GOT HALF A MILLION SIGNATURES

...OR AT LEAST IT **WILL** HAVE BY TIME YOUR RAG HITS THE SHOPS.

ALTHOUGH THE PRODUCER, TOM WHO WAS PUNCHED, HAS HAD TO GO INTO HIDING AFTER HIS HOME ADDRESS, 32 LEAFY LANE, BARNTON, WAS LEAKED TO THE PRESS...

...MEANWHILE, FTV BOSSES ARE CONCERNED THAT RIVAL BROADCASTERS WILL TAKE THE OPPORTUNITY TO TRY TO TEMPT THE TOP-RATED STAR AWAY FROM THEIR NETWORK WITH SIX FIGURE CONTRACTS...

...AND SOURCES CLOSE TO MELLIE, 58, BELIEVE THE CONTROVERSIAL STAR WOULD BE AVAILABLE FOR TALKS WITH SKY AND ITV TO BRING THE SHOW TO THEIR CHANNEL

...AND HERE'S A PICTURE OF ME IN MY CAR, REFUSING TO ANSWER QUESTIONS, LOOKING PALE AND DRAWN, YESTERDAY

GREAT! THAT'S ALL I NEED, ROGER... WE'LL DO A PIECE AND A GAME OF SKIDMARKS BINGO

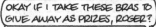

OKAY IF I TAKE THESE BRAS TO GIVE AWAY AS PRIZES, ROGER?

HELP YOURSELF   MR. MELLIE

HEH! HEH!

THERE'S A REPORTER FROM FULCHESTER FM TO SEE YOU

SHOW THEM IN   SURE

WE'VE HAD REPORTS OF A FRACAS IN THE PTV OFFICES IN WHICH A PRODUCER HAD HIS LIP SPLIT OPEN

NO...NO!.. THAT'S SIMPLY NOT TRUE...

...IT WAS HIS NOSE THAT GOT BROKEN

AND WE'RE HEARING THAT IT WAS **YOU** WHO BROKE IT, MR. MELLIE

I'M AFRAID I CAN'T COMMENT ON THAT AS I AM IN THE PROCESS OF BEING SUSPENDED...

RIGHT.

TOM, WILL YOU GET A FUCKING **MOVE ON** AND REPORT ME TO THE FUCKING D.G.?.. WE'RE IN DANGER OF BEING OVERTAKEN BY EVENTS, HERE..

GROAN...

LIGHTS...F.F FLASHING... LIGHTS...

...BUT I THINK IT IS SAFE TO SAY THAT WHEN THE DIRECTOR GENERAL OF FTV... HUGHIE McFEE... SEES THE OUTPOURING OF PUBLIC SUPPORT FOR ME, HE'LL HAVE LITTLE OPTION BUT TO REINSTATE ME AT AN INCREASED SALARY...

BUT THAT'S FOR ANOTHER TIME BECAUSE MY PRIORITY TODAY IS MY CHARITY WORK. I'M OPENING A WING OF A HOSPITAL OR SOMETHING FOR KIDDIES IN WHEEL-CHAIRS OR PENSIONERS OR SOMEBODY

DIDDLE! DEE-DEE-DEE! DEE-DEE!

GREAT... WELL I THINK THAT'S ALL I NEED

LOVELY.

DON'T FORGET TO MENTION THE WEB SITE... WWW. BRINGBACKROGER .CO.UK

HELLO!.. OH, HELLO, MR McFEE... YES, FINE... YES THANKS... YES, HE'S HERE NOW... YES... YES... YES, I'LL TELL HIM...

YES, BYE!

THAT WAS THE D.G., ROGER... HE WANTS TO SEE YOU FOR A VERY IMPORTANT MEET-ING... ONE O'CLOCK... IN THE PTV EXECUTIVE DINING ROOM... DON'T BE LATE

HEH! HEH!.. DON'T WORRY, TOM... THIS IS ALL GOING LIKE A FUCKING SWISS CLOCK

WHY DON'T YOU GET DOWN TO A&E, TOM?.. GIVE A FEW OF THEM T-SHIRTS OUT WHILE YOU'RE DOWN THERE

3:00 PM...   SORRY I'M LATE, HUGHIE... I HAD A BIT OF BUSINESS TO SORT OUT IN THE BAR, IF YOU KNOW WHAT I MEAN

WELL, YOU'RE HERE NOW, ROGER

I TAKE IT YOU'VE HEARD ABOUT THE DUST-UP IN TOM'S OFFICE

YES, ROGER, I HAVE... MOST UNFORTUNATE

MOST UNFORTUNATE INDEED

WELL, YOU CAN SUSPEND ME IF YOU WANT, BUT YOU'LL BE MAKING A BIG MISTAKE, I CAN TELL YOU..

IF YOU DON'T RENEW MY CONTRACT, YOU'LL BE PISSING OFF GOD KNOWS HOW MANY...

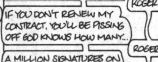
A MILLION SIGNATURES ON THAT PETITION BY NOW... PROBABLY... EVEN THE P.M. IS GOING TO SIGN IT..

...AND I WON'T BE SHORT OF OFFERS... RIVAL STATIONS WILL BE SNIFFING ROUND LIKE 70s STARS ROUND PRIMARY SCHOOL GATES...

ROGER...

I'M GOING TO STOP YOU THERE, ROGER...

ROGER...

ROGER...

...I'M **NOT** GOING TO SUSPEND YOU...

OH, RIGHT..

YOU ARE THE MOST POPULAR PRESENTER ON THE NETWORK, AND SKIDMARKS IS OUR MOST VALUABLE FRANCHISE...

IN FACT, I'M GOING TO RE-COMMISSION THE SERIES FOR ANOTHER 5 YEARS AT LEAST... AND GIVE YOU A 50% SALARY INCREASE INTO THE BARGAIN

FUCK ME! CHEERS!

NO PROBLEM!

...RIGHT, NOW THAT'S THE BUSINESS DONE WITH, HOW ABOUT WE HAVE A SPOT OF LUNCH, ROGER?

ABSOLUTELY... I'M FUCKING STARVING!

...I'LL HAVE THE STEAK AND CHIPS.

OH, I'M AFRAID THAT WITH YOU GETTING HERE SO LATE, THE CHEF HAS GONE HOME... BUT YOU CAN STILL HAVE A COLD MEAT PLATTER OR A BOWL OF SOUP...

SOUP!?!

FUCK OFF! I'M ROGER MELLIE! I'M ROGER FUCKING MELLIE! AND I WANT STEAK AND FUCKING CHIPS, YOU BALD SCOTTISH CUNT!

SMACK!

OOF!

MAJOR
MISUNDERSTANDING

DJ '15

Panel 1: THAT DOESN'T LOOK RIGHT.
YOU SHOULD'VE LEFT A BIGGER GAP BETWEEN "WINTER" AND "SALE".

Panel 2: HMM, YOU RECKON THE GAFFER WILL WANT ME TO RE-DO IT?
BUGGER.

Panel 3: FOR GOD'S SAKE! HOW ABSOLUTELY PATHETIC.
I'M NOT GOING TO CALL IT THAT!

NORMAN the DOORMAN
·251·

Panel 1: ARE YOU EXCITED ABOUT VISITING SANTA IN HIS GROTTO, TIMMY?
OH YES! I CAN'T WAIT, DAD!
TO THE NORTH P...

Panel 2: COME ON, THEN, IT'S OUR TURN. LET'S GO INSIDE AND SAY HELLO TO FATHER CHRISTMAS!

Panel 3: WOAH, WOAH, WOAH...! I'M NOT SURE WHERE THE FUCK YOU THINK YOU'RE GOING, SUNSHINE. BUT IT AIN'T IN HERE.
EX-EXCUSE ME..?

Panel 4: NO TIES WEARING THIS
YES, SORRY..

Mrs BRADY OLD Lady

Panel 1: PULL A CRACKER WITH ME, DOLLY LOVE, BEFORE THE QUEEN?
OOH YES! I LOVE A CRACKER, ME.

Panel 2: HNNNNNG!
GNNNNNNN!

Panel 3: CRACK!

Panel 4: HANG ON, DOLLY. THIS CRACKER'S STILL IN ONE PIECE.

SID THE SEXIST
TYNESIDE'S SILVER-TONGUED CAVALIER

TITS OOT

Panel 1: FOR THIS NEXT PIECE, I NEED A VOLUNTEER FROM THE AUDIENCE... A MAN... A LADIES MAN... SOMEONE WHO KNOWS HIS WAY AROUND THE WOMEN...
HOO LADS, I THINK HE'S JUST CAALLED W' NAME OOT...
DERREN MCKENNA HYPNOTIST
YEEZ LOT SIT DOON. THIS IS A JOB FORRA STALLION.

Panel 2: THANK YOU SIR, AND WHAT IS YOUR NAME?
SIDNEY SMUTT. YUZ CAN CAALL US SID.

Panel 3: LOOK DEEP INTO MY EYES, SIDNEY...DEEP... DEEEEEEEP... YOU ARE COMPLETELY UNDER MY POWER...
!

Panel 4: NOW, SID, I KNOW A GENTLEMAN DOESN'T LIKE TO KISS AND TELL, BUT I WANT YOU TO TELL THE AUDIENCE HERE, THE DIRTIEST THING YOU'VE EVER DONE TO A LADY.
SPARE NO DETAILS, SID, WE'RE ALL GROWN-UPS HERE. WE WANT A COMPLETE BLOW BY BLOW ACCOUNT.
WHOOP!